Lab Manual

Fourth Edition

Jeff S. Foster
Elizabeth A. Lacy

bju press
Greenville, South Carolina

The authors and the publisher have made every effort to ensure that the laboratory exercises in this publication are safe when conducted according to the instructions provided. We assume no responsibility for any injury or damage caused or sustained while performing the activities in this book. Conventional and homeschool teachers, parents, and guardians should closely supervise students who perform the exercises in this manual.
NOTE: The fact that materials produced by other publishers may be referred to in this volume does not constitute an endorsement of the content or theological position of materials produced by such publishers. Any references and ancillary materials are listed as an aid to the student or the teacher and in an attempt to maintain the accepted academic standards of the publishing industry.

Life Science Lab Manual
Fourth Edition

Jeff S. Foster, MS
Elizabeth A. Lacy, MEd

Bible Integration
Wesley Barley, MA

Editor
Adelé Hensley, ELS

Project Coordinator
Don Simmons

Cover Design
Elly Kalagayan

Concept Design
Andrew Fields

Page Design
Dan Van Leeuwen

Page Layout
Linda Hastie

Permissions
Sylvia Gass
Sarah Gundlach
Lily Kielmeyer
Kathleen Thompson

Illustration
Amber Cheadle
Paula Cheadle
Caroline George
Courtney Godbey
Preston Gravely
Brian D. Johnson
Sarah Lyons
Kara Moore
Kathy Pflug
John Roberts
Dave Schuppert
Lynda Slattery
Del Thompson

Photograph credits appear on pages 375–76.

Produced in cooperation with the Bob Jones University Division of Natural Science of the College of Arts and Science and Bob Jones Academy.

ISBN 978-1-60682-202-9

15 14 13 12 11 10 9

Contents

Introduction to LIFE SCIENCE *Lab Manual* v

1 *The World of Life Science*

Applications 1a–c 1

Investigations

1d: Is Measuring Accurate? 9

1e: Popcorn Science 13

2 *Characteristics and Classification of Life*

Applications 2a–i. 15

Investigations

2j: The pH of Life Substances 33

2k: Protein in Life Substances 35

2l: The Action of Enzymes 37

2m: Grouping Plants by Characteristics. . . 39

2n: Making an Insect Collection 41

3 *Cell Structure*

Applications 3a–d 47

Investigations

3e: Diffusion Rates 55

3f: Osmosis. 57

3g: How to Use a Microscope. 59

3h: Observing Cells with a Microscope . . . 63

3i: Turgor Pressure. 65

4 *Cell Activities*

Applications 4a–d 67

Investigations

4e: Aerobic Cellular Respiration 75

4f: Anaerobic Cellular Respiration 77

4g: Starch from Photosynthesis 79

5 *The Cell Cycle and Protein Synthesis*

Applications 5a–d 81

Investigations

5e: The Phases of Mitosis. 89

5f: A Model of DNA, RNA, and Protein Synthesis. 91

6 *Genetics of Organisms*

Applications 6a–e 93

Investigation

6f: Inheritance of Traits 105

7 *Genetic Changes and Biotechnology*

Applications 7a–c 109

Investigation

7d: Observing Radiation Effects on Seedlings 115

8 *In the Beginning*

Applications 8a–d 117

Investigations

8e: The Scale of Noah's Ark 125

8f: Dinosaurs 127

8g: Making a New Gene 129

8h: Evolutionary Family Trees 131

9 *The Microscopic World*

Applications 9a–c 133

Investigations

9d: Graphing Bacterial Growth 139

9e: Observing Protists. 141

9f: Examining a Mushroom 143

10 *Structure and Function of Plants*

Applications 10a–e 145

Investigations

10f: Leaf Design and Function. 155

10g: How Much Water Is Lost During Transpiration? 159

10h: Is Light Necessary for Photosynthesis? 161

10i: Gravitropism in Seedlings 165

11 *Plant Classification and Reproduction*

Applications 11a–d 167

Investigations

11e: Moss Structures 175

11f: Flower Dissection 177

11g: Factors That Affect Germination . . . 179

12 *The Invertebrates*

Applications 12a–g 183

Investigations

12h: Earthworm Dissection 197

12i: Other Sponges, Jellyfish, and Worms 201

12j: Butterfly Metamorphosis 203

13 *The Cold-Blooded Vertebrates: Fish, Amphibians, and Reptiles*

Applications 13a–d 205

Investigations

13e: Fish Respiration Rates 215

13f: Frog Dissection.................... 217

14 *The Warm-Blooded Vertebrates: Birds and Mammals*

Applications 14a–c 221

Investigations

14d: Conserving Body Heat: Wool vs. Down........................ 227

14e: Observing Feathers and Hair....... 229

14f: Man vs. Beast 231

15 *Animal Behavior and Reproduction*

Applications 15a–d 233

Investigations

15e: Myrmecology: The Study of Ants ... 241

15f: An Animal's Response to Its Environment.................. 243

15g: Sexual Reproduction: Means of Amazing Variation 245

15h: Animal Reproduction Worksheet... 247

16 *Relationships in Ecosystems*

Applications 16a–e 249

Investigations

16f: The Biotic Community of the Soil... 259

16g: Backyard Ecosystems............. 261

17 *Relationships Among Organisms*

Applications 17a–d 263

Investigations

17e: Your Food Chain 271

17f: Overcrowding..................... 273

17g: Lichens.......................... 275

17h: Observing Relationships 277

18 *Man's Relationship with the Environment*

Applications 18a–b 279

Investigations

18c: Estimates 283

18d: Recycling Paper.................. 285

19 *Support and Movement*

Applications 19a–d 287

Investigations

19e: Structure of the Skin 295

19f: Observing a Beef Bone 297

19g: Heat from Muscles 299

19h: The Structure of Bones and Muscles 301

20 *Internal Balance*

Applications 20a–d 303

Investigations

20e: Blood............................ 311

20f: Observing a Cow Heart............ 313

20g: Using a Stethoscope.............. 315

20h: Increasing Heart Rate 317

21 *Energy*

Applications 21a–c 321

Investigations

21d: Respiration 327

21e: Digestive Enzymes 331

22 *Control*

Applications 22a–e 333

Investigations

22f: The Skin's Sensation of Temperature 343

22g: The Pupil Reflex 345

22h: Afterimages...................... 347

23 *Health*

Applications 23a–e 349

Investigations

23f: Collecting Bacteria............... 359

23g: Counting Calories................ 363

23h: Burning Calories with Exercise..... 371

Appendixes

Appendix A: Metric System Conversions and Unit Abbreviations 373

Appendix B: Periodic Table of the Elements .. 374

Photograph Credits 375

Introduction to LIFE SCIENCE Lab Manual

Life science isn't just about reading your textbook and learning terms, although that is important. Life science is about doing things! The activities in this lab manual should make science come alive for you. "Doing science" is one of the best ways for you to learn science. It's one thing to read about an organism or a process, listen to your teacher talk about it, and even look at pictures of it. But it's another thing entirely to actually look at the organism yourself or observe a process happening in real time. In this lab manual, you'll complete activities that help you learn the concepts you're studying in class, develop laboratory skills, learn to record and interpret experimental data, build problem-solving skills, and much more. And hopefully you'll have fun while you're at it!

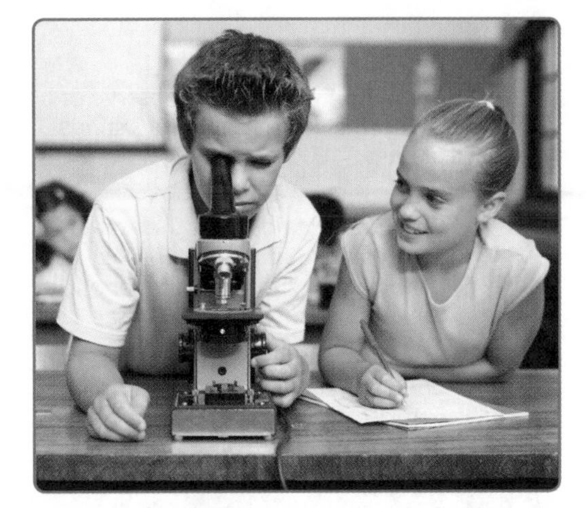

In your investigations, you'll make observations of many fascinating things.

Types of Activities

There are two types of activities in this lab manual—applications and investigations.

Applications

Applications are pencil-and-paper exercises designed to help you learn the information you are studying in class. These exercises will help you build your science vocabulary and remember the important material from your textbook. Some of the exercises are very simple; others are designed to make you think harder. Learning the information in the applications will help you a lot in preparing for tests.

Investigations

Investigations are designed to help you learn more about life science by doing something hands-on. You may perform an experiment, make observations, do library research, collect natural items, or do various other activities. There are several different types of investigations.

Class Investigations. Designed to be done in class, a class investigation often involves your performing an experiment. Usually there are observations to be made and analyzed. Some class investigations will be performed individually, others by groups, and some as demonstrations by your teacher while the class observes.

Research Investigations. A research investigation usually involves your finding information in other sources. Sometimes it involves talking with a person to find out what he knows about something. In these investigations you are given information about a topic and are told how to find out more about it. Often you are asked to prepare an oral or written report about your findings.

Field Investigations. A field investigation involves finding out what something is like. It may mean going to a zoo, the woods, or even your own backyard to make various observations. In field investigations you are told what to look for and where to find it. Sometimes you are asked to prepare an oral or written report about your findings.

Personal Investigations. A personal investigation is one you can do on your own, often at home. It may involve building models, keeping track of data over a period of time, or doing a deeper investigation of a topic you are studying in class.

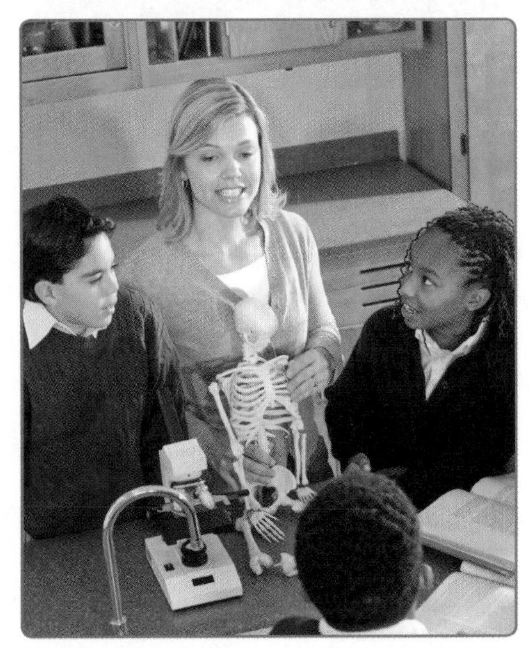

Get ready for some hands-on exploration of God's living creation!

Animals
Animals that you are to observe or collect may inflict dangerous stings or bites.

Body protection
Chemicals, stains, or other materials could damage your skin or clothing. You should wear a laboratory apron and/or latex gloves.

Chemical fumes
Chemical fumes may present a danger. Use a chemical fume hood or make sure the area is well ventilated.

Electricity
An electrical device (hot plate, lamp, or microscope) will be used. Use the device with care.

Extreme temperature
Extremely hot or cold temperatures may cause skin damage. Use proper tools to handle laboratory equipment.

Eye protection
There is a possible danger to the eyes from chemicals or other materials. Wear safety goggles.

Fire
A heat source or open flame is to be used. Be careful to avoid skin burns and the ignition of combustible materials.

Gas
Improper use of gas can result in burns, explosions, or suffocation. Be careful to check that the gas is turned off when you are finished.

Pathogen
Organisms encountered in the investigation could cause human disease.

Plants
Plants that you are to observe or collect may have sharp thorns or spines or may cause contact dermatitis (inflammation of the skin).

Poison
A substance in the investigation could be poisonous if ingested.

Sharp objects
Cuts are possible from broken glassware (broken test tubes, thermometers, or microscope slides) or sharp instruments (scalpels, razorblades, or knives).

Safety

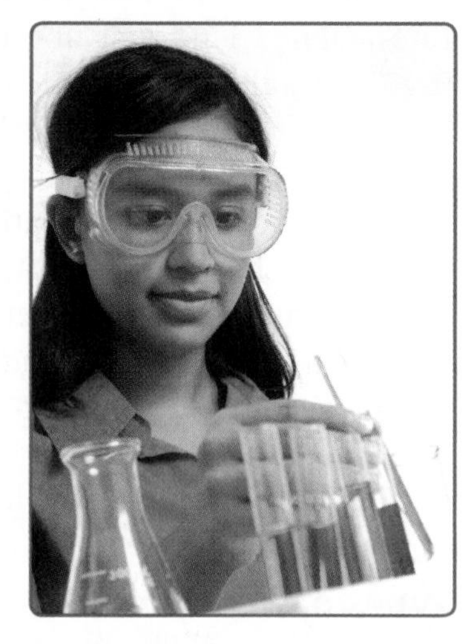

Sometimes you will be asked to use materials or equipment that could be dangerous if used improperly. For this reason you should never play with the equipment used in this class. Never use equipment for any purpose other than the one for which it was designed. In this way, neither you and your friends nor the equipment will be harmed. If your equipment is damaged when you get it, show it to your teacher immediately. If you damage a piece of equipment, report it to your teacher immediately.

The directions in the investigations include safety symbols to alert you to possible danger. The safety symbols are explained on the left. When you see a particular symbol in an investigation, your teacher should explain to you what the danger is and how to protect yourself.

Policies and Procedures

The pages in your lab manual are perforated so they can be easily removed. In order for your teacher to look over your work, grade it, and help you do better work in the future, you may be asked to turn in various pages. Be sure you have your name and other requested information written at the top of the page before you hand it in. When your teacher returns it to you, you should put it in a looseleaf notebook so you don't lose it.

Some investigations ask you to hand in a written report. You will do these reports on your own paper and will not need to turn in a page from your lab manual. When your reports are returned, place them in your notebook as well. Your teacher may wish to check your notebook periodically to review your work. Keep it neat, well-organized, and safe.

Be sure to do your own work on these activities and investigations, unless your teacher tells you it is okay to work together for a particular activity. Sometimes it's easy to ask a friend what answer he put for a question. But that is cheating. Of course, if you are working together as a group on a particular project, it is not cheating to discuss what you are doing. If you have trouble with a section or a specific question, ask your teacher about it. Cheating is lying to your teacher, to yourself, and to God.

Ready . . . Set . . . Explore!

You should have a lot of fun participating in life science activities this year. You'll learn fascinating things as you complete the investigations. After all, you're studying God's living creation, and there are lots of fascinating organisms in the world! We hope these activities will help increase your knowledge of science as well as your love for science. Most importantly, though, we hope they will help you learn more about the Creator and be inspired to love Him more. So get ready to explore the world of life science!

name ______________________

section __________ date __________

1a Searching for the Truth

Directions

Read each of the statements about the great auk carefully. Then decide which of the following categories best describes each statement and place the letter in the blank. You may use each category more than once or not at all.

Categories

A. Observable evidence

B. Universal statement

C. Value judgment

D. Final answer

__B__ 1. There are no great auks alive today.

__C__ 2. The great auk was a beautiful bird.

__A__ 3. By examining preserved specimens in various museums, scientists have determined that the great auks stood about 75 cm high.

__A__ 4. Today common murres (MURS), a smaller type of auk that can fly, live on the islands where the great auks once lived.

__C__ 5. The meat of the great auk was very tasty.

__A__ 6. Great auks nested in large colonies, but their population growth was limited because no auk ever laid more than one egg each year.

__A__ 7. The eggs preserved in museums show that great auk eggs were mottled brown and white.

__A__ 8. The little auk, which is 8 in. long, nests in Greenland and Iceland.

You can learn more about the great auk on p. 390 of the *Life Science* Student Text.

name ____________________

section __________ date __________

1b The Scientific Method

Directions

Select the proper terms from the list to complete the following paragraph. Write your answers on the lines to the left of the paragraph. You may use each term only once or not at all.

analyze	experiment	observations	scientific method
choose	experimental group	predict	survey
control group	experimental variable	presupposition	verify
data	hypothesis	problem	workability

1. scientific method
2. problem
3. hypothesis
4. experiment
5. experimental variable
6. experimental group
7. control group
8. observations
9. data
10. analyze
11. choose
12. verify

John's science teacher said that seeds do not need light to sprout. However, John had always heard that seeds do need light to sprout. He decided to use the __1__ to determine which statement was correct. His __2__ was, do plant seeds need light to sprout? John's __3__ was that plant seeds do need light to sprout. To begin his __4__, he obtained four small cups and filled each one with soil. He then put three seeds in each cup. In his experiment, John planned to have light as the __5__, so he put two of these cups on a sunny window ledge and used them as his __6__. He placed the other two cups inside a dark cabinet and used them as his __7__. Every other day, he added the same amount of water to each of the cups. Every day, he recorded his __8__ of the seeds. Once a seed sprouted, John used a ruler to measure the plant's daily growth. He also made notes about the color of the sprouts. All these notes would serve as his __9__. After two weeks, John made a chart of the results of his experiment. He made the chart to help him __10__ the data. After looking at the chart, John was able to __11__ an answer. Based on his observations, John decided that his hypothesis was wrong. The seeds sprouted equally well in both the dark and light areas. However, from his data he also concluded that soon after the seeds sprouted, differences developed between the two groups. John doubted the results of his experiment. Since he had used only bean seeds, he decided he would need to perform additional experiments in order to __12__ the results of his experiment.

name ______________________

section __________ date __________

1c Defining the Problem and Forming a Hypothesis

Introduction

Before a scientist performs an experiment, he must define the problem and form a hypothesis. The problem is usually given in the form of a question. Its purpose is to limit the scope of the experiment. A hypothesis is a proposed solution to the problem. It describes the specific, testable relationship between the variables being studied. During the experiment, one variable (the experimental variable) is manipulated to observe its effect on another variable (the response variable). The hypothesis is often stated in an *if–then* format. For example, "If the bean plants are given extra fertilizer, then they will produce more beans." In this case, the amount of fertilizer is manipulated to observe its effect on bean production. Both of these variables are easily observed.

Directions

For each of the following topics and problem statements, give the possible variables and write a testable hypothesis relating the two variables. Write a problem statement if none is given.

Example

Topic: Plant growth

Problem: Is the growth of plants related to the amount of fertilizer they receive?

Experimental variable: *amount of fertilizer*

Response variable: *height of plants*

Hypothesis: *If the growth of plants is related to the amount of fertilizer they are given, then plants that receive fertilizer will grow taller than plants that do not receive fertilizer.*

1. Topic: Plant growth

   Problem: Is the color of light related to plant growth?

   Experimental variable: color of light

   Response variable: the height of plant

   Hypothesis: ______________________

2. Topic: Dissolving of solutes

   Problem: Does temperature affect how quickly sugar dissolves in water?

   Experimental variable: temprature of water

   Response variable: speed at which sugar dissolves

   Hypothesis: If the temprature of the water increases, than the sugar will dissolve faster.

3. Topic: Bacterial growth

   Problem: Does temperature affect the growth of bacteria?

   Experimental variable: ______________________________

   Response variable: ______________________________

   Hypothesis: ______________________________

   ____

4. Topic: Test scores

   Problem: Are test scores related to the frequency of studying?

   Experimental variable: ______________________________

   Response variable: ______________________________

   Hypothesis: ______________________________

   ____

5. Topic: Popcorn popping

   Problem: Is the price of popcorn related to the percentage of kernels that pop?

   Experimental variable: ______________________________

   Response variable: ______________________________

   Hypothesis: ______________________________

   ____

6. Topic: Exercise and memory retention

   Problem: Is there a relationship between memory retention and exercise?

   Experimental variable: ______________________________

   Response variable: ______________________________

   Hypothesis: ______________________________

   ____

7. Topic: Smell and taste

   Problem: ______________________________

   Experimental variable: ______________________________

   Response variable: ______________________________

   Hypothesis: ______________________________

   ____

8. Topic: Cricket chirping

   Problem: ______________________________

   Experimental variable: ______________________________

   Response variable: ______________________________

   Hypothesis: ______________________________

   ____

name ______________________

9. Topic: Attracting hummingbirds

    Problem: ______________________

    Experimental variable: ______________________

    Response variable: ______________________

    Hypothesis: ______________________

    ____

10. Topic: Icy roads

    Problem: ______________________

    Experimental variable: ______________________

    Response variable: ______________________

    Hypothesis: ______________________

    ____

Class Investigation

name ______________________

section ___________ date ___________

1d Is Measuring Accurate?

Goals

- ✓ Recognize the potential inaccuracy of measurements made by humans.
- ✓ Practice measuring, recording, and analyzing data.

Materials

Activity 1
yarn
ruler

Activity 2
cross section of a tree trunk or branch

Activity 3
balance
paper (13 cm or 5 in. square)
tablespoon
sand

Activity 4
meter stick, yardstick, ruler, or tape measure

Activity 5
water
graduated cylinder or measuring cup

Activity 6
water sample
thermometer

Procedure

Activity 1: How long is this piece of yarn?

1. Lay the yarn flat on your desk in as straight a line as possible.
2. Lay the ruler next to the yarn and determine the length of the yarn.
3. Record your observation on the Individual Data Chart.

Activity 2: How many growth rings are visible in this cross section of a tree trunk or branch?

1. Count the growth rings from the center of the cross section and work your way to the outside.
2. Record your observation on the Individual Data Chart.

Activity 3: What is the mass of 5 tbsp of sand?

1. Place one square of paper on the balance.
2. Using the tablespoon, place 5 tbsp of sand on the square of paper.
3. Determine the mass of the sand using the method described by your teacher.
4. Record your observation on the Individual Data Chart.
5. Carefully pour the sand back into the container and discard the square of paper.

Activity 4: How tall is ________________?
Choose one person from your group whose height will be measured. Write that person's name in the blank above.

1. Measure the person's height.
2. Record your observation on the Individual Data Chart.

Activity 5: What volume of water is in the container?

1. Pour the water into the measuring container.
2. Observe the lowest point of the curve of the liquid's surface (called the *meniscus*).
3. Record your observation on the Individual Data Chart.
4. Carefully pour the water back into the original container.

Activity 6: What is the temperature of the water sample?

1. Insert the thermometer into the water.
2. Wait for the temperature indicator to reach equilibrium.
3. Record your observation on the Individual Data Chart.

Individual Data Chart

Experiment	Measurement
1	Length of yarn =
2	Number of growth rings =
3	Mass of sand =
4	Height of person =
5	Volume of water =
6	Temperature of water =

Data

On the following charts, record the names of your group members and the data they obtained. Be sure to record the units for each observation.

Activity 1

No.	Name	Data	No.	Name	Data	No.	Name	Data
1			12			23		
2			13			24		
3			14			25		
4			15			26		
5			16			27		
6			17			28		
7			18			29		
8			19			30		
9			20			31		
10			21			32		
11			22			33		

Activity 2

No.	Name	Data	No.	Name	Data	No.	Name	Data
1			12			23		
2			13			24		
3			14			25		
4			15			26		
5			16			27		
6			17			28		
7			18			29		
8			19			30		
9			20			31		
10			21			32		
11			22			33		

Activity 3

No.	Name	Data	No.	Name	Data	No.	Name	Data
1			12			23		
2			13			24		
3			14			25		
4			15			26		
5			16			27		
6			17			28		
7			18			29		
8			19			30		
9			20			31		
10			21			32		
11			22			33		

name ______________________

Activity 4

No.	Name	Data	No.	Name	Data	No.	Name	Data
1			12			23		
2			13			24		
3			14			25		
4			15			26		
5			16			27		
6			17			28		
7			18			29		
8			19			30		
9			20			31		
10			21			32		
11			22			33		

Activity 5

No.	Name	Data	No.	Name	Data	No.	Name	Data
1			12			23		
2			13			24		
3			14			25		
4			15			26		
5			16			27		
6			17			28		
7			18			29		
8			19			30		
9			20			31		
10			21			32		
11			22			33		

Activity 6

No.	Name	Data	No.	Name	Data	No.	Name	Data
1			12			23		
2			13			24		
3			14			25		
4			15			26		
5			16			27		
6			17			28		
7			18			29		
8			19			30		
9			20			31		
10			21			32		
11			22			33		

Summing Up

Answer the following questions based on the experiment that your teacher indicates.

1. Did every member of your group report the same measurements? yes ☐ no ☐
2. Did every member of your group report the values in the same unit (e.g., feet, inches, meters)? yes ☐ no ☐

   If not, convert all the values to the unit that most of the students used to report these measurements.

   Why is it important that everyone's data be reported in the same unit? ____________________

3. Calculate the average value of all the measurements reported. (Add all the measurements and divide the total by the number of measurements.) Be sure to include the units.

   The average measurement is ____________.

   Did any student actually report this average value as his measurement? yes ☐ no ☐

   Would this average value be a good answer for your problem? yes ☐ no ☐ Why?

4. Which value did most students report as their measurement? ____________

   Is this value the same as the average? yes ☐ no ☐

   Would this value be a good answer for the question? yes ☐ no ☐ Why?

5. What value would you choose to answer the question? Why? ____________________
6. What was the smallest measurement reported? ____________
7. What was the largest measurement reported? ____________
8. Is either of these values unreasonable? yes ☐ no ☐ If so, which one and why? ____________
9. Why were so many different values reported for the measurement of the same thing? Give as many reasons as you can. ____________________
10. If your group were to do the activity again, how could you make more accurate measurements?

name ____________________

section ________ date ________

1e Popcorn Science

Procedure and Data

Goal

✓ Use the scientific method.

Materials

hot plate

popcorn kernels of various natural colors

popcorn popper

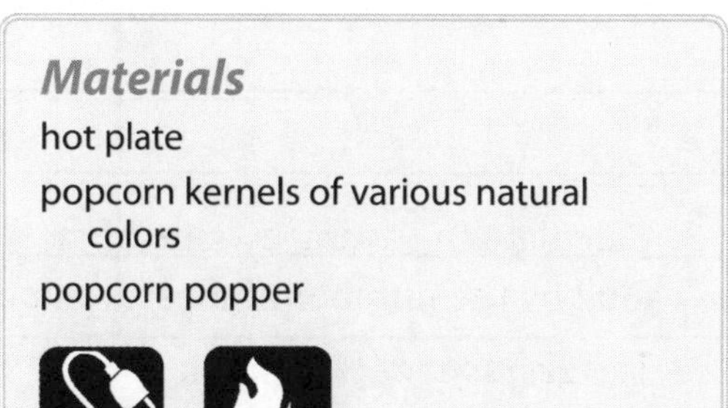

In this investigation you will use the steps of the scientific method. Answer the questions below in complete sentences. Your teacher will guide you with helpful hints, but the answers must be your own.

Define the problem.

1. Your teacher will show you some unpopped popcorn kernels. Describe the kernels. ____________________
2. What color do you think the popcorn will be after it is popped? ____________ Do you know for sure? ________
3. Write a question about popcorn color that could be answered by using the scientific method. ____________________

Form a hypothesis.

Though you may not be certain of the answer to your question, you have probably popped and eaten popcorn before. Thus, you probably have an idea about what the answer to the problem should be. How do you think unpopped kernel color and popped kernel color are related? This statement is your hypothesis; write it as a statement, not a question.

____

Perform the experiment.

1. Explain an experiment you could perform to determine whether your hypothesis is correct or incorrect.

____

2. Your teacher will perform the experiment.

Classify and analyze the data.

In the following chart, record the data from the experiment.

Popcorn Data	
Color of unpopped kernels	Color of popped kernels

Choose an answer.

Was your hypothesis right or wrong? ______________________________

Verify the answer.

1. Is it possible that something could have gone wrong in the experiment to give incorrect results? ________
2. List one thing that could have caused you to get incorrect results. ______________________
____
____
____
3. What could be done to make it more likely that the experiment's results are free of errors? __________
____
____
____
4. Your teacher will help you verify the answer.

Use the answer to predict outcomes.

Suppose another color of popcorn kernel were available. Based on the results of this experiment, what color would it pop? ____________________

name__________

section______ date______

2a Being Alive

Directions

Match the following statements with the correct characteristic of life. Use each characteristic twice.

A. energy needs
B. growth
C. movement
D. reproduction
E. response

A 1. Mushrooms cannot produce their own sugar. They must receive their nutrition from decaying material.

E 2. After being watered, a wilted plant becomes stiff again.

B 3. This characteristic occurs when an organism builds more substance than it uses.

C 4. This characteristic is demonstrated by blood circulating inside an organism's body.

B 5. This characteristic may result in your having to change to a larger shoe size.

D 6. An organism produces other organisms similar to itself.

C 7. A worm inches along the ground.

E 8. Nightfall signals a plant to close its flowers.

D 9. Small new plantlets may form from the sides of a plant.

A 10. Most plants use energy from sunlight to make sugar.

name ______________________

section ____________ date ____________

2b The Cell Theory

Directions

Study the drawing below. On the numbered lines, list all the things clearly visible in the drawing that are made of cells. Do not list things that cannot be seen, such as people in the plane, insects in the grass, and so forth. All the blanks may or may not be used, depending on how specifically some items are identified.

1. ______________________
2. ______________________
3. ______________________
4. ______________________
5. ______________________
6. ______________________
7. ______________________
8. ______________________
9. ______________________
10. ______________________
11. ______________________

name ____________________

section __________ date __________

2c Cellular Functions

Part 1

Directions

In the blanks below, list the four main functions of cells.

1. ____________________
2. ____________________
3. ____________________
4. ____________________

Part 2

Directions

Below is a list of cells or organisms performing various activities. In the spaces provided, indicate which of the four cellular functions each activity illustrates best.

____________________ 1. A bacterium dividing

____________________ 2. A person jerking his hand away from a hot stove

____________________ 3. Cells of the stomach making digestive juices

____________________ 4. A fish swimming away from light and toward shadows

____________________ 5. A plant cell forming a cell wall

____________________ 6. Muscles of your legs working as you run

____________________ 7. A plant forming seeds

____________________ 8. A person enjoying the smell of cookies baking

____________________ 9. A bee flying to its hive

____________________ 10. A bird growing a new feather to replace a lost one

name ____________________

section __________ date __________

2d Molecules and Life

Directions

In each of the following statements, draw a circle around the correct choice in the parentheses. On the lines below each statement, explain why the incorrect choice is not acceptable.

1. Sugars and (starches / enzymes) are important carbohydrates.

   ____

2. Carbohydrates consist of carbon, oxygen, and (nitrogen / hydrogen).

   ____

3. (Enzymes / Nucleic acids) are made of proteins.

   ____

4. Proteins are made of (glucose molecules / amino acids).

   ____

5. The arrangement of nucleotides in (DNA / lipids) is a code.

   ____

6. Fats and (carbohydrates / lipids) are the same thing.

   ____

7. RNA is a (nucleic acid / nucleotide).

   ____

8. Cell membranes are made largely of (lipids / nucleic acids).

   ____

9. The nucleic acid (RNA / cellulose) helps make proteins.

   ____

10. Glucose is a (carbohydrate / protein).

   ____

name ______________________

section __________ date __________

2e The Modern Classification System

Directions

Listed among the following terms are the seven basic taxons in today's classification system. Turn your book sideways and write them in the correct order on the lines below. In the boxes above the lines, write the letter choice corresponding to each taxon. When you complete the exercise, the letter choices will spell a word that relates to the classification system.

N—class	W—kind	S—species
E—family	L—kingdom	R—tribe
U—genus	A—order	T—variety
F—group	I—phylum	

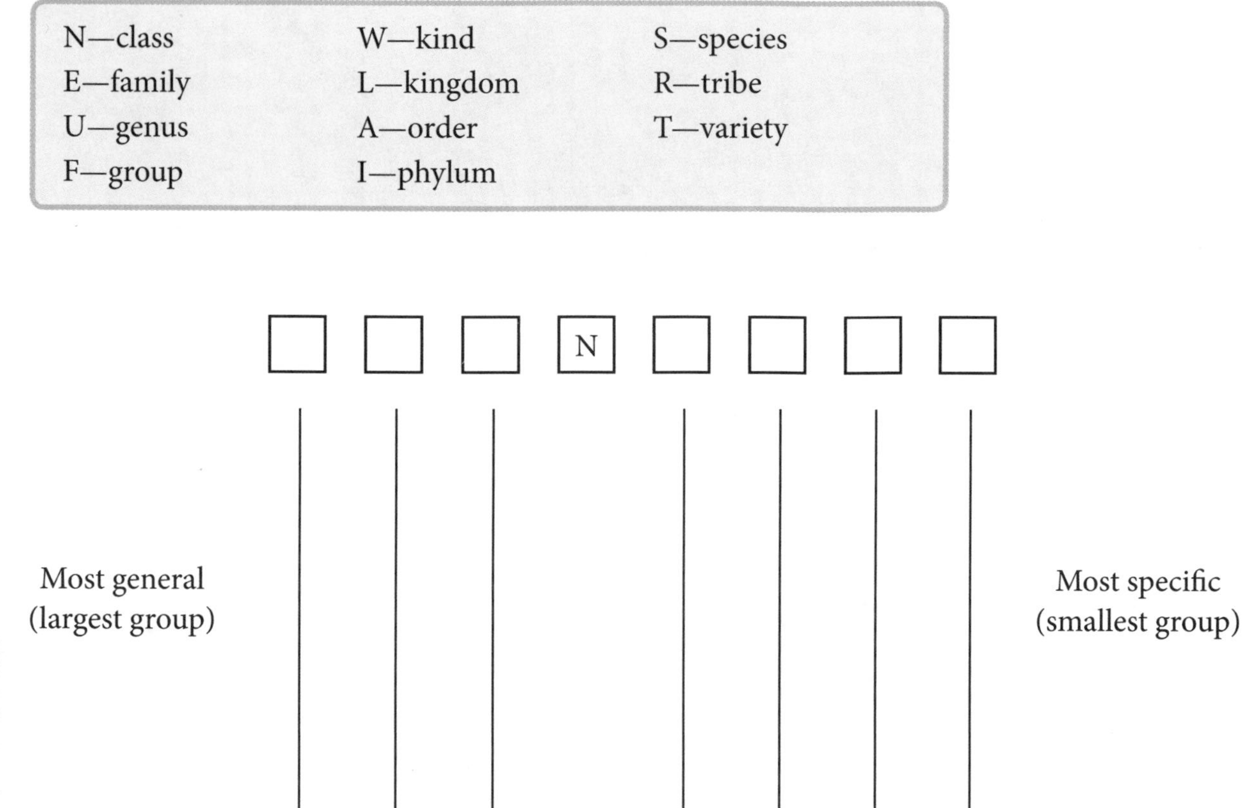

How does the word in the boxes relate to the classification system?

____

____

name ____________________

section __________ date __________

2f Scientific Names

Part 1

Directions

Choose the best answer for each of the following questions.

__B__ 1. How many words are usually included in a scientific name?

A. one
B. two
C. three
D. four

__D__ 2. Which is *not* a requirement for a scientific name?

A. Latin form
B. must not duplicate a name
C. underlined or italicized
D. can never change

__A__ 3. Which of the following is a genus name?

A. *Canis*
B. *familiaris*
C. German
D. shepherd

__C__ 4. Which of the following is a properly written scientific name?

A. *Pisum sativum*
B. Pisum sativum
C. *Pisum Sativum*
D. Pisum Sativum

__C__ 5. What is the scientific name sometimes called?

A. German name
B. common name
C. genus-species name
D. prime name

__A__ 6. What language form is used in a scientific name?

A. Latin
B. German
C. English
D. Spanish

Part 2

Directions

Starting with Question 1 in Part 1, use the letters of your answers (*A*, *B*, *C*, or *D*) and the key below to plot a trail on the map. If all your answers are correct and you correctly plot the trail, your trail will end in the country that answers the question below the map.

> **Key**
> If the answer to a statement is *A*, draw a line 5° northward from your last stopping point.
> If the answer to a statement is *B*, draw a line 5° southward from your last stopping point.
> If the answer to a statement is *C*, draw a line 5° eastward from your last stopping point.
> If the answer to a statement is *D*, draw a line 5° westward from your last stopping point.

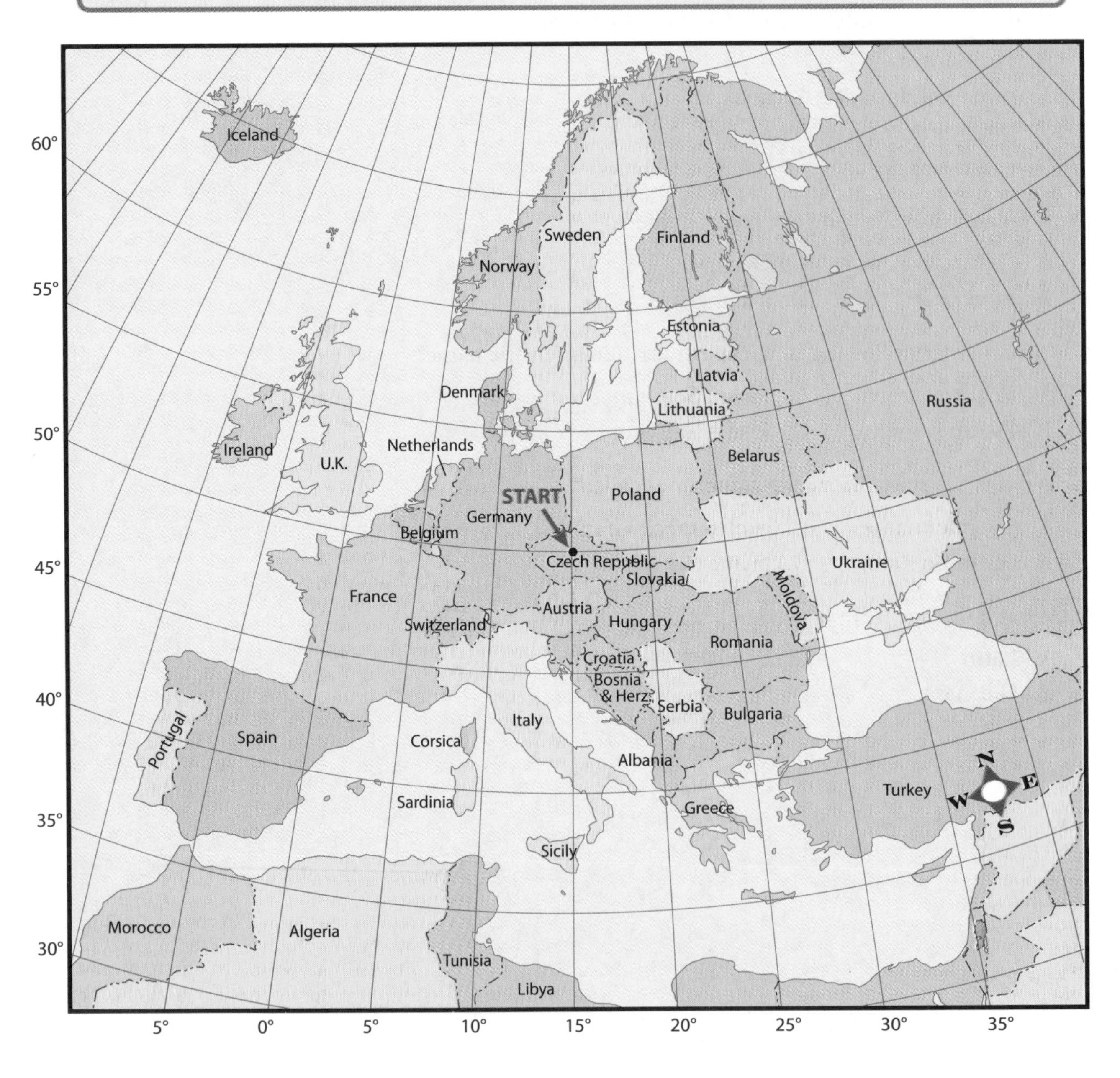

Which country was Carolus Linnaeus's homeland? ______________________

Application

name ______

section ______ date ______

2g The Living Kingdoms

Directions

Using Appendix D, "The Living Kingdoms," in the textbook, fill in the left column with the proper name for each group from the modern classification system. List at least one example of that group in the right column.

Kingdom	Description	Example
Archaebacteria	are unicellular or colonial, do not have true nuclei, and like to live in extreme environments	
Eubacteria	are unicellular or colonial and do not have true nuclei	
Animalia	have tissues but lack chlorophyll and cell walls	
Fungi	are unicellular or colonial, do not have true tissues, lack chlorophyll, and obtain food by secreting enzymes	
Protista	are unicellular or colonial, lack tissues, and may have chlorophyll	
Plantae	have tissues, chlorophyll, and cell walls containing cellulose	

Phylum	Description	Example
Brophyta	plants that lack water-conducting tissues	
Cnidaria	animals that live in water and have stinging cells to paralyze and capture prey	
Echindermata	animals that have spiny skins	
Arthropod	animals that have an exoskeleton	
Anthophta	plants that produce flowers	
Annelida	animals that have soft bodies and are divided into segments	
chordata	animals that have backbones	
Platyhelminthes	animals that are flattened worms	
Mollusca	animals that have soft bodies and, frequently, shells	

Class	Description	Example
Mammalia	vertebrates that have fur or hair	
Insecta	arthropods that have six legs	
Amphibia	smooth-skinned vertebrates whose immature forms breathe with gills and whose mature forms breathe with lungs	
Reptilia	vertebrates that have scales and lungs	
Osteicthyes	vertebrates that have gills and bony skeletons and are covered by scales	
Aves	vertebrates that have feathers and light, hollow bones	

name

section date

2h Using a Dichotomous Key

Directions

Dichotomous keys are used to identify the classification of organisms. Using the dichotomous key on the next page, identify the phylum, subphylum, or class that each of the animals pictured below belongs to.

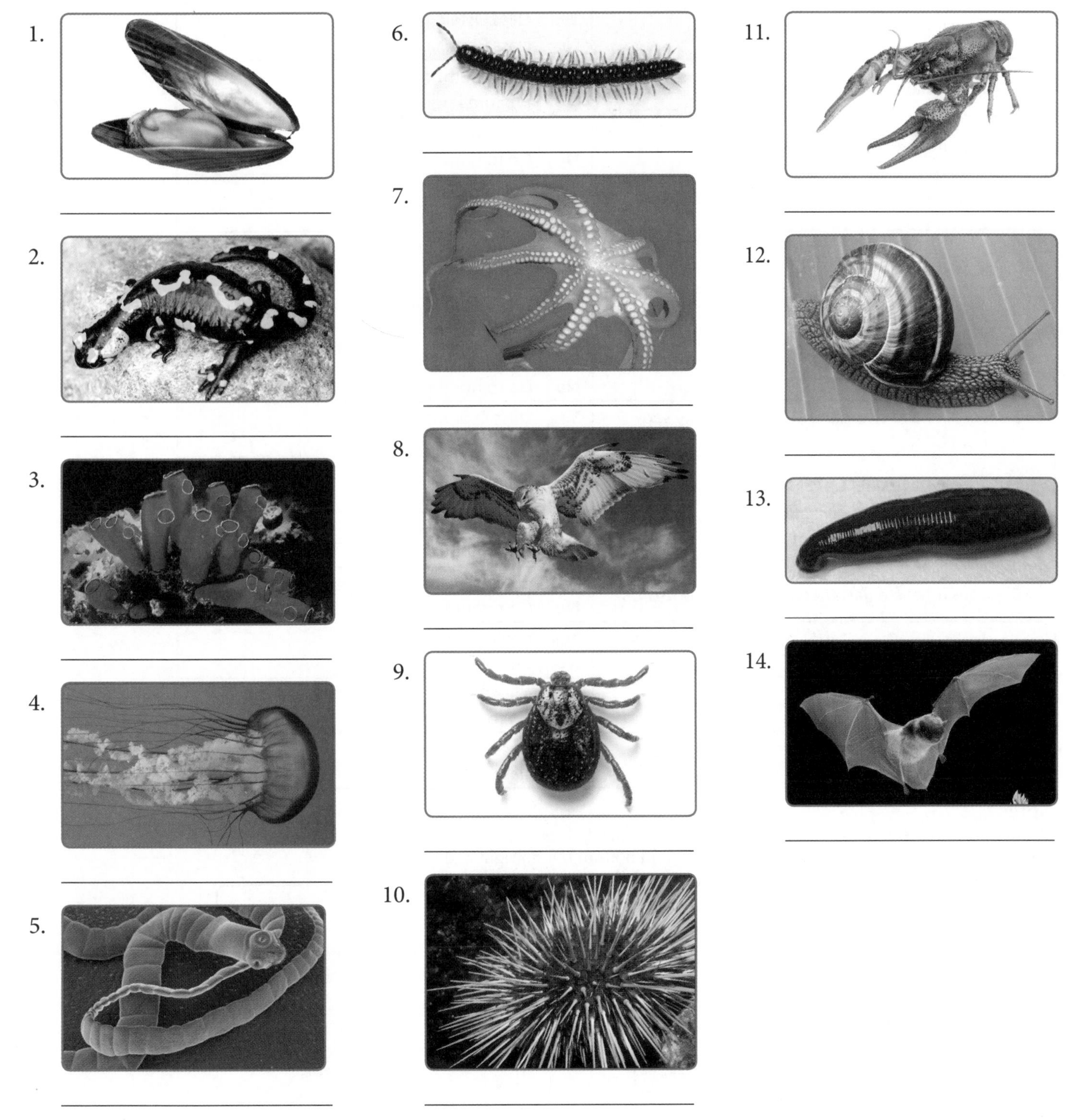

Key to Identification of Animal Phyla and Classes	
1. Does it have a backbone?	**Yes** Go to number 2. **No** Go to number 6.
2. Does it have feathers?	**Yes** class Aves **No** Go to number 3.
3. Does it have hair or mammary glands?	**Yes** class Mammalia **No** Go to number 4.
4. Does it have scales?	**Yes** Go to number 5. **No** class Amphibia
5. Does it have gills?	**Yes** class Osteichthyes **No** class Reptilia
6. Does it have symmetry?[1]	**Yes** Go to number 7. **No** phylum Porifera
7. Does it have radial symmetry?[2]	**Yes** Go to number 8. **No** Go to number 9.
8. Does it have tentacles or stinging cells?	**Yes** phylum Cnidaria **No** phylum Echinodermata
9. Does it have an exoskeleton?	**Yes** Go to number 10. **No** Go to number 14.
10. Does it have gills?	**Yes** subphylum Crustacea **No** Go to number 11.
11. Does it have more than eight legs?	**Yes** Go to number 12. **No** Go to number 13.
12. Does it have two pairs of legs per body segment?	**Yes** class Diplopoda **No** class Chilopoda
13. Does it have only six legs?	**Yes** class Insecta **No** class Arachnida
14. Does it have the body of a worm?	**Yes** Go to number 15. **No** Go to number 17.
15. Does it have a flattened body top to bottom?	**Yes** phylum Platyhelminthes **No** Go to number 16.
16. Does it have a segmented body?	**Yes** phylum Annelida **No** phylum Nematoda
17. Does it have a two-part shell?	**Yes** class Bivalvia **No** Go to number 18.
18. Does it have tentacles?	**Yes** class Cephalopoda **No** class Gastropoda

Notes

[1]An organism has symmetry if it can be divided into equal halves.
[2]An organism has radial symmetry if it has a top and bottom but no right and left sides.

Hints

Organism 6 has an exoskeleton but no gills.
Organism 7 does not have radial symmetry.
Organism 9 has an exoskeleton but no gills.
Organism 10 has radial symmetry.
Organism 11 has gills.
Organism 12 does not have tentacles.
Organism 14 has hair but not feathers.

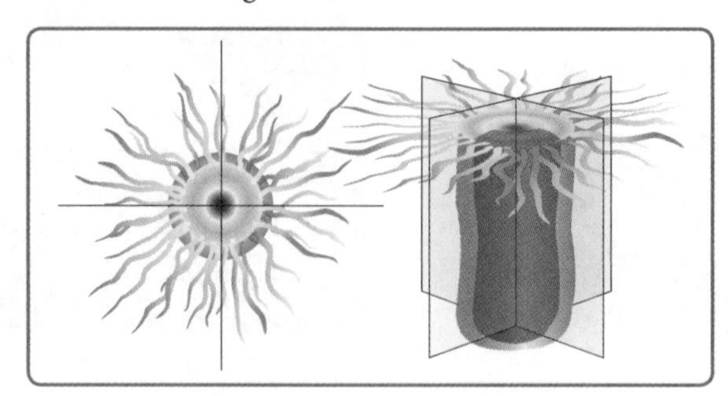

Radial symmetry

name ____________________

section __________ date __________

2i Classification Review

Directions

Choose a word from the list to correctly complete each sentence below. Each word may be used only once.

classify	kind	phylum
common	kingdom	scientific
English	Latin	taxonomy
Galileo	Linnaeus	three
genus	observe	two

1. God commanded all living things to reproduce after their ____________________.
2. To arrange things in groups is to ____________________.
3. ____________________ proposed the classification system that is widely used today.
4. A scientific name consists of ____________________ words.
5. A scientific name follows the language form of ____________________.
6. A(n) ____________________ name could apply to many organisms, but a(n) ____________________ name only applies to one organism.
7. The largest taxon in the modern classification system is the ____________________.
8. *Streptococcus pyogenes* is the bacterium that causes strep throat. *Streptococcus* is the organism's ____________________ name.
9. The taxon above *class* is ____________________.
10. The science of classifying living organisms is called ____________________.

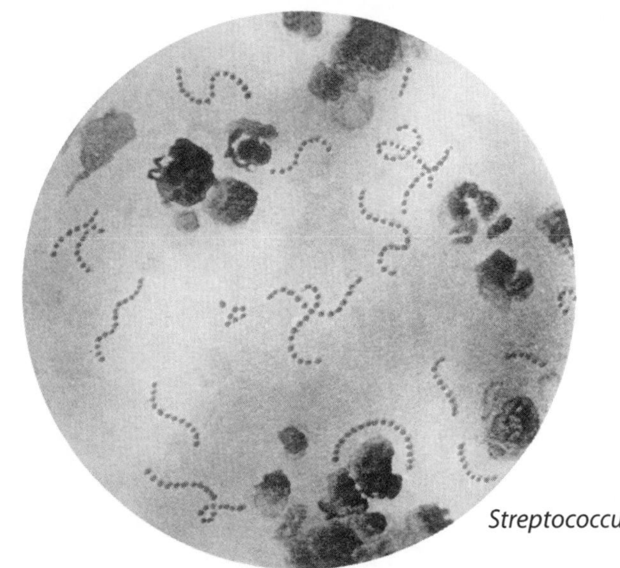

Streptococcus pyogenes

name ______________________

section ____________ date ____________

2j The pH of Life Substances

Procedure

1. Obtain each of the materials to be tested that are listed in the table below. Those that are not liquid should be dissolved or mixed in a small amount of distilled water. Sweat should be touched to the pH paper directly; do not use the pH meter.
2. Determine the pH of each material by dipping one piece of pH paper in each material and observing the color change. Match the color with the color scale on the pH paper container. You should determine a number value for the pH. Values less than 7 are acidic, values greater than 7 are basic, and values equal to 7 are neutral. Record your results in the data table.
3. Your teacher will explain how to use the pH meter. Use the pH meter to determine the pH of each of the materials. Record your results in the data table.
4. Based on your measurements, decide whether each substance is an acid or a base and record your decisions in the last column of the table.

Goals

- ✓ Measure the pH of common substances.
- ✓ Recognize that many substances produced by living things are acids and bases.

Materials

materials to be tested (see table below)
distilled water
pH meter
pH paper

Data

pH Data

Material	pH paper	pH meter	Acid or base?
aloe	X		X
apple juice	3-4		acid
banana	4-5		acid
coconut milk	X		X
coffee (black)	5-6		acid
egg white	8		base
egg yolk	7-8		nuetral or base
honey	3-4		acid
lemon juice	2-3		acid
milk	6-7		acid or nuetral
pineapple juice	3-4		acid
rainwater	4-6		acid
saliva	6-8		acid, nuetral or base
salmon (canned)	X		X
sweat	X		X
tuna (canned)	5-6		acid
vinegar	2-3		acid
Worcestershire sauce			

Summing Up

1. How many of the substances tested were acids?

   Of the 13 substances 8 were acids

2. Which gave the more precise pH measurement—the pH paper or the pH meter?

   ph meter

3. Do you think acids and bases are found in living things? Why or why not?

   Yes. All of the substances in this investigation came from living things, and some acids and some were bases.

4. If you wanted to find the pH of cytoplasm, how would you do it?

   Crush the cells to release cytoplasm for testing or insert microelectrodes into the cytoplasm of indvidual cells.

name ______________________

section __________ date __________

2k Protein in Life Substances

Procedure

1. Obtain each of the materials listed in the table below. Those that are not liquid should be ground, mixed, or dissolved in a small amount of distilled water.
2. Determine whether each material contains protein by mixing 3 mL of the material with 1 mL of biuret solution in a test tube. If the material contains protein, it will turn violet (or pink). Record your results in the data table.

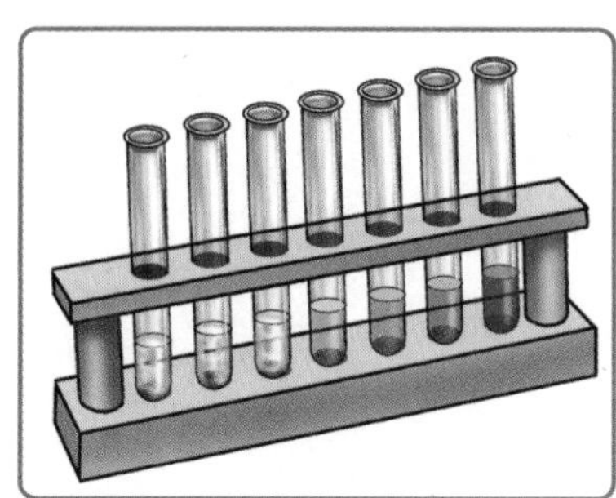

Goal

✓ Determine whether some common substances contain protein.

Materials

materials to be tested (see table below)
distilled water
biuret solution
goggles
test tube rack
test tubes
graduated cylinder, 10 mL
pipets

Data

Protein Data

Material	Color after biuret solution (pink or violet/no change)	Protein present? (yes/no)
apple juice	no change	no
banana	no change	no
beans (boiled)		
coconut milk		
egg white	violet	yes
egg yolk		
flour	violet	yes
gelatin		
honey	no change	no
lemon juice	no change	no
milk	violet	yes
rainwater		
saliva	violet	yes
salmon (canned)		
starch		
sugar		
syrup	no change	no
tuna (canned)	violet	yes
vegetable oil	no change	no
vinegar	no change	no

Summing Up

1. How many of the substances tested contain protein?

Of the 12 substances 5 were protein.

2. Do you think proteins are found in living things? Why or why not?

Yes. All of the substances with protein came from living things (although not all substances from living things had protein.

name ______

section ______ date ______

21 The Action of Enzymes

Goal
✓ Observe the action of enzymes.

Materials
mixing bowls
measuring cup
milk
hot plate
thermometer
measuring spoons (1 tbsp)
sugar
vanilla
rennet tablets
water
stirring spoons

Procedure

1. Label one mixing bowl *A* and another *B*.
2. Heat 0.95 L (4 c) of milk until lukewarm (about 45 °C, 113 °F).
3. In each bowl, combine 0.47 L (2 c) of milk, 45 mL (3 tbsp) of sugar, and 15 mL (1 tbsp) of vanilla.
4. Crush one rennet tablet and mix it with 15 mL (1 tbsp) of cold water until it is dissolved.
5. Add the dissolved rennet tablet to bowl A and stir the solution for about 10 seconds.
6. Cover both bowls and allow them to sit undisturbed for 10 minutes.

Data

After 10 minutes, uncover the bowls and compare the contents. Note differences and similarities such as color, consistency, taste, and smell. Record your observations below.

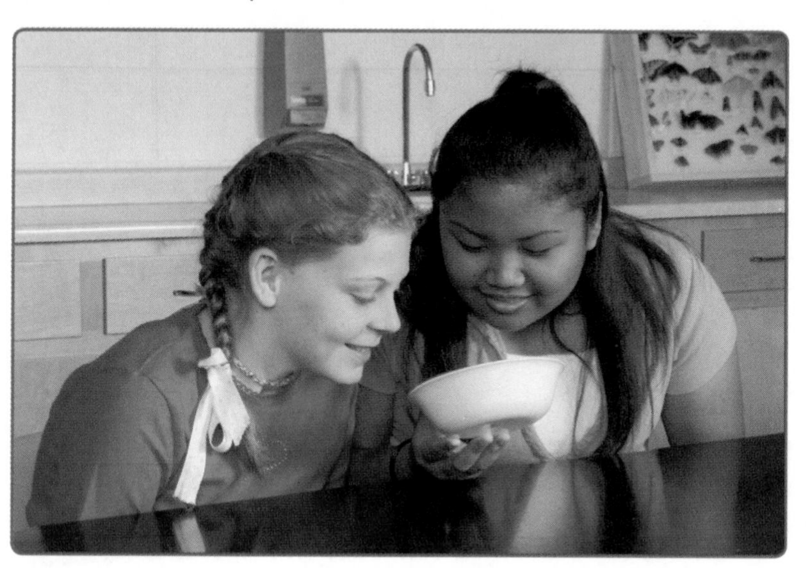

Bowl A: ______

______

Bowl B: ______

______

Summing Up

1. Rennet tablets contain an enzyme called rennin. What are enzymes?

___

___

___

2. The sugar and the vanilla were flavorings in the experiment. The rennin acted on the milk. What did it do to the milk?

___

___

___

Field Investigation

name ______________________

section ____________ date ____________

2m Grouping Plants by Characteristics

Goal

✓ Identify and observe plant traits that could be used to classify plants.

Materials

various plant specimens

Procedure and Data

When thinking of kinds of plants, most people list flowers, trees, and shrubs. However, within these three general categories there are many varieties. There are differences between varieties, even though at first glance they may appear identical. By taking a closer look at plants, you will be able to find many differences between them.

1. Make a collection of several different types of the same kind of plant. Be sure your collection is of only one kind of plant. For example, you can collect branches of several different types of oaks. Different types of maples, pines, roses, or azaleas are also possibilities. Various types of marigolds, philodendrons, chrysanthemums, ferns, or similar plants would also be good specimens to collect. If the plant is small, you may collect the entire plant. If the plant is a large shrub or a tree, collect only a portion of a stem.
2. Carefully observe the plants you have collected. Note the similarities and differences between them. Compile two lists, one that describes the similarities between the various specimens and one that describes the differences.

Kind of plant: ______________________________

List up to ten similarities shown by your specimens.

1. ______________________________
2. ______________________________
3. ______________________________
4. ______________________________
5. ______________________________
6. ______________________________
7. ______________________________
8. ______________________________
9. ______________________________
10. ______________________________

List up to ten differences shown by your specimens.

1. ______________________________
2. ______________________________
3. ______________________________
4. ______________________________
5. ______________________________
6. ______________________________
7. ______________________________
8. ______________________________
9. ______________________________
10. ______________________________

name

section date

Field Investigation

2n Making an Insect Collection

Procedure

1. Catch as many different adult insects as you can without damaging them. Immature insects, such as nymphs and larvae (grubs, caterpillars, and the like), are sometimes difficult to identify and often require special killing-and-mounting procedures. Do not collect these forms.

Goals

- ✓ Use a dichotomous key to identify organisms.
- ✓ Gain experience in collecting organisms.
- ✓ Become familiar with orders of insects.

Ideas for Catching Insects

1. Look under stones, boards, and logs.
2. Collect mushrooms and put them in a closed jar. As the mushrooms dry, insects that were inside will come out.
3. Dig up and turn over a shovelful of earth. Watch closely and capture any insects that scurry away.
4. Check around outdoor lights at night.
5. At night, put a light over a tub of water that contains a spoonful of kerosene. In the morning, collect the insects in the tub.
6. If time permits, collect caterpillars and grubs, but do not kill and identify them until they become adults. The pupa stage may be as short as two weeks or as long as several months.
7. Leave an open sandwich outside for an hour or two. Insects will be attracted to the food.
8. Attach an insect net to an automobile and drive along at dusk about 25 mi/h. The net will trap many flying insects. This method works very well along country roads.
9. Use an insect net to capture flying insects. Disturbing bushes and tall grass will often arouse many flying insects.
10. Check pool filters for beetles and other large insects that have fallen into the water.

Materials

box to hold collected insects temporarily
killing jar (made from a large-mouth jar with a screw lid or a coffee can with a plastic lid, cotton or a sponge, cardboard, and ethyl acetate or rubbing alcohol)
ethyl or isopropyl (rubbing) alcohol
hand lens
materials for displaying insects
straight pins
clear fingernail polish
paper triangles
mothballs

2. Kill the insects you catch.
    - Make a killing jar by following the directions in the box on page 42. You can kill many insects by placing them in your killing jar as soon as you catch them. Leave them in the killing jar until they are dead.
    - You can kill beetles quickly by dropping them into a small jar of ethyl alcohol or isopropyl (rubbing) alcohol (70%–80%). Beetles sometimes survive in killing jars for long periods of time.
    - Do not place butterflies and moths into your killing jar. They may ruin their wings by flapping around inside the jar. Kill a butterfly or moth by squeezing firmly on its thorax. This can be done with the insect inside a zippable sandwich bag.

Method for killing butterflies and moths

How to Make a Killing Jar

Use a large-mouth jar with a screw lid or a coffee can with a plastic lid. Make several jars of various sizes if you plan to catch several insects at one time.

Place a half-inch-thick layer of cotton in the bottom of the jar or can. (You may use a sponge instead of cotton.)

Pour a killing agent such as ethyl acetate or rubbing alcohol onto the cotton or sponge. Keep the killing jar tightly closed as much as possible. The more you keep the jar covered, the fewer times you will have to add more killing agent to the cotton or sponge. If the sponge or cotton becomes too dry, add more killing agent.

Cover the cotton or sponge with cardboard that has holes punched in it and has been cut to fit the inner diameter of the can or jar. This keeps the insects from coming into direct contact with the killing agent.

An alternative to putting the cotton in the bottom of the jar is to put it in a much smaller container with holes in it that is fastened to the lid of the jar.

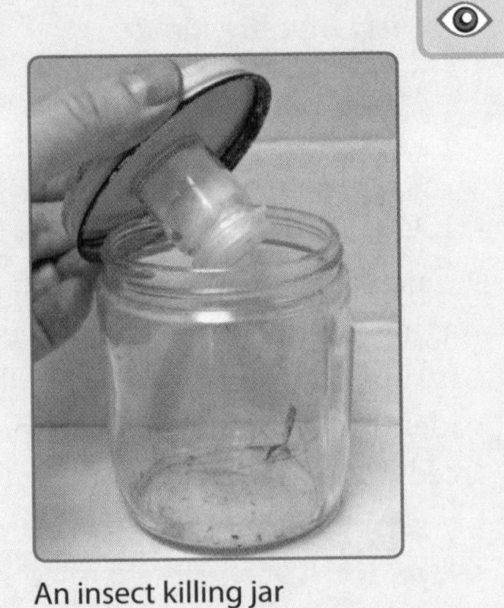
An insect killing jar

- Some insects can also be killed by placing them in the freezer for a few hours or overnight, but do not store them there. Be careful when removing them from the freezer. If moisture collects on them, they will need to be dried out before being put into an airtight container. If insects stay moist, they will often deteriorate. Do not freeze grasshoppers or katydids because it could change their color.

3. Mount the insects.
    - You can mount most insects by sticking pins through the thorax (not the wings) and into a piece of cardboard or foam board. Make sure that the insects are suspended in the air on the pins and are not tacked against the cardboard or foam board. Be sure the insect is dead before you mount it. Pin your insects soon after they are dead because they become brittle with time.
    - To mount beetles (order Coleoptera), place the pin through the right wing and abdomen, not through the thorax.
    - Mount tiny insects (such as mosquitoes, gnats, and fruit flies) onto small triangles of stiff paper. Touch a triangle of paper to a small drop of clear fingernail polish; then touch the polish on the paper to the insect. Once the polish dries, pin the paper triangles to the cardboard or foam board.
    - To mount butterflies and moths, spread their wings out with strips of paper pinned to the cardboard or foam board.

How to mount a butterfly or moth

4. Protect your mounted insects.
    - Others may want to handle your specimens. Keep your collection away from children and pets, and allow friends to look but not to touch. Some insects are very fragile.

name________________________

- For temporary storage of your insects, glue a flat piece of foam board or thick, corrugated (having ridges) cardboard to the bottom of a box. (A shoe box works well.) Stick the pins with insects on them into the foam board or cardboard.
- Protect your dead insects from hungry live insects by attaching mothballs inside the collection box. Loose mothballs may damage insects; therefore, put holes in a tiny box or bag filled with mothballs, tape it shut, and tape it into the corner of the storage box.

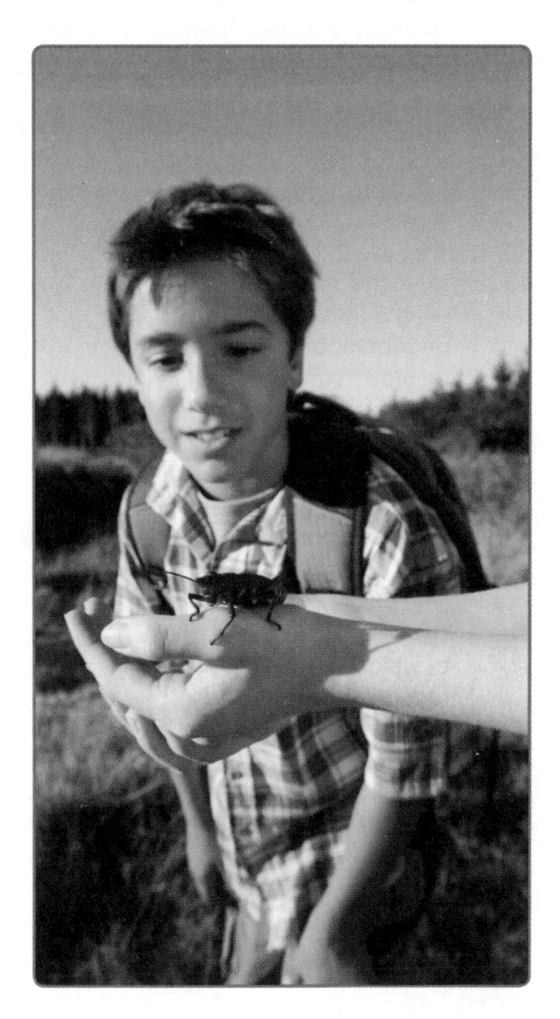

5. Identify your insects.
   - Use the classification key on pages 44–46 to determine the correct order for each of your specimens. If your specimen does not exactly fit the limited descriptions given in the key, choose the description that you think best fits your specimen.
   - Once you have determined the order to which an insect belongs, use books on insects to identify the specimen by common name. Field guides to insects are helpful. Your teacher may be able to suggest specific books to help you. Online resources can be helpful as well, but be sure to confirm the identification by finding multiple reputable sites that give the same identification.
6. Label and display your insects.
   - Print on a rectangular piece of paper the information that applies to each insect according to your teacher's instructions. (See the example below.) Printed labels usually look more professional than handwritten ones.

Insect Label Information

Order: Orthoptera
Common Name: red-legged grasshopper
Date Collected: September 2013
Place Collected: field; Murray, KY

   - Attach the label for each specimen under that specimen. You may pin it to the foam board or cardboard with the same pin that goes through the specimen as long as the specimen does not obstruct the view of the label.
   - Devise a method to display your insect collection. You may display your insects temporarily on a piece of cardboard or foam board, or you may display them in a collection box.
   - Be sure to arrange your specimens in orderly rows when placing them in your display. Also, group your specimens by classified order.

Key to Identification of Common Insect Orders		
1. Does the organism have six legs?	**Yes** Go to number 2. **No** Either this organism is not an insect or it is a larval form (such as a caterpillar), which cannot be identified with this key.	
2. Does the insect have wings? (NOTE: Typical membranous wings may be hidden under a thick, hard outer pair of wings.)	**Yes** Go to number 3. **No** Go to number 16.	unicorn beetle (wings open) 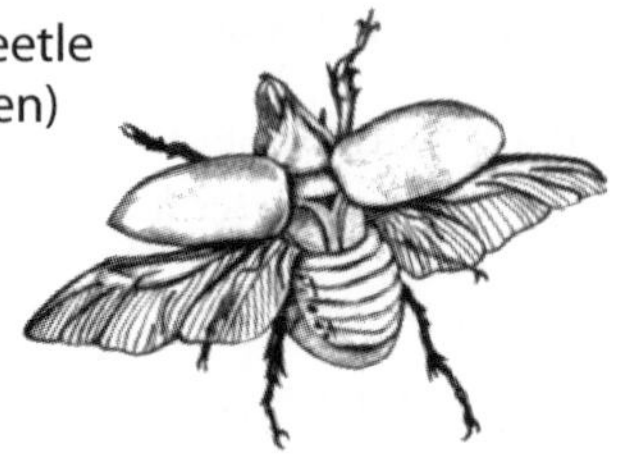
3. Does the insect have two pairs of wings? (NOTE: One pair of covering structures counts as a pair of wings. Also see note regarding bees, wasps, and ants at number 12.)	**Yes** Go to number 4. **No** order Diptera (flies, mosquitoes, gnats)	 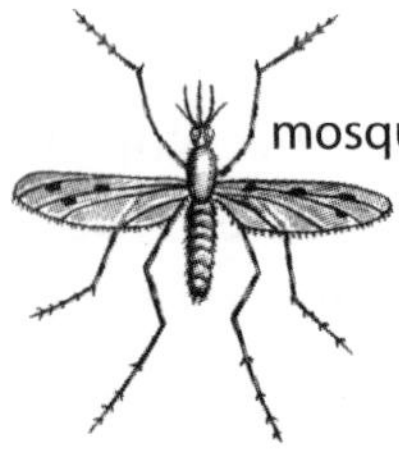 mosquito bluebottle fly
4. Are both pairs of wings made of the same substance and a similar thickness?	**Yes** Go to number 10. **No** Go to number 5.	
5. Are the outer wings hard, and do they meet in a straight line in the center of the insect's back?	**Yes** Go to number 6. **No** Go to number 7.	
6. Does the insect have obvious pincerlike structures extending from its abdomen?	**Yes** order Dermaptera (earwigs) **No** order Coleoptera (beetles)	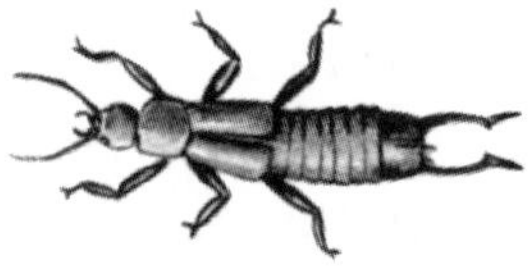 earwig  unicorn beetle (wings closed)
7. Does the outer pair of wings have a leathery section next to the body and membranous tips that overlap when the insect is at rest?	**Yes** order Hemiptera (chinch bugs, squash bugs, stinkbugs) **No** Go to number 8.	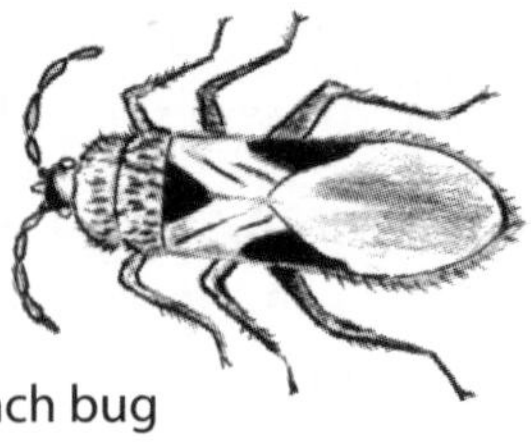 chinch bug

name ______________________

8. Are the hind legs enlarged for jumping?	**Yes** order Orthoptera (grasshoppers, crickets, katydids) **No** Go to number 9.	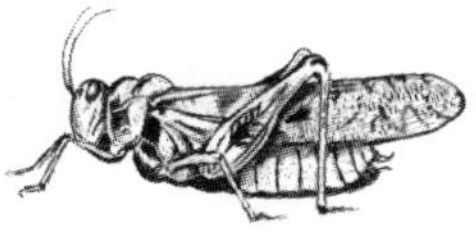 grasshopper,  cricket
9. Are the front legs used for grasping prey?	**Yes** order Mantodea (mantids) **No** order Orthoptera (cockroaches)	 praying mantis, 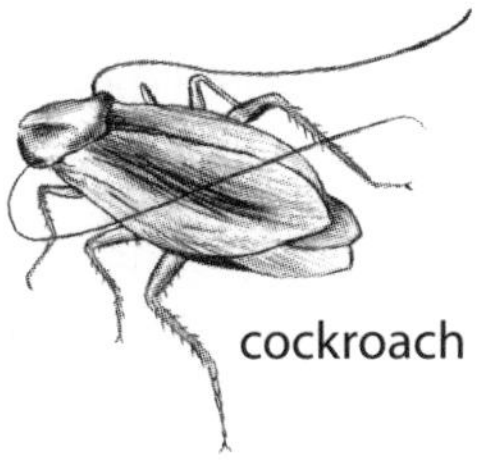 cockroach
10. Are the insect's wings covered with scales that rub off easily?	**Yes** order Lepidoptera (moths, butterflies) **No** Go to number 11.	 moth, 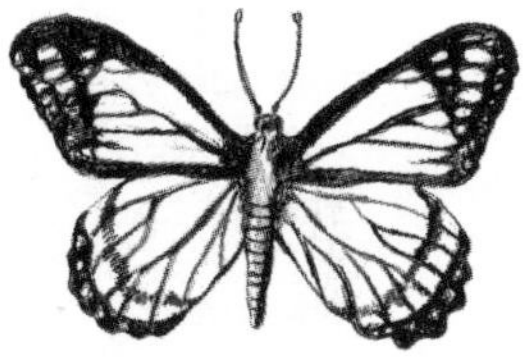 butterfly
11. Do the insect's wings slope down from its body when it is at rest?	**Yes** order Hemiptera (cicadas, aphids, treehoppers, leafhoppers) **No** Go to number 12.	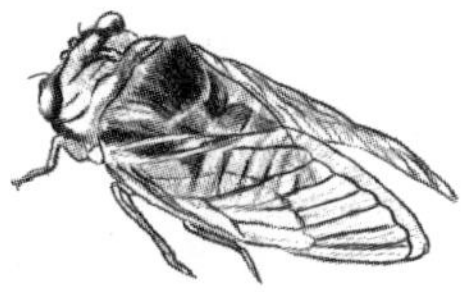 cicada, 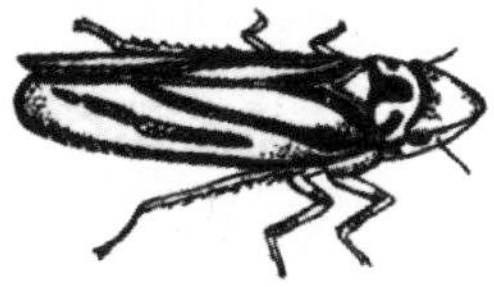 leafhopper
12. Do the insect's wings have very few vertical crossveins?	**Yes** order Hymenoptera (bees, wasps, ants). (NOTE: Male and female ants have wings early in life. Members of this order may have wings that look like one pair instead of two pairs because the wings are hooked together by rows of tiny hooks.) **No** Go to number 13.	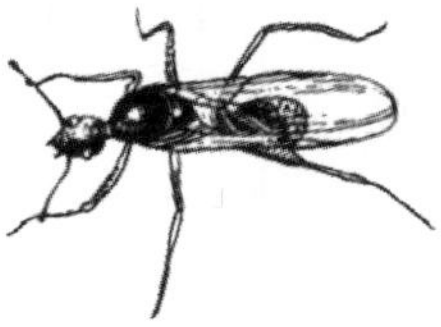 ant (young), 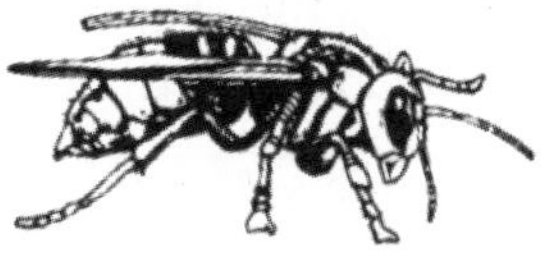 hornet
13. Are there two or three long, threadlike tails extending from the insect's abdomen?	**Yes** order Ephemeroptera (mayflies) **No** Go to number 14.	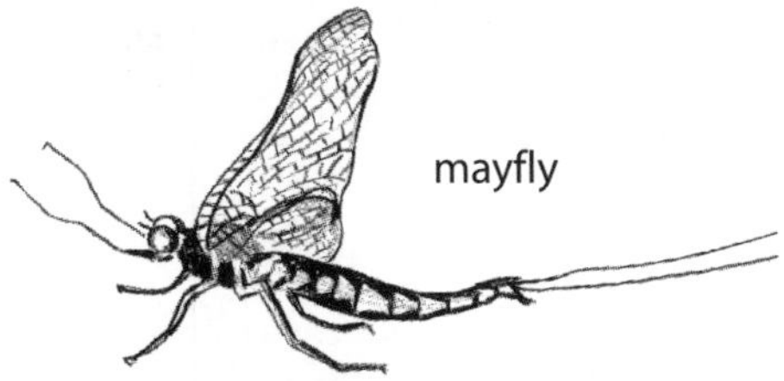 mayfly
14. Are the insect's antennae short and not obvious?	**Yes** order Odonata (dragonflies) **No** Go to number 15.	 dragonfly

15. Do the insect's wings have very distinct veins?	**Yes** order Neuroptera (ant lions, lacewings, dobsonflies) **No** order Isoptera (termites)	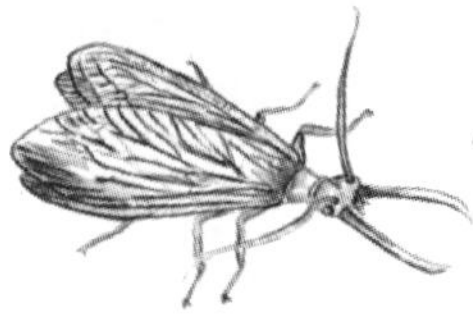 dobsonfly  termite (winged)
16. Is the insect narrow waisted (pinched in between the thorax and abdomen)?	**Yes** order Hymenoptera (ants, bees, wasps) **No** Go to number 17.	 ant (wingless)
17. Does the insect have two short tails extending from its abdomen?	**Yes** order Hemiptera (aphids, scale insects, leafhoppers) **No** Go to number 18.	 aphid (wingless)
18. Is the insect small with a soft, plump body and a small head?	**Yes** order Isoptera (termites, white ants in some stages) **No** Go to number 19.	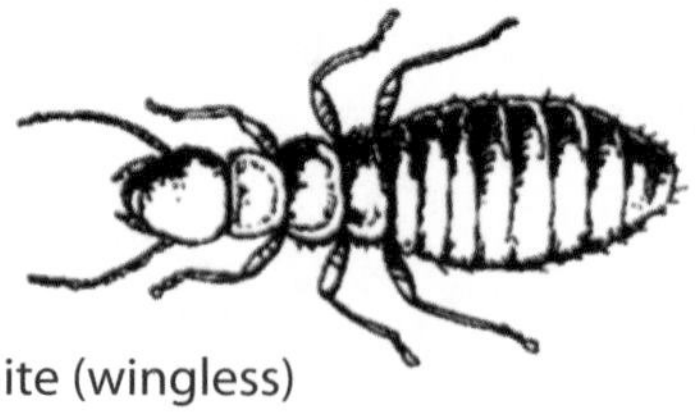 termite (wingless)
19. Is the insect tiny with a narrow body flattened on the sides, and is it able to jump with its hind legs?	**Yes** order Siphonaptera (fleas) **No** Go to number 20.	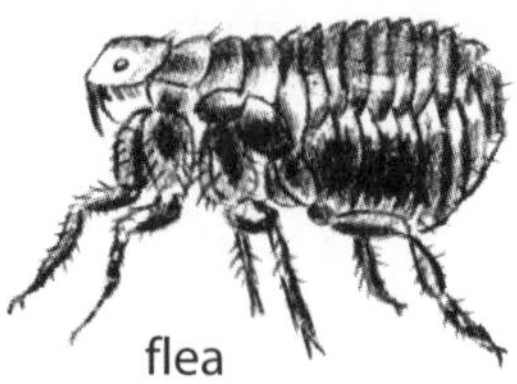 flea
20. Does the insect have a very delicate body with long, jointed, threadlike tails and antennae?	**Yes** order Thysanura (silverfish, bristletails) **No** Go to number 21.	 silverfish
21. Does the insect have a stick- or twig-shaped body?	**Yes** order Phasmida (walking sticks) **No** order Orthoptera (certain grasshoppers or crickets in adult and/or nymph stages)	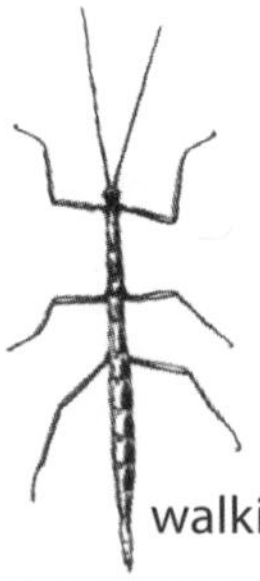  wingless grasshopper walking stick

name ____________________

section __________ date __________

3a Membranes and Their Important Properties

Directions

Match each term below with the correct statement. Then write the number of the statement in the corresponding lettered hexagon in the figure below. If you complete the figure correctly, you will find that the numbers in each diagonal and vertical row of three hexagons will add up to the same number. Write that number in the blank at the bottom.

A. lipid

B. active transport

C. osmosis

D. selective permeability

E. passive transport

F. diffusion

G. fluid mosaic

______ 1. Allows some molecules through but not others

______ 2. Movement away from an area of high concentration

______ 3. Does not require energy to pass through a membrane

______ 4. Requires the use of energy to pass through a membrane

______ 5. Movement of water through a selectively permeable membrane without requiring energy

______ 6. Accounts for most of the molecules that compose membranes

______ 7. Describes a common model of the cell membrane

The common total is _____.

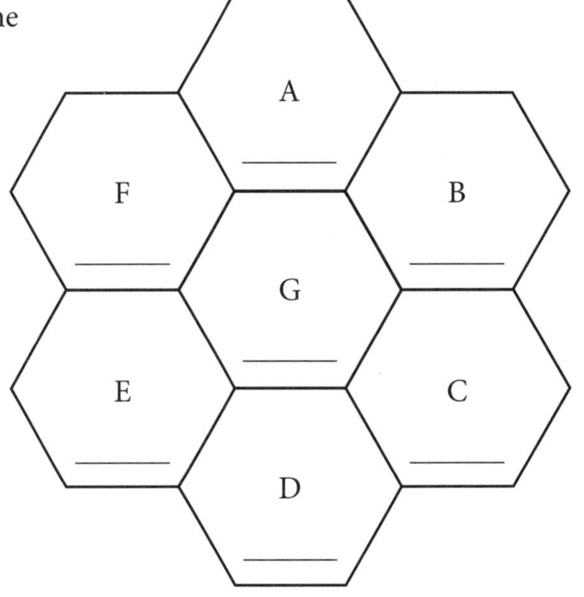

name ______________________

section __________ date __________

Application

3b The Compound Light Microscope

Directions

Match each term below with the correct definition. Not all terms will be used. Then label the diagram using the entire list of terms.

A. arm
B. base
C. body tube
D. coarse adjustment knob
E. compound light microscope
F. diaphragm
G. eyepiece (ocular)
H. fine adjustment knob
I. mirror or light source
J. objectives
K. specimen
L. stage

F 1. Used for varying the amount of light reaching the specimen

k 2. The object viewed through a microscope

E 3. Uses two sets of lenses to produce an enlarged image

L 4. Where the slide is placed

J 5. The lenses nearest the object being viewed

D 6. Used for general focusing

G 7. Contains the lens(es) that you look into

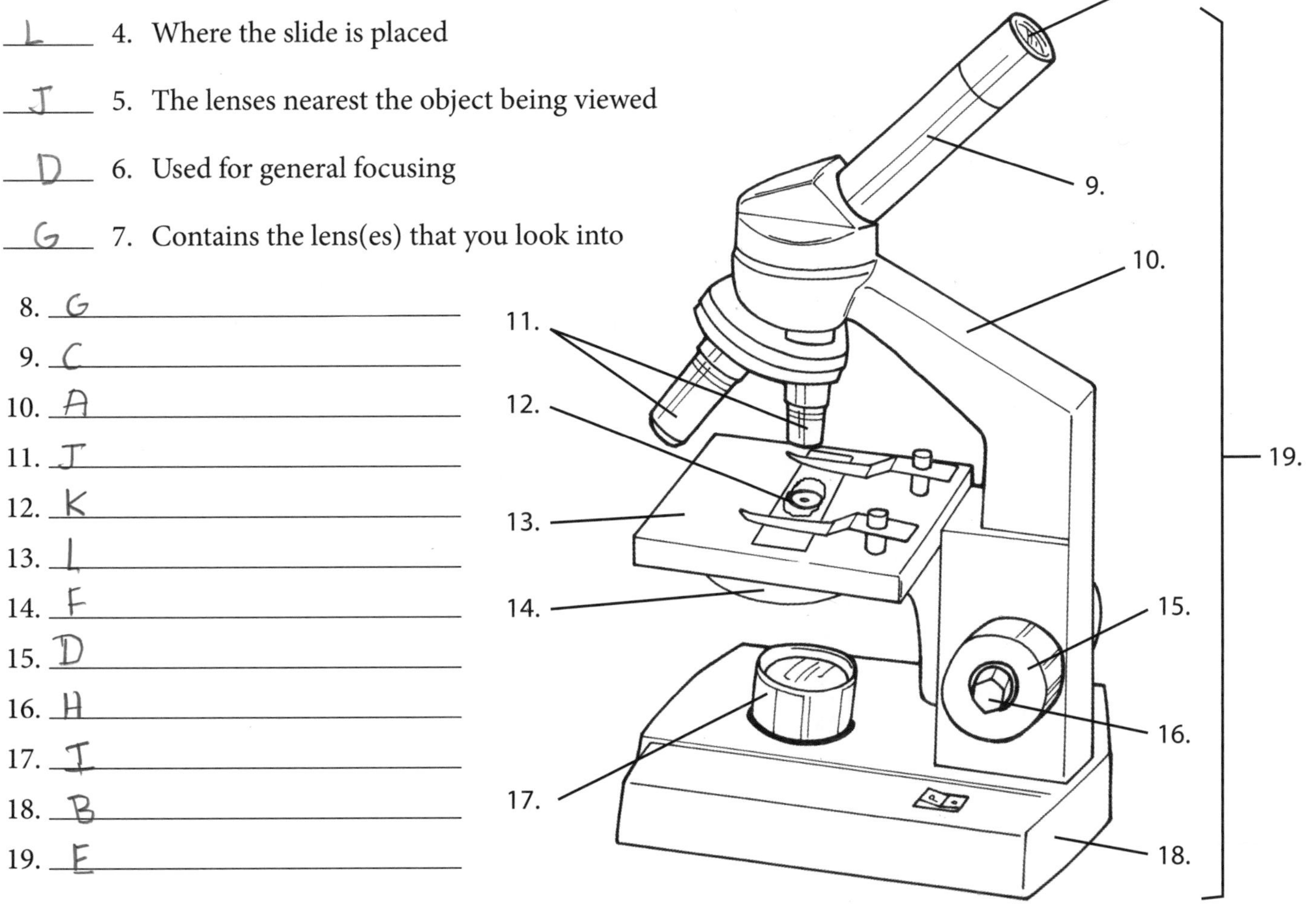

8. G
9. C
10. A
11. J
12. K
13. L
14. F
15. D
16. H
17. I
18. B
19. E

Application

name ____________________

section __________ date __________

3c Typical Parts of Cells

Directions

The cell membrane and a couple of other structures involved with cell membranes have been drawn for you. These and other cellular structures are described under the blanks beside the cell. In each blank, write the name of the structure that is being described. Then draw the structure in the cell diagram if it has not been drawn already. Draw a line from the name of the structure to the drawing of the structure. The cell membrane has already been labeled for you as an example.

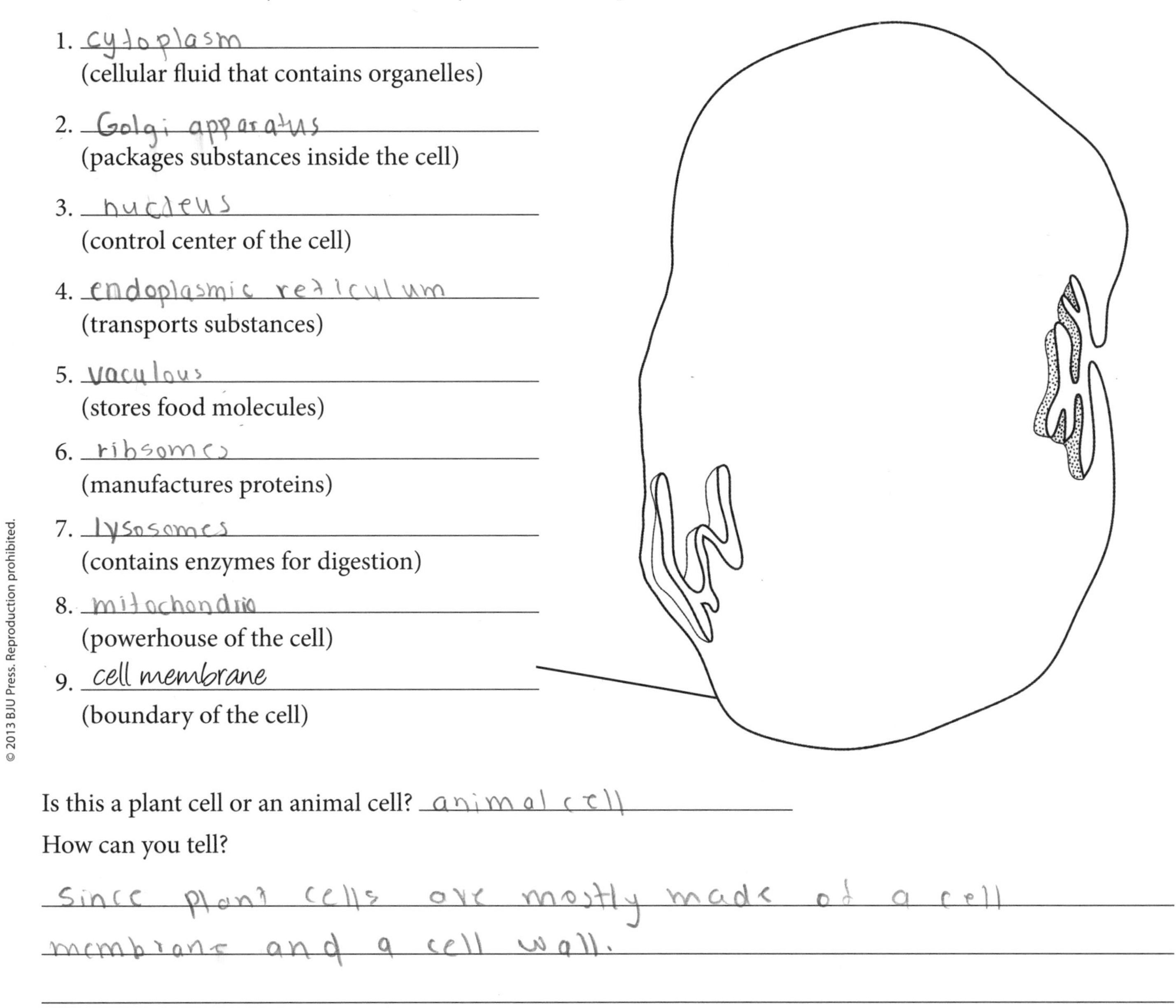

1. cytoplasm
   (cellular fluid that contains organelles)
2. Golgi apparatus
   (packages substances inside the cell)
3. nucleus
   (control center of the cell)
4. endoplasmic reticulum
   (transports substances)
5. vaculous
   (stores food molecules)
6. ribsomes
   (manufactures proteins)
7. lysosomes
   (contains enzymes for digestion)
8. mitochondria
   (powerhouse of the cell)
9. cell membrane
   (boundary of the cell)

Is this a plant cell or an animal cell? animal cell

How can you tell?

since plant cells are mostly made of a cell membrane and a cell wall.

Application

name ____________________

section __________ date __________

3d Review

Directions

Read the following statements. If the statement is true, write *True* in the blank provided. If the statement is false, draw a line through the word or words that make the statement false. Then in the blank, write the word or words necessary to make the statement true.

true ______ 1. Some cells completely lack some organelles.

longer ______ 2. Flagella are usually ~~shorter~~ longer than cilia.

true ______ 3. Lysosomes contain enzymes that break down other substances.

true ______ 4. A cell membrane's structure is described by the fluid mosaic model.

true ______ 5. Most cells are too small to be seen without a microscope.

true ______ 6. The Golgi apparatus collects and packages materials from the cytoplasm.

true ______ 7. The nuclear membrane has pores.

water ______ 8. In osmosis, ~~salt~~ water molecules diffuse through a membrane.

true ______ 9. DNA contains coded messages that determine the characteristics of a cell.

true ______ 10. Vacuoles may contain food, water, fats, wastes, or chemicals.

DNA ______ 11. Chromosomes are made of the molecule RNA.

true ______ 12. When molecules diffuse through a cell membrane, they move from an area of higher concentration to an area of lower concentration.

outside ______ 13. A cell wall is located inside the cell membrane.

true ______ 14. Chloroplasts are organelles that contain the chemical chlorophyll, which is used in photosynthesis.

true ______ 15. A selectively permeable membrane allows only certain molecules to pass through it.

active ______ 16. Passive transport requires energy.

true ______ 17. Organs are groups of tissues that work together to accomplish a particular function.

name____________________

section__________ date__________

Class Investigation

3e Diffusion Rates

Part 1: Stirred vs. Unstirred Water

Goals

- ✓ Observe diffusion.
- ✓ Measure different rates of diffusion.
- ✓ Determine how certain factors affect diffusion rates.

Materials

250 mL beakers (2)
water (hot and cold)
ink or dark food coloring
measuring spoons
stirring rod or spoon
stopwatch or a clock with a second hand

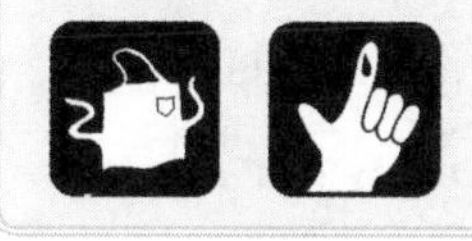

Procedure

1. Fill two clean glass beakers with about 235 mL (1 c) of water each.
2. Place the two beakers next to each other and wait for the water to become still.
3. Measure two identical amounts of ink or dark food coloring (about 5 mL, or 1 tsp).
4. Using a stirring rod or a spoon, stir the water in one beaker. Then immediately pour one portion of ink into the beaker of stirred water and the other portion of ink into the beaker of unstirred water. Be sure to pour both portions of ink at the same time.

Data

Record the time required for each beaker to complete diffusion. Diffusion is complete when all the water in the beaker is the same color; no streaks or currents will be visible.

Stirred water: __________ minutes __________ seconds
Unstirred water: __________ minutes __________ seconds

Summming Up

1. What is diffusion?

____
____
____
____

2. Diffusion is an example of which type of transport?

   active ☐ passive ☐ neither ☐ both ☐

3. In which beaker did diffusion take place more rapidly?

   stirred ☐ unstirred ☐

4. Explain why diffusion occurred more rapidly in one beaker.

____
____
____

Part 2: Hot vs. Cold Water

Procedure

1. Set up two beakers of water as you did in Part 1. This time, however, one beaker should contain very hot water, and the other beaker should contain very cold water.
2. Prepare two identical amounts of ink or dark food coloring as before. Do not stir the water in either beaker.
3. Pour equal portions of ink into each beaker and start timing. Be sure to pour both portions of ink at the same time.

Data

Record the time it takes for each beaker to complete diffusion.

Hot water: __________ minutes __________ seconds
Cold water: __________ minutes __________ seconds

Summing Up

1. In which beaker did diffusion take place more rapidly?

   hot water ☐ cold water ☐

2. Explain why diffusion took place more rapidly in one beaker.

   ____

   ____

   ____

3. What other factors could affect the rate of diffusion?

   ____

   ____

   ____

4. How is the diffusion you observed in this lab different from osmosis? How is it similar?

   ____

   ____

   ____

   ____

5. Would you expect the results of this experiment to be the same if you used a lighter color of food coloring instead of ink or dark food coloring? Why or why not?

   ____

   ____

   ____

   ____

name ____________________

section ____________ date ____________

3f Osmosis

Goal

✓ Demonstrate and observe osmosis.

Materials

thistle tube
clear corn syrup
selectively permeable membrane
rubber band or string
500 mL beaker
distilled water
clamp
ring stand
wax pencil or tape
metric ruler

Procedure

1. Put your finger over the narrow end of a thistle tube; then pour syrup into the thistle-shaped bulb. The syrup should fill the bulb and go down the tube a couple of centimeters (about an inch). The tube should not be completely filled with syrup.
2. Keeping your finger over the end of the tube, have another student place the membrane over the open end of the bulb. Secure the membrane with a string or rubber band so that no syrup can leak out when the bulb is turned downward.
3. Turn the thistle tube so that the bulb is pointed down and remove your finger from the end of the tube. Allow the syrup to settle.
4. Place the bulb of the thistle tube in a beaker of distilled water as shown in the diagram.
5. Using a wax pencil or a piece of tape, mark the level of syrup in the tube.
6. Every 10 minutes, measure how many millimeters above the original mark the syrup has risen. Record this in the data chart. Continue these observations as long as your class period lasts.
7. If possible, leave the apparatus set up overnight and observe the results the next day.

Data

Osmosis Data

Time	Level of syrup (in mm)
10 minutes	
20 minutes	
30 minutes	
40 minutes	
50 minutes	
60 minutes	
after 24 hours	

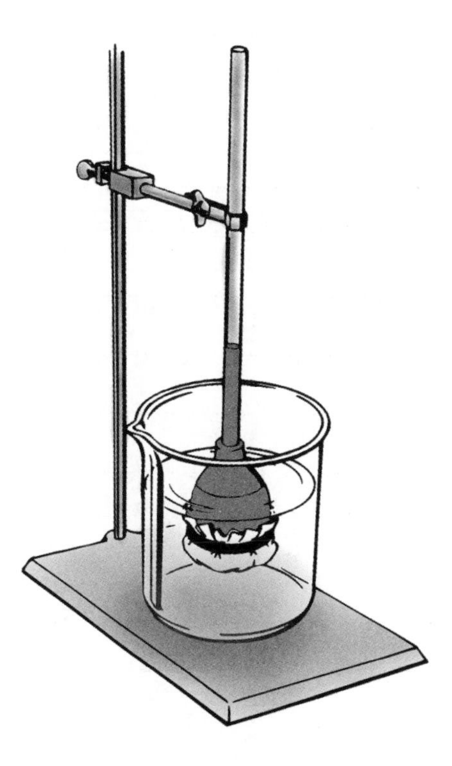

Summing Up

1. What is osmosis?

2. What caused the level of syrup to rise in the tube?

3. Why do syrup molecules remain in the tube and not pass from the tube into the beaker of water?

4. If you left this apparatus set up for a long period of time, the action you observed would
   continue indefinitely. ☐ come to a stop. ☐
   Why?

5. Osmosis is an example of which type of transport?
   active ☐ passive ☐ neither ☐ both ☐

Class Investigation

name____________________

section__________ date__________

3g How to Use a Microscope

Goals

- ✓ Demonstrate the proper way to set up and focus a compound light microscope.
- ✓ Practice using a compound light microscope.

Materials

microscope
glass slides
cover slips
eyedropper
newspaper or other printed materials

Setting Up

Using a Microscope

Always follow these instructions to properly obtain, set up, and return your microscope.

Carry the microscope properly.

Excessive jarring and bumping may bring the lenses out of adjustment. To avoid damaging the microscope, observe the following rules:

1. If it is necessary to take a microscope out of a cabinet or cupboard, be careful not to bang the microscope against the sides of the cabinet.
2. Carry the microscope with one hand under the base and the other hand holding the arm of the microscope.
3. Be sure to keep the microscope close to your body in an upright position so that the eyepiece does not slip out of the body tube.
4. Place the microscope gently on the table and position it about 8 cm (3 in.) from the edge.

Prepare the microscope properly.

You may need to clean your microscope before using it. Observe the following rules while you clean it:

1. Use only lens paper to clean the lens surfaces and the mirror. Wipe the lenses in one direction across the diameter of each lens.
2. Consult your instructor if any material remains on your eyepiece or objectives.
3. Under no circumstances should you attempt to take your microscope apart.

Return the microscope properly.

When you have finished using the microscope, you should observe the following rules:

1. If the microscope has a built-in light source, be sure the switch is off.
2. Make sure the body tube is straight up and down (if your model is one that inclines).
3. Position the lowest-power objective directly under the body tube.
4. Adjust the body tube to its lowest position.
5. Carefully return the microscope to the place where you obtained it.

Calculating the Magnifying Powers on a Microscope

1. Compute the magnifying powers on your microscope. On page 61 of your textbook, you will find instructions for determining the powers available on a microscope.
2. Fill in the table on page 60 regarding your microscope. Your microscope may have only two or three objectives. If so, use only the first two or three lines of the table.

3. In this manual, the term *low power* refers to a total magnification of about 100×. The term *high power* refers to a total magnification of about 400×.

	Objective power		Eyepiece power		Total magnification
Objective 1	________×	times	________×	equals	________×
Objective 2	________×	times	________×	equals	________×
Objective 3	________×	times	________×	equals	________×
Objective 4	________×	times	________×	equals	________×

Procedure

Viewing a Specimen

Prepare your microscope for viewing.

1. Open the diaphragm on your microscope to its largest setting.
2. If your microscope has an electric light source, plug it in and turn it on.
3. If your microscope has a mirror, adjust it until you are able to see a bright light through the eyepiece (ocular). You should try to use the brightest light source available, but you should not use direct sunlight.

Prepare a microscope slide for viewing.

1. Carefully clean and dry a glass slide and a cover slip. Once you have cleaned them, handle the slide and cover slip only by the edges. This will prevent you from viewing fingerprints by mistake.
2. Place a single drop of water on the center of your slide.
3. Cut a letter *e* from a piece of newspaper and place it on the drop of water.
4. Carefully place the cover slip on top of the drop of water. If air bubbles appear near the piece of paper, gently tap the cover slip with a pencil. If too many bubbles remain, take the slide apart and start over.
5. Place the slide on the stage of your microscope and position it so that the piece of newspaper is centered over the opening in the stage. Clip the slide in place.

Focus the microscope on low power.

1. Position the low-power objective so that it is directly under the body tube of your microscope. On most microscopes the objectives will click into place.
2. While looking at the side of your microscope, turn the coarse adjustment knob until the objective *almost* touches the cover slip.
3. Look through the objective and *slowly* turn the coarse adjustment knob so that the body tube goes up (or the stage goes down) until you are able to see the newspaper.

   NOTE: Never turn the coarse adjustment knob so that the body tube goes down (or the stage goes up) while you are looking through the eyepiece! You could cause the objective to push into the slide and break the objective.
4. If you have raised the objective more than an inch from the cover slip, you have raised it too far. Look at the side of your microscope and turn the coarse

name______________________________

adjustment knob until the objective almost touches the cover slip. Then look through the eyepiece and start raising the body tube again.

5. If you are still unable to see the newspaper, try the following:
   - Check to make sure the newspaper is directly above the center of the opening in the stage and directly under the objective.
   - Adjust the diaphragm to a slightly smaller setting and then try to focus the microscope again.
6. If you still cannot see the newspaper, ask your teacher for help.
7. Once you have found the newspaper by using the coarse adjustment knob, use the fine adjustment knob to obtain a clear image. You can adjust the fine adjustment knob either direction, but you should never have to turn it more than a full turn in either direction.
8. Often you will need to readjust your fine adjustment knob while you are viewing something through the microscope.

Note what happens when you move your slide.

1. While looking through the objective, move your slide slightly to the left. What happens to the image that you are viewing?

____

____

2. Move your slide slightly to the right. What happens to the image that you are viewing?

____

____

3. Move your slide so that it goes away from you slightly. What happens to the image?

____

____

4. Move your slide so that it comes toward you slightly. What happens to the image?

____

____

5. Describe what the newspaper and the printed *e* look like under the low power of a microscope.

____

____

Focus your microscope on high power.

1. Move your slide so that an edge of the newspaper crosses the center of the area you see through the microscope. Be sure this is in the very center.
2. Carefully rotate the objectives so that the high-power objective is directly below the body tube.

3. Adjust the fine adjustment knob. The image should be in focus when you turn the knob less than a full turn.
4. If necessary, adjust the amount of light coming through the diaphragm.
5. If you cannot see a good image through your microscope, return to low power and focus again. Make sure that your newspaper is in the center of the area you are viewing through the microscope. Try to focus on high power again. If you still have problems, ask your teacher for help.
6. Move the slide around and observe the newspaper and the letter *e* on high power.
7. What is the difference between the image you see under low power and the image you see under high power?

____

____

____

____

____

8. Make slides of printed letter *e*'s from magazines and other sources. What differences do you notice between different kinds of paper and between different forms of printing?

____

____

____

____

____

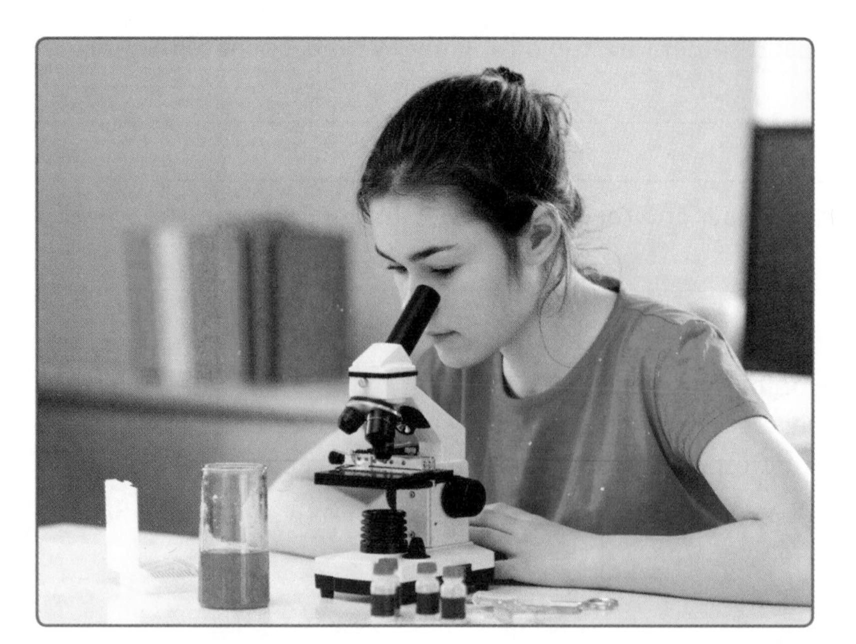

name ____________________

section __________ date __________

Class Investigation

3h Observing Cells with a Microscope

Goals

✓ Observe and compare different kinds of cells.

✓ Practice using a compound light microscope.

Materials

microscope
prepared slides of various cells
glass slides
cover slips
eyedropper
single-edged razorblades
toothpicks
cork
elodea
flower
geranium leaf
onion
potato
protozoan specimen
iodine solution
methylene blue

Procedure

Use a microscope to observe several prepared slides (slides that have preserved tissues mounted on them) that your teacher has chosen. Prepared slides usually have specimens that have been stained for easier viewing.

Observe several slides of fresh specimens that your teacher has prepared. Some fresh specimens must be stained to be seen clearly; other specimens have natural color and do not need to be stained.

On the data chart, list the names of the cells you observed and record your observations and descriptions.

Data

Name of cell	Observations and descriptions of cell*

*Describe the size, shape, color, and number of cells seen and list any cellular parts that you can identify.

Summing Up

1. Based on your observations, what conclusions can you draw regarding the differences between plant and animal cells?

____

____

____

____

2. Which two or three cellular structures did you see most often?

3. Did you see anything moving inside the fresh cells? If you did, what cells were they and what do you think was moving?

4. What other observations did you make regarding cells?

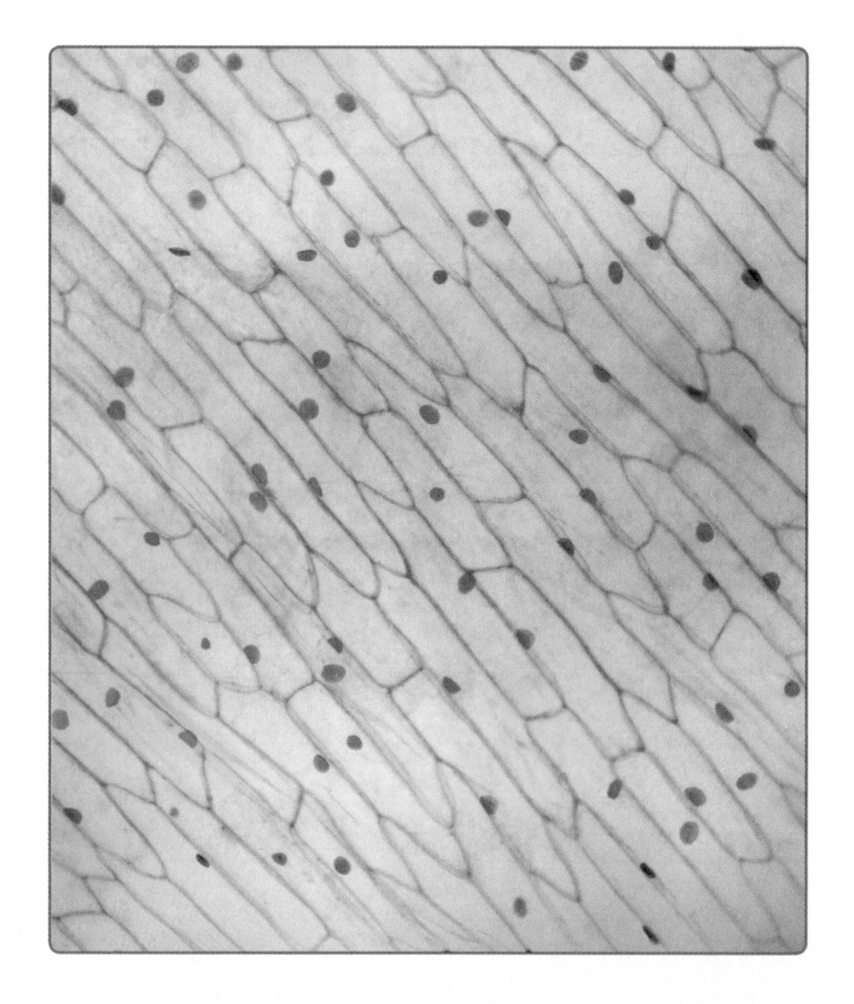

Class Investigation

name ____________

section ____________

3i Turgor Pressure

Goals

✓ Observe the … plant cells.

✓ Demonstrate turgor pressure.

Materials

dishes
water
salt water
knife
potato

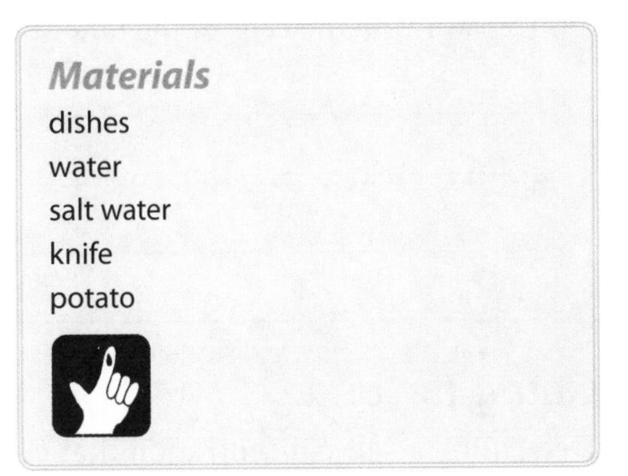

Procedure

1. Place about 5 cm (about 2 in.) of water in a dish. Label the dish *fresh water.*
2. Place the same amount of salt water in a dish. Label the dish *salt water.*
3. Cut two thin strips of potato about the thickness of thin french fries and at least 5 cm long. You should be able to completely submerge them in the water of the dishes. The two potato strips should be as nearly identical as you can make them.
4. Place one strip of potato in the fresh water and the other in the salt water.
5. Leave the strips undisturbed for 30 minutes.
6. After 30 minutes, take the potato strips out of the fresh water and the salt water and record your observations.

Data

- Describe the potato strip in fresh water.

____

- Describe the potato strip in salt water.

____

Summing Up

1. What is turgor pressure?

____

____

____

____

2. What conditions are necessary for plant cells to have turgor pressure?

____

____

____

____

cellular organelle helps maintain turgor pressure in plant cells? ____________________

the end of your experiment, which of the two potato strips had greater turgor pressure? How can you tell?

____

____

____

____

5. Explain why the cells of the other potato strip lost turgor pressure.

____

____

____

____

Going Beyond

Determine a salt concentration that equals the solute concentration in the potato's cells by placing potato strips in a range of saltwater concentrations. The highest concentration that does not change the crispness of the potato from its original crispness would have the same solute concentration as the cytoplasm of the potato's cells. Be sure to cut all strips from the same potato.

name ____________________

section __________ date __________

4a Division of Labor

Directions

Write your responses in the spaces provided.

1. What is meant by "division of labor"? Give two examples (not mentioned in Chapter 4) of division of labor.

2. Read Romans 12:4–8 and 1 Corinthians 12:12–25. Describe the division of labor in the body of Christ, and discuss the benefits and responsibilities of members in the body of Christ. Are you a member of the body of Christ?

Application

name ____________________

section __________ date __________

4b Cellular Respiration

Directions

Use the definitions to help unscramble the terms.

1. ragus	sugar	The most common energy source in cellular respiration
2. tacmlyosp	cytoplasm	Where the first part of cellular respiration occurs
3. rebcaio	aerobic	Type of cellular respiration that requires oxygen
4. ticcla	lactic	Acid produced in muscles during anaerobic respiration
5. TAP	ATP	The usable form of energy for the cell
6. ithmodoraicn	mitochondria	Organelles associated with cellular respiration
7. temfatrenoin	fermentation	Type of cellular respiration that produces alcohol or lactic acid
8. cduorprse	producers	Organisms that can make their own source of energy
9. smunseroc	consumers	Organisms that must obtain energy by eating other organisms
10. borcan oidxied	carbon dioxide	Gas that is produced as a byproduct during cellular respiration

name ____________________

section __________ date __________

4c Photosynthesis

Directions

Below are several groups of terms. In each group, three of the four terms are related to one another. Draw a line through the unrelated term, and then write a sentence using the remaining three terms. Your sentence should show how the terms are related. You may slightly change the form of the term in your sentence (for example, *product* to *products* or *stored* to *storage*).

1. photosynthesis / cellulose / sugar / oxygen

2. light energy / consumers / photosynthesis / chemical energy

3. consumer / photosynthesis / chlorophyll / pigment

4. chlorophyll / chloroplasts / oxygen / organelles

5. sugar / light / carbon dioxide / water

6. sugar / oxygen / pigments / products

7. sugar / cellulose / cell walls / oxygen

8. producers / food / photosynthesis / respiration

9. sugar / light / pigments / absorb

10. membrane / mitochondria / chloroplast / chlorophyll

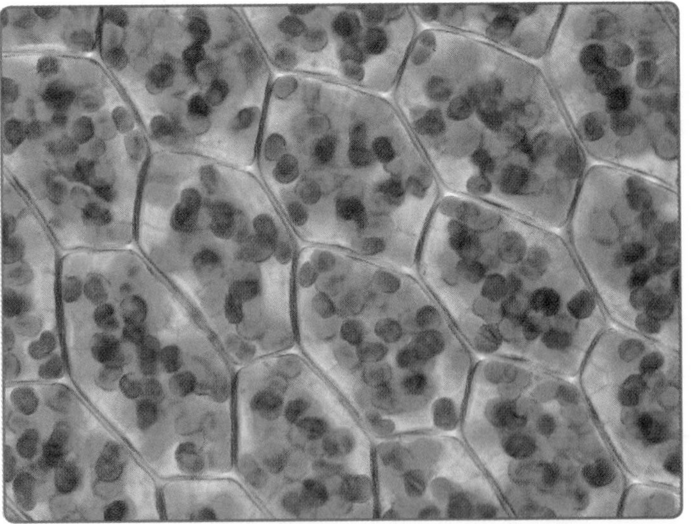

Wednesday 21

name ______________________

section ____________ date ____________

Application

4d Review

Directions

Choose the correct set of words to complete the following statements about photosynthesis, aerobic cellular respiration, and anaerobic cellular respiration. You may use each answer only once.

Photosynthesis

A. carbon dioxide
B. cells
C. cellulose
D. chloroplasts
E. oxygen
F. photosynthesis
G. sugar
H. water

1. __D__ are located in __B__.
2. __A__ and __H__ are reactants.
3. __C__ is made from __G__.
4. __F__ produces sugar and releases __E__.

Aerobic Cellular Respiration

A. aerobic
B. aerobic cellular respiration
C. ATP
D. energy
E. mitochondria
F. molecule
G. sugar
H. with

1. __G__ is broken down to release __D__.
2. __B__ occurs in the cell's __E__.
3. __A__ cellular respiration occurs __H__ oxygen.
4. The primary __F__ produced by aerobic cellular respiration is __C__.

Anaerobic Cellular Respiration

A. alcoholic
B. anaerobic
C. carbon dioxide
D. fermentation
E. lactic acid
F. muscles
G. without
H. yeast

1. __B__ cellular respiration occurs __G__ oxygen.
2. __A__ fermentation occurs in __H__.
3. __E__ fermentation can occur in human __F__.
4. __C__ is a gas produced in alcoholic __D__.

Tuesday 20

Class Investigation

name ____________________

section __________ date __________

4e Aerobic Cellular Respiration

Goal

✓ Observe the consumption of oxygen by aerobic cellular respiration.

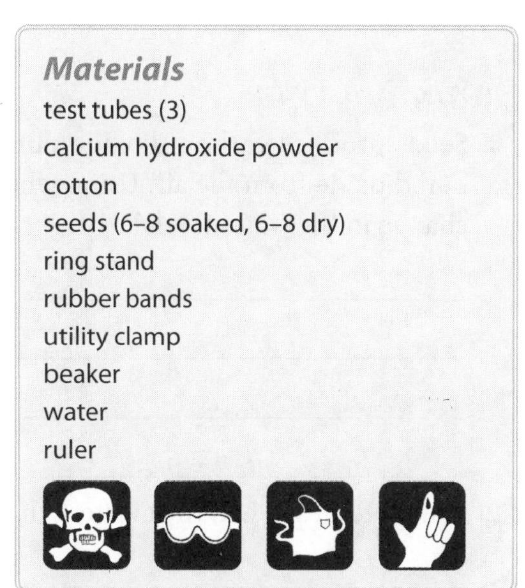

Materials

test tubes (3)
calcium hydroxide powder
cotton
seeds (6–8 soaked, 6–8 dry)
ring stand
rubber bands
utility clamp
beaker
water
ruler

Procedure

1. Label the test tubes *A*, *B*, and *C*.
2. Place about half an inch (about 13 mm) of calcium hydroxide powder in each test tube.
3. Insert a ball of cotton into each test tube, and use a pencil to push the cotton all the way to the calcium hydroxide. Check to make sure the calcium hydroxide remains in place by turning the test tube upside down.
4. Put 6–8 presoaked seeds in test tube A, and insert a ball of cotton on top of the seeds so that they remain in place when turned upside down.
5. Put 6–8 dry seeds in test tube B, and insert a ball of cotton on top of the seeds so that they remain in place when turned upside down.
6. Insert a second ball of cotton into test tube C, leaving a space between the cotton balls equal to the space taken up by the seeds in test tubes A and B.
7. Bundle the three test tubes together with a rubber band. Secure one of them in the utility clamp on the ring stand so that all three test tubes are suspended upside down.
8. Fill the beaker about four-fifths full of water.
9. Carefully lower the utility clamp so that the three test tubes are at least three-fourths submerged upside down in the beaker of water. Be sure to keep the test tubes vertical (do not tilt them as you lower them) so that no water enters the mouths of the test tubes.

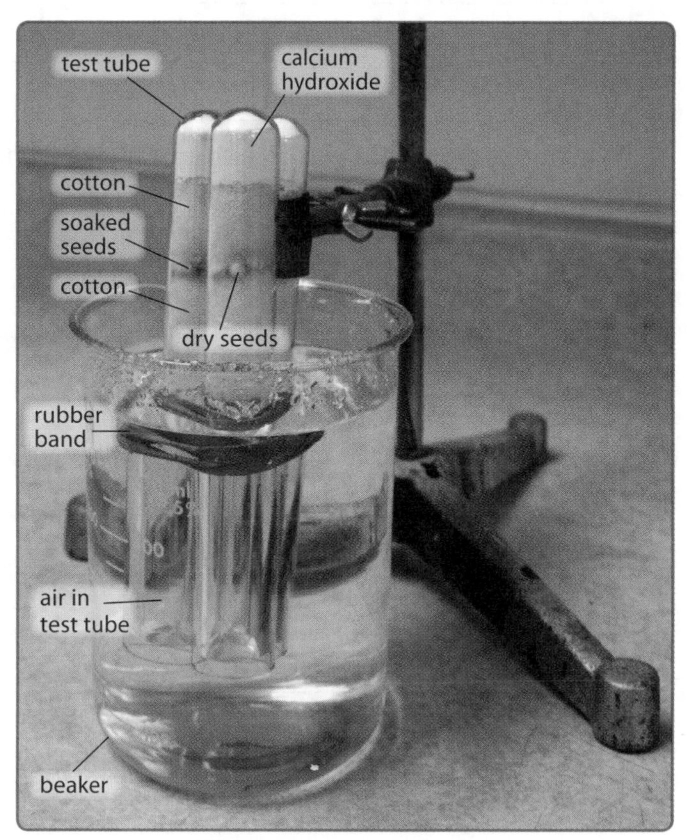

Data

1. Observe the level of water in each of the test tubes. Ideally they should all start at the same level. After five minutes, measure and record the water levels in each of the test tubes.

   Test tube A 0 mm Test tube B 0 mm Test tube C 0 mm

2. Leave the assembly undisturbed for at least 48 hours. As time progresses, the water should rise in the test tubes. Then measure and record the water levels in each of the test tubes.

   Test tube A 25 mm Test tube B 8 mm Test tube C 4 mm

Summing Up

1. Seeds produce carbon dioxide during cellular respiration, and calcium hydroxide absorbs carbon dioxide from the air. Using what you have learned about cellular respiration, why was there a change in the water levels?

   As the seeds absorb oxygen from the air for use in cellular respiration, and the calcium hydroxide absorbs carbon dioxide produced during cellular respiration, the level of water in the test tubes goes up filling space

2. Which test tube had the greatest change in the water level? Why?

   Test tube A. The presoaked seed are going through cellular respiration to produce energy for germanation. Because the cellular respiration is aerobic, it is using up oxygen gas allowing the water level to rise.

3. Which test tube had the second greatest change in the water level? Why?

   Test tube B. The dry seeds may not be germanating but they are still performing a small amount of aerobic cellular respination because they are still living, but in a dormant state.

4. What was the purpose of test tube C? Did it show any change in water level? Why or why not?

   It served as a control for comparison. There was probably a slight change. There was some carbon dioxide in the air in the test tube initially, and this carbon dioxide was absorbed by the calcium hydroxide.

Tuesday 20

name ______________________

section ____________ date ____________

4f Anaerobic Cellular Respiration

Goal

✓ Observe the products of anaerobic cellular respiration.

Materials

Thermos vacuum flasks (2)
two-hole rubber stoppers (2, to fit in the vacuum flasks)
thermometers (2)
glass tubing (2 pieces)
balloons (2)
string
tape
apple juice (600 mL)
sugar (120 mL)
yeast (1 package)

Procedure

1. Label the vacuum flasks *A* and *B*.
2. Prepare two rubber stoppers.
   - Place a thermometer through one hole in each stopper.
   - Place a short section of glass tubing through the other hole in each stopper.
   - Tie a balloon to the top end of each glass tubing piece. Carefully tape each balloon so that no air can escape from it. The balloons should be stretched before attaching them to the glass tubing. Fully inflate them a few times before putting them on the glass tubing.
3. Pour 300 mL (10 fl oz) of apple juice into each vacuum flask.
4. Add 60 mL (4 tbsp) of sugar to each vacuum flask.
5. Pour one package (0.25 oz) of yeast into flask A. Do *not* pour yeast into flask B. Place the covers on the flasks and shake them well. Remove the covers and place the stoppers in each vacuum flask. Be sure that each balloon is deflated. (See illustration.)

Data

Wait for three minutes and then record your observations on the chart below. Observe the vacuum flasks for the next three days and record your observations on the chart below.

Flask A			Flask B		
	Temperature	Condition of balloon		Temperature	Condition of balloon
Initial	22°C	Flat	Initial	20°C	
24 hours	24°C	inFloted	24 hours	21°C	FLAT
48 hours	22°C	slowly inflate	48 hours	22°C	
72 hours	22°C	stays the same	72 hours	21°C	

Summing Up

1. After what period of time was the temperature in flask A the highest?

   24 hr ☑ 48 hr ☐ 72 hr ☐ The temperature did not change. ☐

2. After what period of time was the temperature in flask B the highest?

   24 hr ☐ 48 hr ☑ 72 hr ☐ The temperature did not change. ☐

3. After what period of time did the balloon on flask A expand the most?

   24 hr ☑ 48 hr ☐ 72 hr ☐ The balloon did not expand. ☐

4. After what period of time did the balloon on flask B expand the most?

   24 hr ☐ 48 hr ☐ 72 hr ☐ The balloon did not expand. ☑

5. Define anaerobic cellular respiration.

   Anaerobic cellular respiration is the process by which cells break down sugar and release energy without using oxygen.

6. What are the products of anaerobic cellular respiration?

   Energy (ATP), carbon dioxide, and either alchohol or lactic acid are the products of anaroebic cellular respiradion.

7. In which of the two vacuum flasks did anaerobic cellular respiration occur?

   flask A ☑ flask B ☐

   Explain why you chose that answer.

   The temprature in flask A increased, indacating that energy was released. The balloon on Flask A expanded, indacating that a gas (carbon dioxide) was given off.

name ____________________

section __________ date __________

4g Starch from Photosynthesis

Procedure

1. Place a healthy geranium in a dark area for two days (a cabinet or cupboard works well). During this time, energy reserves (starch) in the leaf will become depleted since the plant will be unable to obtain energy from light (through photosynthesis).
2. Cut pieces of aluminum foil into rectangles that are each large enough to cover half of a leaf.
3. Use paper clips to attach the aluminum foil pieces to the upper surface of leaves that are still attached to the plant. (See illustration.) Be sure that the edges of foil adhere closely to each leaf or even bend down slightly over the edges of the leaf. Be sure to leave half of the leaf exposed.
4. Place the plant in a sunny window or another well-lit area for one or two days.
5. Heat the alcohol in a beaker until it is hot but not boiling. You should use enough alcohol to cover the leaves that will be placed in the beaker.
6. Remove the leaves with aluminum foil from the plant. Remove the aluminum foil.
7. Immerse the leaves in the hot alcohol for about five minutes. During this time, the chlorophyll will be removed from the leaves.
8. Rinse the leaves with water, and place each leaf flat in a petri dish.
9. To test for the presence of starch, cover each leaf in the petri dish with iodine solution for five minutes.
10. Rinse off the iodine solution and examine the leaves.

Goals

- ✓ Observe that the presence of starch can indicate photosynthesis has occurred.
- ✓ Demonstrate that light is necessary for photosynthesis.

Materials

geranium or coleus plant
aluminum foil
paper clips
alcohol (70% ethanol or 70% isopropyl)
250 mL beaker
hot plate or other heat source (not an open flame)
water
petri dishes
iodine solution

Data

Make a drawing of the leaves in the space below.

Summing Up

1. Why did you have to put the plant in a dark area for two days?

2. Did starch form in the covered or uncovered part of the leaf? ____
3. What does the presence of starch indicate?

4. What does the absence of starch indicate?

5. What would you have discovered during the test for starch if, after covering the leaves, you set the plant in a dark area for one or two days before testing for starch? Why?

6. What would be the problem with covering both the top and bottom of the leaf? In other words, what might the leaf need or give off that the foil might interfere with if the bottom of the leaf had also been covered?

Going Beyond

On a separate sheet of paper, explain an experiment that you could do (similar to this investigation) that would use different colors of plastic wrap or cellophane to determine what color(s) of transmitted light are most useful in photosynthesis.

Monday 2, 2021

name ______________________

section ____________ date ____________

Application

5a The Cell Cycle

Directions

Below is a series of diagrams illustrating each stage of the cell cycle. Beside the diagrams is a column for the name of the stage being illustrated and another column for a description of what is happening in that stage. Fill in the missing names or descriptions. In your descriptions be sure to use the following words if they apply: *chromosomes*, *sister chromatids*, and *spindle*.

Cell Diagram	Cell Division Stage	Description
	Interphase	The genetic material is duplicated.
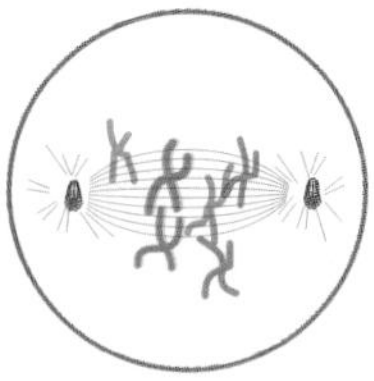	prophase	First stage of mitosis: The nuclear membrane disappears and the chromosomes coil up. The spindle begins to form.
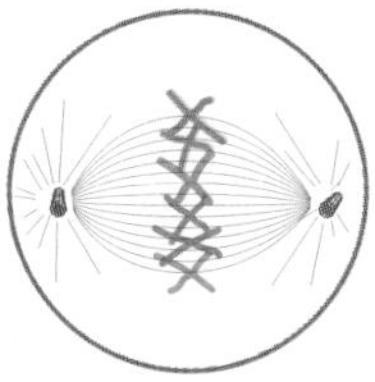	Metaphase	Second stage of mitosis: chromosomes (sister chromatids) line up at the center of the spindle
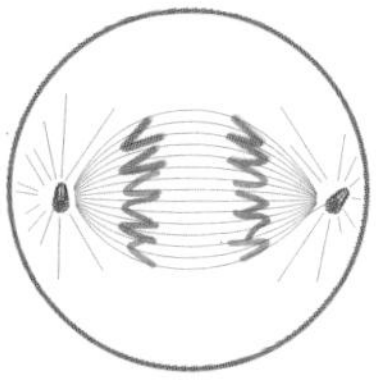	anaphase	Third stage of mitosis each pair of sister chromatids sperates into two daughter chromosomes, which begin to move to the other side of the cells
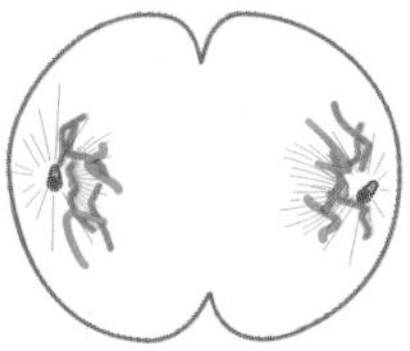	Telophase	Final stage of mitosis: The daughter chromosomes reach the ends of the spindel and begin to uncoil. New nuclear membranes form around each group of chromosomes.
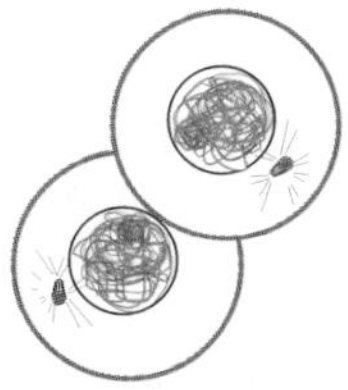	Cytokinesis	Cytoplasm divides, forming two daughter cells.

Tuesday 28, 2021

name __________

section ________ date ________

5b Sexual and Asexual Reproduction

Directions

Complete the table below by answering the questions and filling in the missing words from the list provided.

amoebas	spores
budding	union of egg and sperm
planarians	yeast
regeneration	

Type	Must mitosis occur?	Must meiosis occur?	Are offspring identical to parent?	Example
cell division of a unicellular organism	yes	no	yes	amoeba
budding	yes	no	yes	yeast
regeneration	yes	no	yes	planarians
union of egg/sperm	no	yes	no	dogs
spores	yes	no	yes	bread molds

Monday 27, 2021

name ____________________

section __________ date __________

Application

5c Genes and Mitosis

Directions

Use the definitions below to choose the right words to fill in the blanks.

1. r e G e n e r a t i o n
2. s p o r E
3. a N a p h a s e
4. m E t a p h a s e
5. p r o p h a S e
6. t e l o p h A s e
7. g e N e s
8. s p i n D l e
9. M e i o s i s
10. m I t o s i s
11. c h r o m a T i d s
12. c y t O k i n e s i s
13. n u c l e u S
14. b u d d I n g
15. a S e x u a l

1. The regrowing of missing body parts
2. A cell with a hard, protective coat around it
3. The phase of mitosis that follows metaphase
4. The phase of mitosis in which the chromosomes are lined up in the middle of the spindle
5. The first phase of mitosis
6. The last phase of mitosis, after which cytokinesis takes place
7. Contain the information needed for cell functions
8. The structure on which chromosomes move during mitosis
9. Must precede sexual reproduction
10. Another name for cell division
11. The duplicate chromosomes that appear during mitosis
12. The dividing of the cytoplasm during cell division
13. The area where chromosomes are normally found in a cell
14. A form of asexual reproduction in yeast
15. The form of reproduction based on mitotic cell division

name ______________________

section ____________ date ____________

5d How Genes Function

Directions

Below are several groups of terms. In each group, three of the four terms are related to one another. Draw a line through the unrelated term, and then write a sentence using the remaining words. Your sentence should show how the words are related. You may slightly change the form of the term in your sentence (for example, *chromosome* to *chromosomes* or *replicate* to *replication*).

1. sugar / phosphate / amino acid / base

2. uracil / DNA / adenine / thymine

3. DNA / uracil / replication / nucleotides

4. DNA / transcription / RNA / amino acids

5. Mendel / Watson / Crick / DNA

6. proteins / replication / amino acids / ribosomes

7. sequence / factors / amino acids / nucleotide

8. phosphate / chromosomes / DNA / genes

9. protein / thymine / RNA / uracil

10. protein synthesis / chromosome / tRNA / amino acids

Class Investigation

name ____________________

section __________ date __________

5e The Phases of Mitosis

Procedure

1. Focus your microscope on one of the root tips on the prepared slide.
2. Locate the area just above the root cap. (See page 214 of your textbook.) In this area, mitosis occurs rapidly to form new root cells so that the root can grow. When this root tip was prepared for microscope viewing, many of the cells in this area were in various phases of mitosis. The root tip was then treated with special stains to allow you to see the chromosomes.
3. To see the chromosomes in the various phases of mitosis, you will need to focus your microscope on high power.
4. Scan your slide by slowly moving the slide back and forth. Look for cells in the various phases of mitosis.
5. Find what you think is a good example of one of the phases of mitosis. Position that cell in your microscope's viewing field.
   - What phase of mitosis do you believe this is?

     ____
   - Why do you think that you are viewing a good example of this phase of mitosis?

     ____

     ____
   - Ask your teacher to check your cell to be sure it shows a good example of the phase you think you are viewing.
6. After your teacher has approved everyone's slides, move from one microscope to another, viewing the various phases of mitosis *in order*. Carefully note the sequence of the positions of the chromosomes in mitosis.

Goals

- ✓ Observe the phases of mitosis in plant cells.
- ✓ Describe the sequence of the phases of mitosis.

Materials

microscope

prepared slides of onion, hyacinth, or lily root tips showing the phases of mitosis

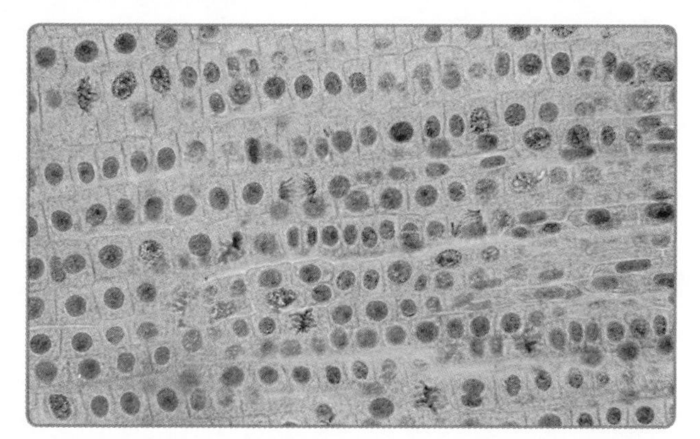

This micrograph of an onion root tip shows cells in various stages of mitosis. Which stages can you identify?

Illustration of an onion root tip

Summing Up

1. Write a brief description of the positions of chromosomes during each phase of mitosis as you saw them in the various microscopes.

   Prophase: ____________________

   ____

   ____

   Metaphase: ____________________

   ____

   ____

   Anaphase: ____________________

   ____

   ____

   Telophase: ____________________

   ____

   ____

2. What other observations about mitosis did you make while looking at these cells? ____________________

   ____

   ____

   ____

   ____

name

section date

Class Investigation

5f A Model of DNA, RNA, and Protein Synthesis

Goal

✓ Model the processes of DNA replication, RNA transcription, and protein synthesis.

Materials

nucleotides
scissors
tape
construction paper (assorted colors)
ribosome pattern

Procedure

1. Obtain a set of nucleotides from your teacher. If they are not already cut out, cut them out.
2. As a class, build a DNA molecule on a large table or on the floor.
   - Make one side of a DNA molecule; then tape the nucleotides together.
   - Make another strand of nucleotides to match your one-sided DNA molecule to form a complete DNA molecule. Remember how the bases pair: A–T and G–C.
3. Replicate your DNA molecule.
   - Unzip your DNA molecule.
   - Match the proper nucleotides to each side of the molecule to form two identical DNA molecules.

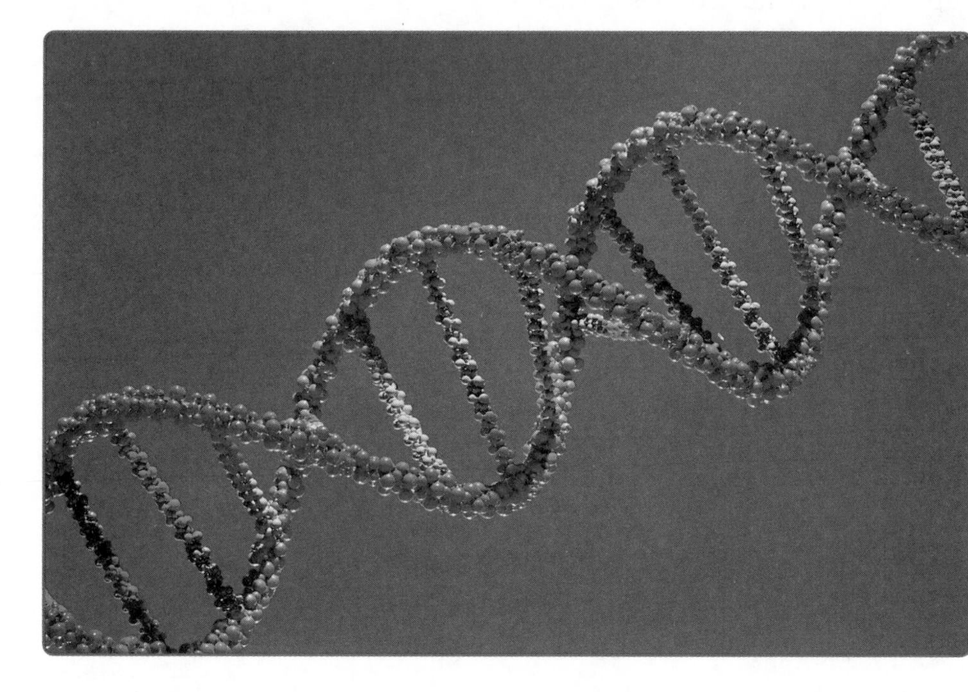

4. Transcribe a messenger RNA (mRNA) molecule.
   - Unzip one DNA molecule.
   - Add the proper nucleotides to one side to form an mRNA molecule. Remember that nucleotides in RNA can be different from those in DNA.
   - Remove the mRNA strand from the side of the DNA and zip the DNA molecule back together.

5. Manufacture a protein.
    - Make several differently colored and differently shaped amino acids from construction paper. Each amino acid should have a diameter of about 8 in.
    - Use the ribosome pattern provided by your teacher to make a ribosome from construction paper.
    - Make transfer RNA (tRNA) molecules. Each tRNA molecule should be three nucleotides long and should be able to line up on your mRNA molecule. Tape the nucleotides of each tRNA molecule together.
    - Attach an amino acid to each of the tRNA molecules.
    - Slide the end of the mRNA molecule over the ribosome.
    - Line up the nucleotides of the tRNA molecule with the proper nucleotides of mRNA on the ribosome.
    - Detach the amino acid from the tRNA molecule and tape it to the other amino acids that are lined up.
    - Remove the tRNA after it has released its amino acid.
    - Slide the ribosome along the mRNA until the next three nucleotides are in it. Line up the proper nucleotides of the tRNA molecule and attach its amino acid to the chain of amino acids.
    - Continue the process for the length of the mRNA.

name ______________________

section ____________ date ____________

6a Modern Genetics

Part 1

Directions

Black-footed albatrosses can have red beaks or white beaks. Beak color in these birds is controlled by a simple dominant/recessive inheritance pattern. An uppercase *R* represents the dominant allele that causes red beaks. A lowercase *r* represents the recessive allele that, when expressed in the absence of a dominant allele, causes white beaks. Using this information, complete the chart below.

Genotype	Dominant or recessive trait expressed?	Purebred or hybrid?	Color of beak
RR	Dominant	purebred	red
rr	Recessive	Purebred	white
Rr	Dominant	Hybrid	red

Part 2

Directions

Write the proper terms next to the following definitions.

__________________ 1. The monk who studied genetics during the 1800s

__________________ 2. An organism whose two alleles for a trait are the same

__________________ 3. The particles that, according to Mendel, cause inherited characteristics

__________________ 4. A test mating of organisms

__________________ 5. The study of inherited characteristics

__________________ 6. The modern term for Mendel's term *factor*

__________________ 7. The organism Mendel observed in his study of genetics

__________________ 8. The type of trait that masks the presence of another trait

__________________ 9. The number of years Mendel's work went unnoticed

__________________ 10. The type of trait that can be masked

__________________ 11. An organism formed when two organisms with different alleles are crossed

__________________ 12. What Mendel transferred from one flower to another

______________________ 13. The number of alleles each person has for a particular trait

______________________ 14. The passing of characteristics from parents to offspring

______________________ 15. The physical expression of an organism's genes

______________________ 16. The different forms of a gene for a particular trait

______________________ 17. The genes an organism has for a trait

name ______________________

section __________ date __________

6b Genes, Chromosomes, and Heredity

Directions

Write the answer to each question in the space provided.

1. How many chromosomes do normal human cells contain? 46
2. If an organism's normal chromosome number is 12, how many chromosomes would be in each of its egg or sperm cells? 6
3. Is a zygote that results from the union of a sperm and an egg haploid or diploid? diploid
4. Suppose someone reported that an animal's normal chromosome number was 17. Why would you say he is probably wrong?

   Chromosomes come in pairs, so it should be an even number.

5. What does each small box inside a Punnett square represent?

   Each box represents a possible genotype of the offspring.

6. How does incomplete dominance differ from simple dominant/recessive traits?

   In incomplete dominance the two alleles are expressed through "blending".

7. Human ABO blood types are an example of what type of inheritance pattern? multiple alleles
8. Do human males have *Y* chromosomes? yes
9. In humans, is it the mother's egg or the father's sperm that determines the sex of the child?

   It is the father's sperm.

10. Why should you not make fun of someone with an inherited disorder?

    God created all people with their own talents and God created everyone in his own image.

name ______________________

section __________ date __________

6c Review

Directions

Read the following statements. In the blank, write *True* if the statement is true. If the statement is false, draw a line through the word or words that make the statement false. Then in the blank, write the word or words necessary to make the statement true.

true 1. If two pea plants that are purebred for tall height are crossed, all their offspring will also be tall.

true 2. Punnett squares show possible combinations of gametes.

true 3. Mendel used pea plants in his experiments to discover how organisms inherit traits.

23 4. Humans normally have ~~46~~ pairs of chromosomes in every cell.

true 5. A cross between two organisms purebred for different traits will produce hybrid offspring.

recessive/dominant 6. In hybrid tall pea plants, the allele for the ~~dominant~~ characteristic is hidden by the allele for the ~~recessive~~ characteristic.

true 7. Hybrids are organisms that have alleles that are not alike.

true 8. A carrier has one allele for a certain trait but does not express that trait himself.

true 9. A sex-linked trait is caused by a gene located on the *X* or *Y* chromosome.

true 10. In incomplete dominance, two different alleles for the same characteristic both influence the expression of that characteristic.

codominance 11. A brown-and-white-spotted calf produced by a brown bull and a white cow illustrates ~~incomplete dominance~~.

true 12. Polygenic inheritance deals with characteristics that are each controlled by several different sets of genes.

impossible 13. It is ~~possible~~ for parents to pass to their children a gene that they do not have.

on X and one Y 14. In humans, a female has two *X* chromosomes, and a male has ~~two *Y* chromosomes~~.

true 15. Down syndrome can be caused by having one extra chromosome.

Tuesday 10, 2021

name ______________________

section ____________ date ____________

6d Punnett Squares

Directions

Punnett squares are used to represent simple genetic crosses. You can learn a lot about organisms by using Punnett squares. Fill in the Punnett squares diagrammed below to answer the questions.

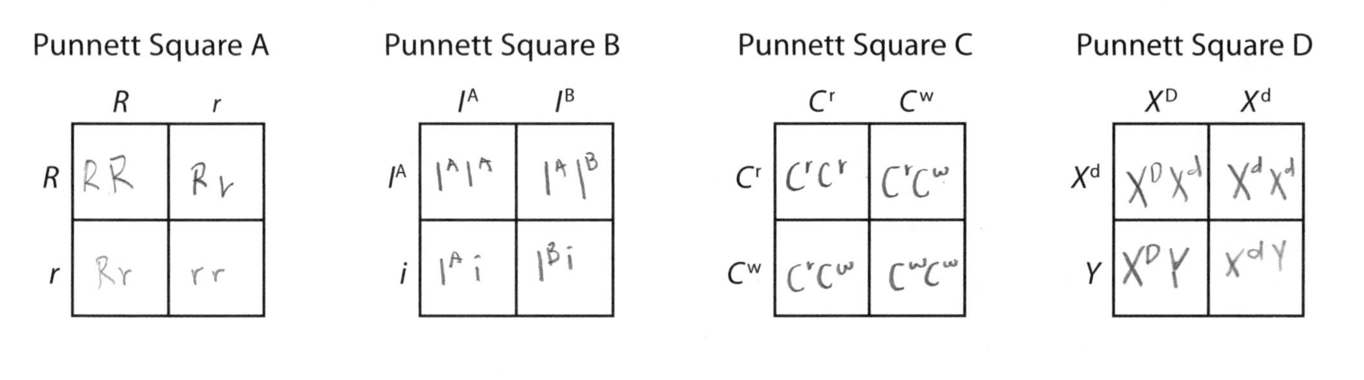

Simple Dominance (Punnett Square A)

1. For this characteristic, round peas are dominant over wrinkled peas. What are the phenotypes of the parents?

Both parents exhibit the dominant phenotype, round peas, because both have a dominant allele.

2. If there were 1000 offspring in the F_1 generation, approximately how many would you expect to exhibit the recessive trait (wrinkled peas)? How many would you expect to be hybrid?

About 250 (25%) should express the recessive trait, wrinkled peas. About 500 (50% should be hybrid (genotype Rr).

Multiple Alleles (Punnett Square B)

3. What human trait does this Punnett square represent?

Punnett square B involves human ABO blood types.

4. What is the phenotype of the mother?

Blood type AB

5. Is it possible for this couple to have a child with type O blood? If not, give an example of a cross that could produce a child with type O blood.

No, it is not possible because only the father has a recessive allele. To have Blood type O, the child must have two recessive alleles. $I^A i$ and $I^A i$ I^B and $I^A i$

Tuesday 10/2021

6. Is it possible for this couple to have a child with a hybrid phenotype? Explain.

Yes, it is possible. If a child received a recessive allele from the father, he would be hybrid for either type A or type B blood (depending on which allele he recieved from the mother).

7. If this couple had seven children, which blood type would you expect to be the most common? Why?

You would expect type A blood to be the most common. The Punnett square predicts that 50% of the offspring would have type A, 25% should have type AB, and 25% should have type B.

Incomplete Dominance (Punnett Square C)

8. How many different phenotypes are possible in the offspring of these parents?

There are three phenotypes possible

9. How many different genotypes are possible in the offspring of these parents? What are the genotypes?

Three genotypes are possible – C^rC^r, C^wC^w, C^rC^w

Sex-Linked Traits (Punnett Square D)

10. Assume that this cross involves Duchenne muscular dystrophy, a recessive trait carried on the *X* chromosome. What are the phenotypes of the parents?

The mother does not have Duchenne musculer dystrophy because she has a dominant allele, but she is a carrier for the trait.

11. Is it possible for this couple to produce a son with Duchenne muscular dystrophy? A daughter? If so, which box or boxes of the Punnett square show this possibility?

Yes

Application

name ____________________

section __________ date __________

6e Genetics Problems

Directions

These problems involve simple dominance, incomplete dominance, multiple alleles, and sex-linked traits. If there is a Punnett square in the margin, be sure to work the problem using the Punnett square, even if you can figure out the answer without it.

Problems Dealing with Simple Dominance

1. One of the characteristics Mendel studied in his pea plants was the color of the pods. Usually the pea pods were green (the dominant characteristic), but sometimes they were yellow (the recessive characteristic). If Mendel crossed a plant purebred for green pods (*GG*) with a plant purebred for yellow pods (*gg*), what would you expect the offspring to be like? Place an *X* in the correct box or boxes.
   - A. ☒ The offspring would have green pods.
   - B. ☐ The offspring would have yellow pods.

2. If Mendel crossed a plant that was purebred for green pods (*GG*) with a plant that was hybrid for green pods (*Gg*), what would you expect the offspring to be like? Place an *X* in the correct box or boxes.
   - A. ☒ The offspring would have only green pods.
   - B. ☐ The offspring would have only yellow pods.
   - C. ☐ The offspring would have some green pods and some yellow pods.

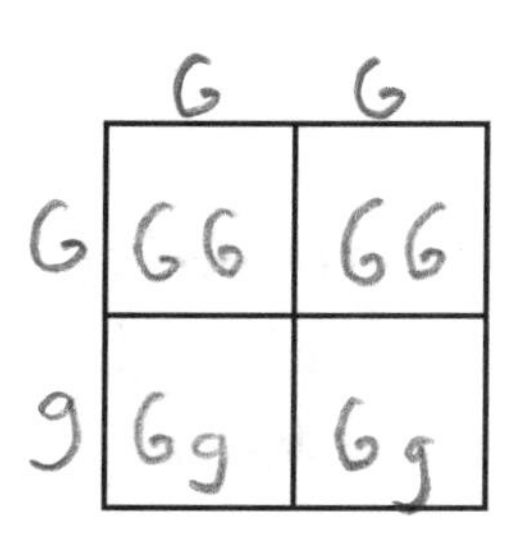

3. In the cross from Question 2, which of the following would you expect to be true of the offspring? Place an *X* in the correct box or boxes.
   - A. ☐ They would all be purebred for yellow pods.
   - B. ☐ They would all be purebred for green pods.
   - C. ☐ Some would be purebred for yellow pods, and some would be purebred for green pods.
   - D. ☒ Some would be purebred for green pods, and some would be hybrid for green pods.
   - E. ☐ Some would be purebred for yellow pods, and some would be hybrid for green pods.

4. Short hair is a dominant characteristic in most dogs. If a person crossed two hybrid short-haired dogs, what would you expect the puppies to look like? Place an *X* in the correct box or boxes.
   - A. ☐ All the puppies would have short hair.
   - B. ☐ All the puppies would have long hair.
   - C. ☒ Most of the puppies would have short hair, but some would have long hair.
   - D. ☐ Most of the puppies would have long hair, but some would have short hair.
   - E. ☐ Not enough information is given.

Tuesday 10/2021

5. In the Cross family, Kim, Kim's father, and Grandmother Cross have blue eyes. Kim's mother and Grandfather Cross have green eyes. Green is the dominant characteristic. Which of these statements could be true for the Cross family? Place an *X* in the correct box or boxes.

   A. ☒ Kim's mother is hybrid for green eyes.

   B. ☐ Kim's mother could be either hybrid or purebred for green eyes.

   C. ☐ Grandfather Cross is purebred for green eyes.

   D. ☒ Grandfather Cross is hybrid for green eyes.

   E. ☐ Grandfather Cross could be either hybrid or purebred for green eyes.

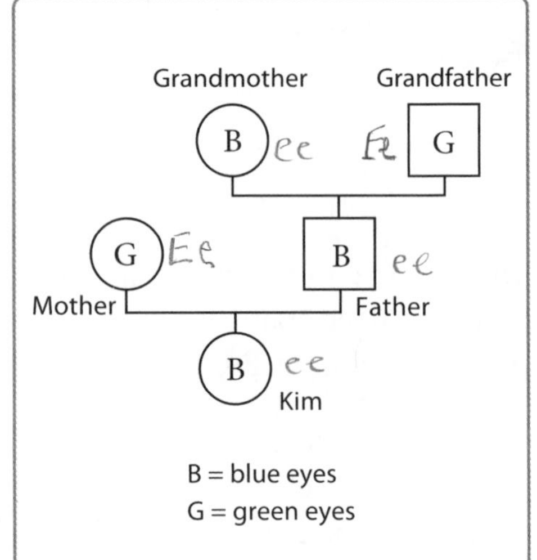

Problems Dealing with Incomplete Dominance

6. In snapdragons, white and red are purebred characteristics and pink is a hybrid characteristic. If a gardener crossed a red snapdragon (C^rC^r) with a white snapdragon (C^wC^w), what flower color(s) could be produced? (The uppercase *C* stands for *color*, while the superscripts *r* and *w* represent the alleles for color, *red* and *white*.) Place an *X* in the correct box or boxes.

   A. ☐ red

   B. ☐ white

   C. ☒ pink

7. What flower color(s) could be produced if two pink snapdragons were crossed? Place an *X* in the correct box or boxes.

   A. ☒ red

   B. ☒ white

   C. ☒ pink

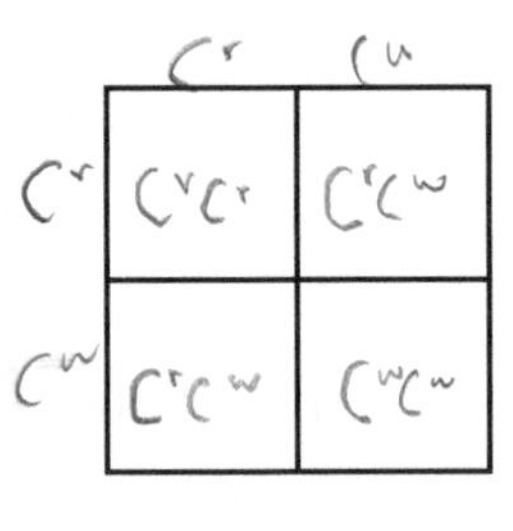

Problems Dealing with Multiple Alleles

8. If a man with type O blood (*ii*) marries a woman with type AB blood (I^AI^B), what blood type(s) might their offspring have? Place an *X* in the correct box or boxes.

   A. ☒ type A

   B. ☒ type B

   C. ☐ type AB

   D. ☐ type O

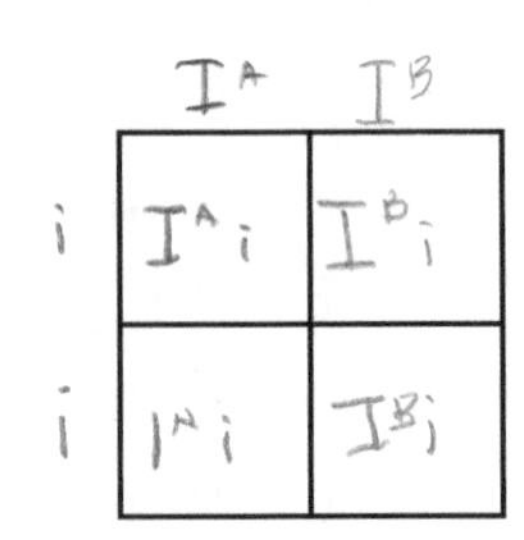

Tuesday 10, 2021

name____________________________

9. If a man with type A blood marries a woman with type B blood, what blood type(s) might their offspring have? Place an *X* in the correct box or boxes.

   A. ☒ type A
   B. ☒ type B
   C. ☒ type AB
   D. ☒ type O

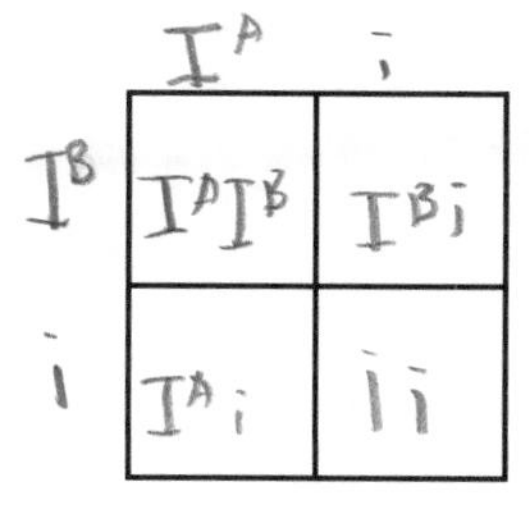

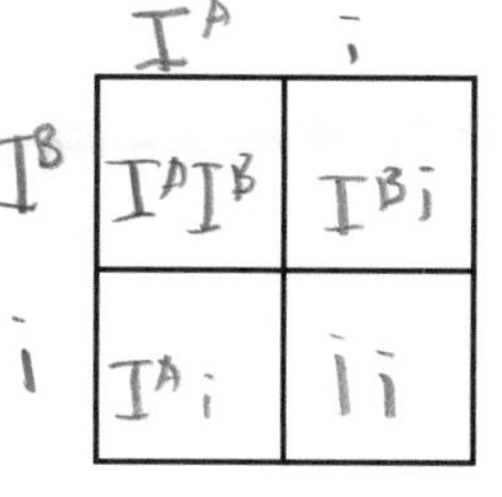
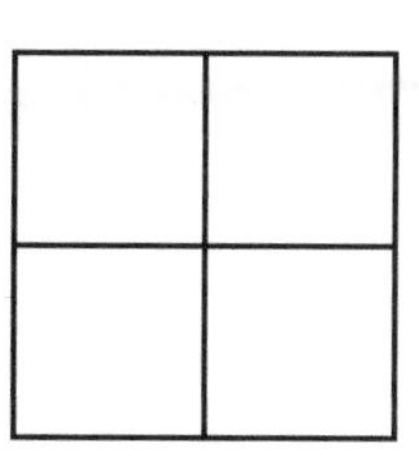

Problems Dealing with Sex-Linked Traits

10. If a hemophiliac male (X^hY) marries a normal woman (X^HX^H), what type(s) of children could they have? (Hemophilia is a recessive characteristic.) Place an *X* in the correct box or boxes.

   A. ☒ They could have a normal son (X^HY).
   B. ☐ They could have a hemophiliac son (X^hY).
   C. ☐ They could have a normal daughter (X^HX^H).
   D. ☒ They could have a daughter who is a carrier (X^HX^h).
   E. ☐ They could have a hemophiliac daughter (X^hX^h).

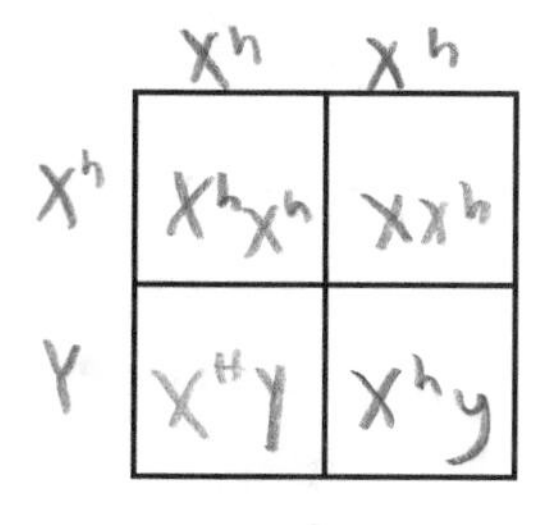

11. If a woman who is a carrier for Duchenne muscular dystrophy (X^DX^d) marries a man who has the disease (X^dY), what type(s) of children could they have? (Duchenne muscular dystrophy is a recessive trait.) Place an *X* in the correct box or boxes.

   A. ☒ They could have a normal son (X^DY).
   B. ☒ They could have a son who has the disease (X^dY).
   C. ☒ They could have a daughter who is a carrier (X^DX^d).
   D. ☐ They could have a normal daughter (X^DX^D).
   E. ☒ They could have a daughter who has the disease (X^dX^d).

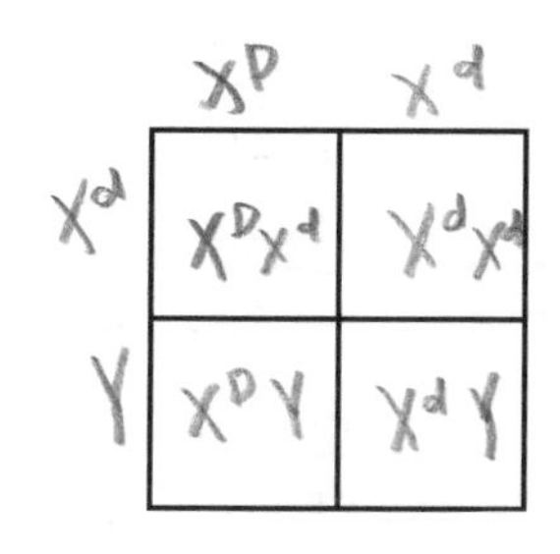

12. If a woman who is a carrier for hemophilia marries a normal male, what type(s) of children could they have? Place an *X* in the correct box or boxes.

   A. ☒ They could have a normal son.
   B. ☒ They could have a son who has the disease.
   C. ☐ They could have a son who is a carrier.
   D. ☒ They could have a daughter who is a carrier.
   E. ☒ They could have a normal daughter.
   F. ☐ They could have a daughter who has the disease.

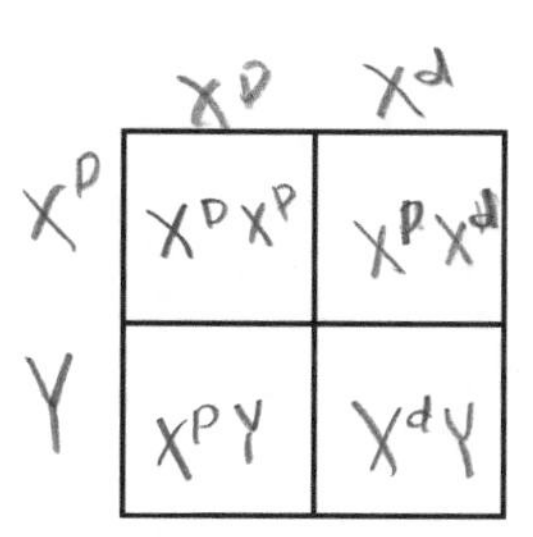

Class Investigation

name ______________________

section ____________ date ____________

6f Inheritance of Traits

Goals

✓ Illustrate the relationship between the inheritance of traits and the inheritance of chromosomes.

✓ Model the expression of dominant, recessive, and incompletely dominant traits.

Materials

bags with parent chromosomes
potato
toothpicks
coins (penny, nickel, and quarter)
popped popcorn
puffed-corn cereal
miniature marshmallows (green, yellow, pink, and white)
chenille wire
pushpins or thumbtacks (green, red, white, and yellow)

Procedure

In this investigation you will build an imaginary creature called a spudoodle. The traits of your organism will be determined by the genes on the chromosomes your spudoodle inherits from its parents. The spudoodle chromosome number is 16. Thus, the spudoodle you build will have 8 chromosome pairs. One chromosome in each pair will come from its mother and one from its father.

1. Obtain two bags from your teacher, each containing the chromosomes of a potential spudoodle parent.
2. Remove the chromosomes of one potential parent from one bag and turn the chromosomes face down so you cannot see the letters on them. Organize the chromosomes by length. Put the two longest ones together, then put the two second-longest ones together, and so on. Sort the chromosomes for the other potential parent in the same manner, but be careful not to mix the chromosomes of the two parents together.
3. Pick one chromosome from each parent's longest pair of chromosomes. Keeping them face down, put the two chromosomes you selected in a separate "baby spudoodle" pile. Do the same for the second-longest chromosome pairs and so on for all the chromosome pairs.
4. Return the remaining parent chromosomes to their bags, and move them out of your way.
5. Arrange the baby spudoodle's chromosomes in pairs by length. The baby spudoodle should have 8 pairs of chromosomes. Now turn the chromosomes over so that the letters on them are facing up.
6. Look at the table on the next page. In the "My Spudoodle's Genotype" column, record your baby spudoodle's genotype (the two-letter code of each chromosome pair) for each trait. Then indicate your spudoodle's phenotype for each trait.
7. Have a classmate check to see that your spudoodle's recorded phenotypes are consistent with your recorded genotypes, putting a check mark for each trait in the last column of the table and then signing the bottom of your table.

8. Assemble your baby spudoodle according to the traits coded for by its chromosomes. Use toothpicks to attach marshmallows and popcorn or puffed-corn cereal. Look at the spudoodle in the photo on the next page to see where the various body parts belong. It is best to put the mouth on first and put the legs on last. Use these materials for your spudoodle's traits:
   - Hair—toothpicks
   - Mouth—coins (quarter, nickel, or penny)
   - Ears—popcorn or puffed-corn cereal
   - Eyes—green or white marshmallows
   - Dorsal spines—yellow, pink, or white marshmallows
   - Tail—chenille wire
   - Legs—green, red, or white thumbtacks
   - Nose—one or two yellow thumbtacks
9. When you are finished, name your spudoodle and place it in the spudoodle holding area designated by your teacher.

Possible Genotypes	Possible Phenotypes	My Spudoodle's Genotype	My Spudoodle's Phenotype	Spudoodle Check
HH or *Hh* *hh*	hair no hair			
AA *Aa* *aa*	large mouth medium mouth small mouth			
EE or *Ee* *ee*	popcorn ears puffed-corn ears			
BB or *Bb* *bb*	green eyes white eyes			
DD *Dd* *dd*	yellow dorsal spines pink dorsal spines white dorsal spines			
RR or *Rr* *rr*	curly tail straight tail			
GG *Gg* *gg*	green legs red legs white legs			
NN or *Nn* *nn*	two-nostril nose one-nostril nose			
Signature of classmate who checked your spudoodle:				

name ______________________

Summing Up

1. What is your spudoodle's name?

____

2. List the spudoodle body parts that have traits controlled by simple dominant/recessive genes.

____

3. List the spudoodle body parts that have traits controlled by incompletely dominant genes.

____

4. Does the inheritance of the longest pair of chromosomes have any effect on spudoodle eye color? Why or why not?

____

____

5. What alleles (letters) would a baby spudoodle need to inherit from its parents for it to have red legs?

____

Does it make any difference which allele comes from the mother spudoodle? __________

6. Is it possible for a spudoodle with yellow dorsal spines to have a baby spudoodle with white dorsal spines? Why or why not?

____

____

____

____

Application

name ______________________

section __________ date __________

7a Mutations

Directions

Fill in the missing letters to complete the words in the following statements. The circled letters form a brief definition of *mutation*.

1. A mutation that changes the sequence of bases in DNA is called a (_) _ _ _ mutation.
2. A _ (_) R _ mutation can affect offspring.
3. Mutations usually occur R _ (_) _ _ _ _ _ in the genetic material.
4. When God _ _ _ S (_) _ the physical creation (Gen. 3:17), a major change occurred in living things.
5. A mutation that results in the death of a cell or organism is a _ _ (_) H _ _ mutation.
6. A seedless watermelon that has three sets of chromosomes results from a change in _ _ _ (_) D _.
7. B _ _ _ _ (_) _ _ _ _ _ _ _ is the use of living organisms to make new, more desirable organisms or products.
8. A _ _ _ _ T _ (_) mutation will not affect an organism's offspring.
9. A _ (_) _ _ M _ _ _ _ _ _ change may involve entire chromosomes or the arrangement of genes on a chromosome.
10. A _ _ T (_) _ _ _ _ is a change in genetic material.
11. Some mutations have so little effect that they are considered (_) _ _ T _ _ _.
12. A mutation in a _ _ (_) M _ _ _ - _ _ O _ _ _ _ _ _ gene causes albinism.
13. Many human genetic D _ _ _ _ _ (_) _ _ are the result of gene mutations.

A brief definition of *mutation* is

_ _ _ _ _ _ _   _ _ _ _ _ _ .
1 2 3 4 5 6 7   8 9 10 11 12 13

name ____________

section ________ date ________

7b Our Use of Genetics

Directions

Below are examples of how people use genetic information. Choose the term from the list below that best describes what is being done in the examples. Each term may be used more than once.

A. cloning
B. crossbreeding
C. genetic engineering
D. simple selective breeding

__B__ 1. A farmer decides to mate his Hereford cow that gives the most milk with an exceptionally large Angus bull.

__A__ 2. After years of breeding roses, a man finally grows a beautiful, strong, fragrant rose that resists certain diseases and insects. He then grafts stems of this rose onto roots of other rose plants to produce many rose plants that are genetically alike.

__B__ 3. A grapevine that cannot withstand cold winter temperatures but can produce sweet grapes is used to pollinate flowers of a different variety of grapevine that can withstand severe winter temperatures but cannot produce sweet grapes.

__D__ 4. A golden retriever that has won several prizes is mated with a golden retriever that has won in many dog shows.

__A__ 5. A beautiful black tulip was found growing in a man's yard. A company purchased the bulb of this tulip and carefully grew the bulb so that it would produce many smaller bulbs, each of which grows into black tulip plants.

__C__ 6. Using a virus, scientists add a lethal gene to a protozoan's genes.

__A__ 7. You cut a potato into several sections, each of which contains an eye (bud), and plant the sections.

__B__ 8. In an attempt to produce a peach without fuzz, a scientist pollinates a peach flower with pollen from a plum.

__C__ 9. A gene that produces a human hormone is isolated and put into a bacterial cell. The bacterium then grows and uses the gene to produce the hormone. Later the hormone can be purified and used to treat people who need the hormone.

__D__ 10. You save seeds from your largest pumpkin to plant next year.

Application

name ____________________

section __________ date __________

7c Review

Part 1

Directions

In the spaces provided, explain the difference between the terms given.

1. gene mutation / chromosomal change

2. somatic mutation / germ mutation

3. identical twins / fraternal twins

4. inbreeding / crossbreeding

5. reproductive cloning / therapeutic cloning

6. embryonic stem cells / somatic stem cells

Part 2

Directions

In the spaces provided, answer the questions.

1. At what two times did God cause global changes to His creation?

2. There are several ways in which a cell in an organism can have a gene mutation that will not significantly affect the organism. List three ways and explain why they would be insignificant.

3. Discuss the following statement: "Mutations are sometimes helpful." Give one example from the chapter.

4. Describe gene therapy and its limitations.

5. Is a change in ploidy always harmful to an organism? Give an example to support your answer.

6. How is the process of education similar to the differentiation of cells?

Class Investigation

name ______________________

section __________ date __________

7d Observing Radiation Effects on Seedlings

Procedure

Irradiated seeds are seeds that have been exposed to radiation. They are usually sold in kits that contain a control group (seeds that have not been exposed to radiation) and four groups that have been exposed to different amounts of radiation. Sow each group of seeds in a different flowerpot. Record the number of seeds sown in each group. Label each pot with the type of seed and the amount of irradiation. Place all the pots in a warm, well-lit area. After one week observe the plants and compare their growth.

Goals

- ✓ Observe examples of radiation-induced mutations.
- ✓ Compare the rate of mutation with the amount of radiation.

Materials

flowerpots
irradiated seeds
nonirradiated seeds
potting soil

Data

Record your data from this experiment in the table below.

Plant Name: ______________________

Group	Number of seeds planted	Number of live seedlings after one week	Average seedling height	Number of unusual seedlings
control				

Describe any unusual seedlings.

____

____

____

____

____

____

Summing Up

1. Did exposure to radiation increase or decrease how tall the seedlings grew?

   increase ☐ decrease ☐

2. Did exposure to radiation increase, decrease, or have no effect on the number of unusual seedlings?

   increase ☐ decrease ☐ no effect ☐

3. Did more or fewer seeds germinate with increased radiation?

   more ☐ fewer ☐

4. Why was it important to include a control group in your observations?

   ____

   ____

   ____

5. Why was it necessary to place all the flowerpots in the same conditions (temperature and light)?

   ____

   ____

   ____

6. How do you think radiation caused the differences that you have observed?

   ____

   ____

   ____

7. Do you think that giving the irradiated seeds a better environment, such as richer soil or fertilizer, would help them grow as well as the control group? Why or why not?

   ____

   ____

   ____

   ____

Going Beyond

Explain an experiment that you could do to determine whether the offspring of the irradiated seeds would show the same unusual characteristics.

____

____

____

____

____

name________________________

section__________ date__________

8a What the Bible Teaches About Creation

Directions

Complete the words in the following statements by filling in the missing letters. The circled letters will spell a word representing a belief system that must be accepted by faith.

1. "In the beginning God __ __ E __ __ E __" (Gen. 1:1).
2. Man is __ __ __ P O __ __ __ B __ __ to God.
3. God created by __ __ R __ __ __ acts.
4. God specially __ R __ __ __ __ D man.
5. God S __ __ __ __ __ __ S His creation.
6. "All things were made by __ __ __" (John 1:3).
7. God reveals His P __ __ __ __ in creation.
8. God created __ __ __ in His own image.
9. __ __ __ __ U __ __ __ __ __ __ M contradicts God's Word.
10. God has revealed the __ __ Q __ __ __ C __ of Creation.
11. The __ __ __ __ __ M __ __ __ shows God's handiwork (Ps. 19:1).

__ __ __ __ __ __ __ __ __ __ __
1 2 3 4 5 6 7 8 9 10 11

name ______________________

section __________ date __________

Application

8b Review

Directions

In each of the following statements, circle the correct choice in the parentheses. On the lines that follow each statement, tell why the incorrect choice is wrong.

1. Biblical creationism and evolutionism are both accepted by (faith / scientific evidence).

____

____

2. God (did / did not) reveal enough about Creation to contradict evolutionary theory.

____

____

3. God created (but does not sustain / and sustains) what He created.

____

____

4. God (created / did not create) animals and man in the same way.

____

____

5. Creation has (degenerated / stayed the same) since God created it.

____

____

6. The (literal view / progressive creationism theory) is the most accurate interpretation of Genesis 1.

____

____

7. The fact that many fossils are found in a random order all over the world supports the (evolutionary theories of fossil formation / belief in a global flood).

____

____

8. Using biblical genealogies, we can determine the earth's age to be about six (thousand / billion) years old.

____

____

name ____________________

section __________ date __________

8c Defining Concepts of Evolution

Directions

In the spaces provided, explain the difference between the terms given.

1. evolution / theory of evolution

2. theory of evolution / biological evolution

3. theory of inheritance of acquired characteristics / mutation theory of evolution

4. theory of natural selection / mutation-selection theory (Neo-Darwinism)

5. gradualism / punctuated equilibrium

6. homologous structures / vestigial structures

name ____________________

section __________ date __________

8d A Record of Evolution

Directions

Use the clues below to choose the right word to fit in the blanks. The letters in the shaded rectangle will spell out one of the supposed proofs of evolution. Answer the question at the bottom once you have determined what the supposed proof is.

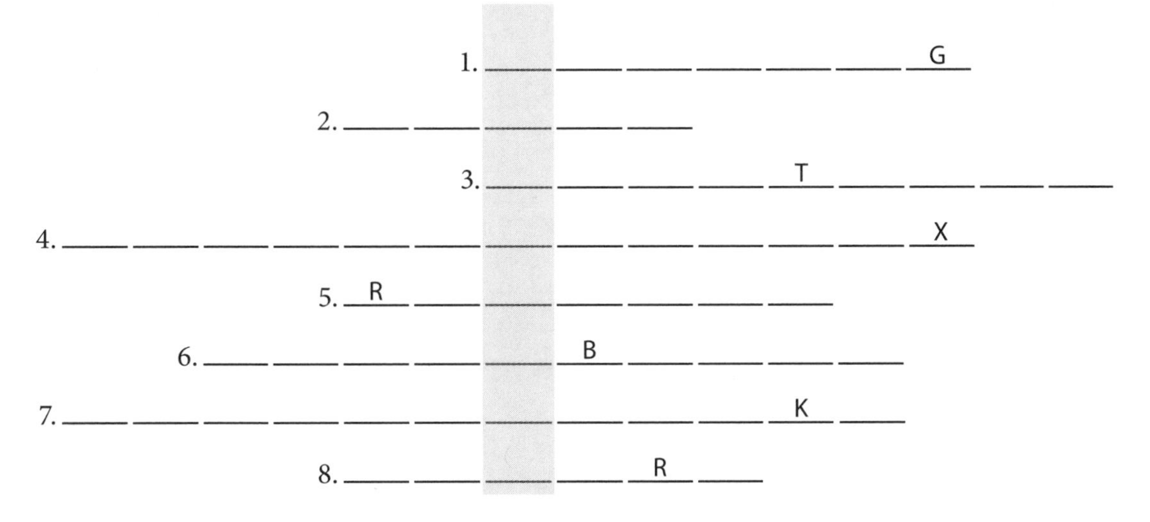

1. Four square miles of rock layers in California contain fossils of this type of fish.
2. Many Christians believe that the ____ is the best explanation for most fossils.
3. Some scientists claim these genetic errors provide the changes that drive evolution.
4. This extinct organism was probably a bird.
5. Christians should avoid saying that two different groups of organisms are ____.
6. These extinct organisms would probably be classified as arthropods.
7. Evolutionists believe these organisms existed but have found no physical evidence. (two words)
8. Fossils are found in ____ of rock.

If someone spoke to you using the supposed proof of evolution that appears in the rectangle above, what would you tell him?

name ______________________

section ____________ date ____________

Personal Investigation

8e The Scale of Noah's Ark

Introduction

Genesis 6:15 states that Noah's ark was 300 cubits long, 50 cubits wide, and 30 cubits high. A cubit is the distance between the end of the longest finger and the elbow. Although some Bible scholars disagree about the exact size of a cubit used by Noah, most agree that a cubit about 0.46 m (18 in.) long is probably accurate.

Using the metric equivalent of a cubit (0.46 m), we can estimate that the ark was about 138 m (453 ft) long, 23 m (75 ft) wide, and 14 m (46 ft) high. According to Genesis 6:16, the ark had three internal decks. If the ark were a boxlike structure, it would have had over 9500 m^2 (102,000 ft^2) of deck space. In other words, the deck space of the ark was greater than the size of 20 basketball courts.

Goals

- ✓ Create a two-dimensional diagram of the ark.
- ✓ Understand the scale of the ark and its capacity for holding animals.

Materials

paper
ruler
scissors
encyclopedia, other reference materials, or online sources

Procedure

It is difficult for most people to visualize the size of such a structure. To help visualize the size of the ark, draw a cross section (lengthwise) of the ark to scale. Consider using a scale in which 1 cubit equals about 3 mm (0.12 in.). Your ark would then be 90 cm (35 in.) long, 15 cm (6 in.) wide, and 9 cm (3.5 in.) high.

If a man were 1.8 m (6 ft) tall, he would be 4 cubits tall. Based on the scale you used to draw the ark, he would be 1.2 cm (0.5 in.) tall. Draw a figure of a man 1.2 cm tall, cut it out, and place it on the ark drawing.

Look up the average sizes of various land animals that were probably taken on the ark. Make drawings of these animals using the same scale that you used to draw Noah's ark. Cut out these animals and place them on your drawing of the ark.

Remember that the drawing you have made of Noah's ark is only two-dimensional. The ark was actually 23 m (75 ft) wide. Thus the ark was able to hold many more animals than you can put on your diagram. Bring your diagram to class and discuss it with your classmates and teacher.

name ______________________

section __________ date __________

Research Investigation

8f Dinosaurs

Goals

- ✓ Learn to separate conjectures (guesses) from conclusions that are supported by physical evidence.
- ✓ Gain new knowledge about several dinosaurs.

Materials

encyclopedia, other reference materials, or online sources

Part 1

The term *dinosaur* was first used by Sir Richard Owen in 1842. At this time scientists, and even people digging just for fun, were discovering large animal bones for the first time. *Dinosaur* means "terrible or monstrous lizard," but most dinosaurs were not monstrous or terrible. Some scientists believe that the average size of the reptiles called dinosaurs was probably about that of a chicken or dog.

Much has been written about dinosaurs. Some of the material that has been written is probably true. By carefully observing an animal's bones, scientists can tell about its size, its method of movement, the general types of food it might have eaten, and a few other things. By observing a skeleton, however, scientists cannot easily tell when the animal lived, where it lived, how it interacted with its young, or what other kinds of organisms lived around it. Often, however, evolutionary paleontologists (scientists who study "prehistoric" life) guess at this kind of information.

Read the following description of an imaginary dinosaur. Then answer the questions on the next page.

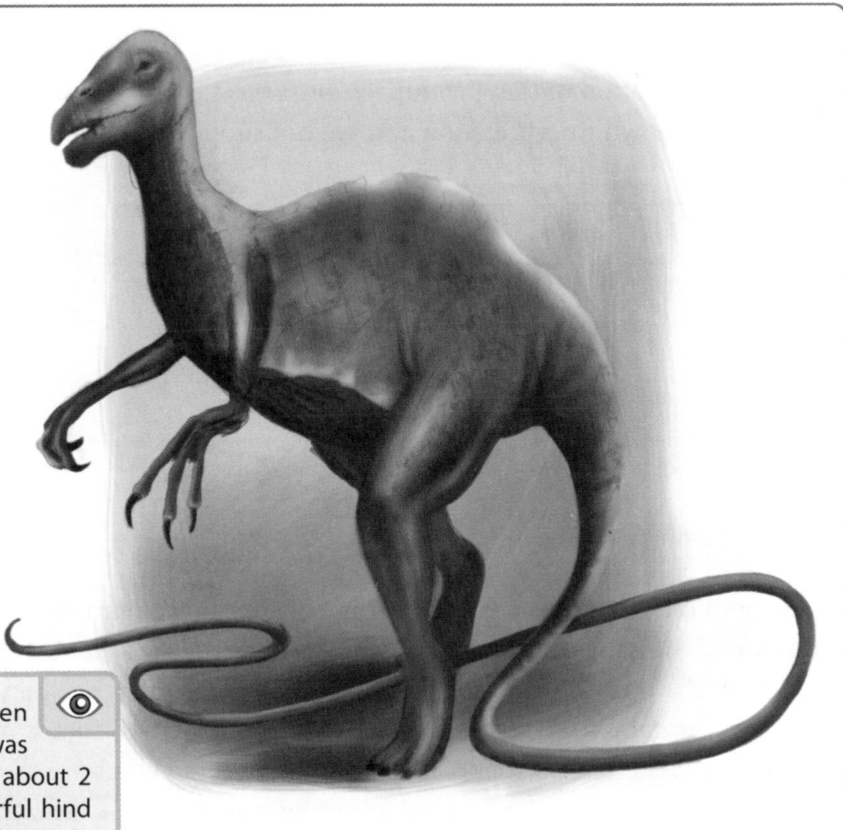

The *Adentoflagellosaurus* has recently been identified and named from one skeleton that was excavated in the deserts of Africa. Standing about 2 m (6.6 ft) tall, it walked upright on its powerful hind legs, which allowed it to run 20 km/h (12 mi/h). Lacking teeth, it survived on ants, termites, and related soft-bodied social insects, which it crushed with its thick gums. Because it had short, strong toes with 4 cm (1.6 in.) hooked claws on the front feet, it was able to tear into the mounds and hills where these insects lived.

This fascinating reptile had a long, thin tail that grew up to 8 m (26 ft). The *Adentoflagellosaurus* could crack its tail like a whip, producing a loud noise that would startle and frighten away larger predators. This sound probably also functioned in communication with other members of its herd.

Decide whether each of the following statements from the description is supported by physical evidence or is just a guess. Then check the appropriate box.

Statement				
stood 2 m tall	supported by evidence	☒	guess	☐
powerful hind legs	supported by evidence	☒	guess	☐
ran 20 km/h	supported by evidence	☐	guess	☒
had no teeth	supported by evidence	☒	guess	☐
ate small insects	supported by evidence	☐	guess	☒
had thick gums	supported by evidence	☐	guess	☒
4 cm hooked claws	supported by evidence	☒	guess	☐
dug into mounds	supported by evidence	☐	guess	☒
thin 8 m tail	supported by evidence	☒	guess	☐
cracked tail like a whip	supported by evidence	☐	guess	☒
used tail to communicate	supported by evidence	☐	guess	☒
lived in a herd	supported by evidence	☐	guess	☒

Study the illustration of the *Adentoflagellosaurus*. List any features that you think are just the artist's own interpretation and are not supported by physical evidence.

- skin color
- skin texture
- any feature that was not persorved in the fossil.

Part 2

Read about dinosaurs in an encyclopedia or other source and choose several different dinosaurs. Find other encyclopedias, books, and websites that discuss dinosaurs and read about the ones you chose. Try to determine the difference between information that scientists gather through observation and information that is probably based on guesswork. Write a brief report about the dinosaurs you chose. Your report should begin with the material that you believe to be true. If you include any material that is evolutionary, indicate the error it promotes. If possible, include drawings of the dinosaurs you discuss in your report.

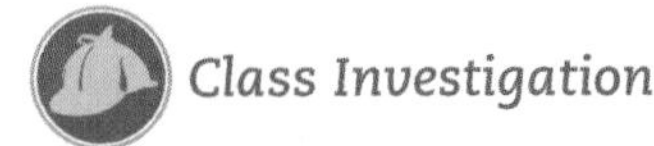

name____________________

section__________ date__________

8g Making a New Gene

Goals

- ✓ Model the improbability that gene mutations will produce a new, beneficial gene.
- ✓ Illustrate the harmful nature of mutations.

Materials

numbered spinner
paper

Introduction

One way to demonstrate what it would take to produce a new gene by mutations is to compare a gene to a sentence. The sentence used in this investigation consists only of three-letter words, which represent codons. The letters in the words represent nucleotides. (Recall from Chapter 5 that genes are made of nucleotides that are read in groups of three called codons.)

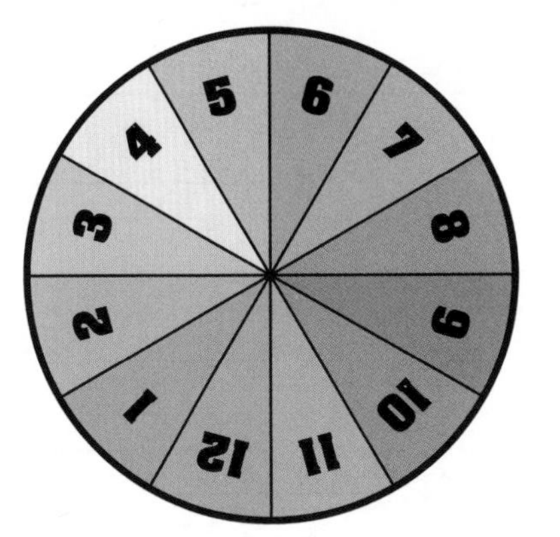

Procedure

Before you begin this activity, make a numbered spinner from the plastic lid of a coffee can or margarine container, a split-tack fastener or cotter pin, and a pointer cut from another plastic lid. The spinner should have 12 numbered sectors (see diagram). Take 26 small pieces of paper and write a different letter of the alphabet on each. Keep these in a container from which you will randomly select letters.

1. Use your numbered spinner to randomly select which letter position (numbered 1–12) in the sentence will mutate. Record this number in the "Position to change" column in the Data section.
2. Randomly pick a lettered piece of paper from your supply of letters. Record this letter in the "New letter" column in the Data section. Return the lettered paper to the container.
3. Rewrite the sentence in the space provided, substituting the letter selected from the container for the letter in the position you selected with the numbered spinner.
4. Beginning with the newly formed sentence from the previous turn, repeat Steps 1–3 until all the spaces for new sentences have been filled.

Data

Position to change	New letter	1 H	2 I	3 S	4 M	5 O	6 P	7 W	8 A	9 S	10 W	11 E	12 T

Summing Up

1. Did some letter positions never mutate? ______
2. Did some letter positions mutate more than once? ______
3. How many mutations (letter substitutions) did it take for you to make a new, grammatically correct sentence?

   ______
4. If the sentence used in this investigation were twice as long, would it be more likely or less likely that a new, correct sentence could be produced by this type of mutation?

   ______
5. Genes consist of thousands of nucleotides (letters). How do you think this would affect the likelihood of mutations making a new, beneficial gene?

   ______

Research Investigation

name ____________________

section __________ date __________

8h Evolutionary Family Trees

Goals

- ✓ Compare various evolutionary family trees.
- ✓ Note the variations between trees proposed by different scientists or groups.

Materials

none

Introduction

Scientists who support evolution do not agree on the way in which biological evolution took place. Since these scientists use evolutionary family trees to illustrate the path of evolution, there are almost as many different trees as there are opinions of how evolution took place.

Procedure

Below are four different evolutionary family trees for vertebrates (animals with backbones). Look for significant differences in evolutionary paths and in common ancestors on these trees. Mark the significant differences on the trees and compile a list of these differences on page 132.

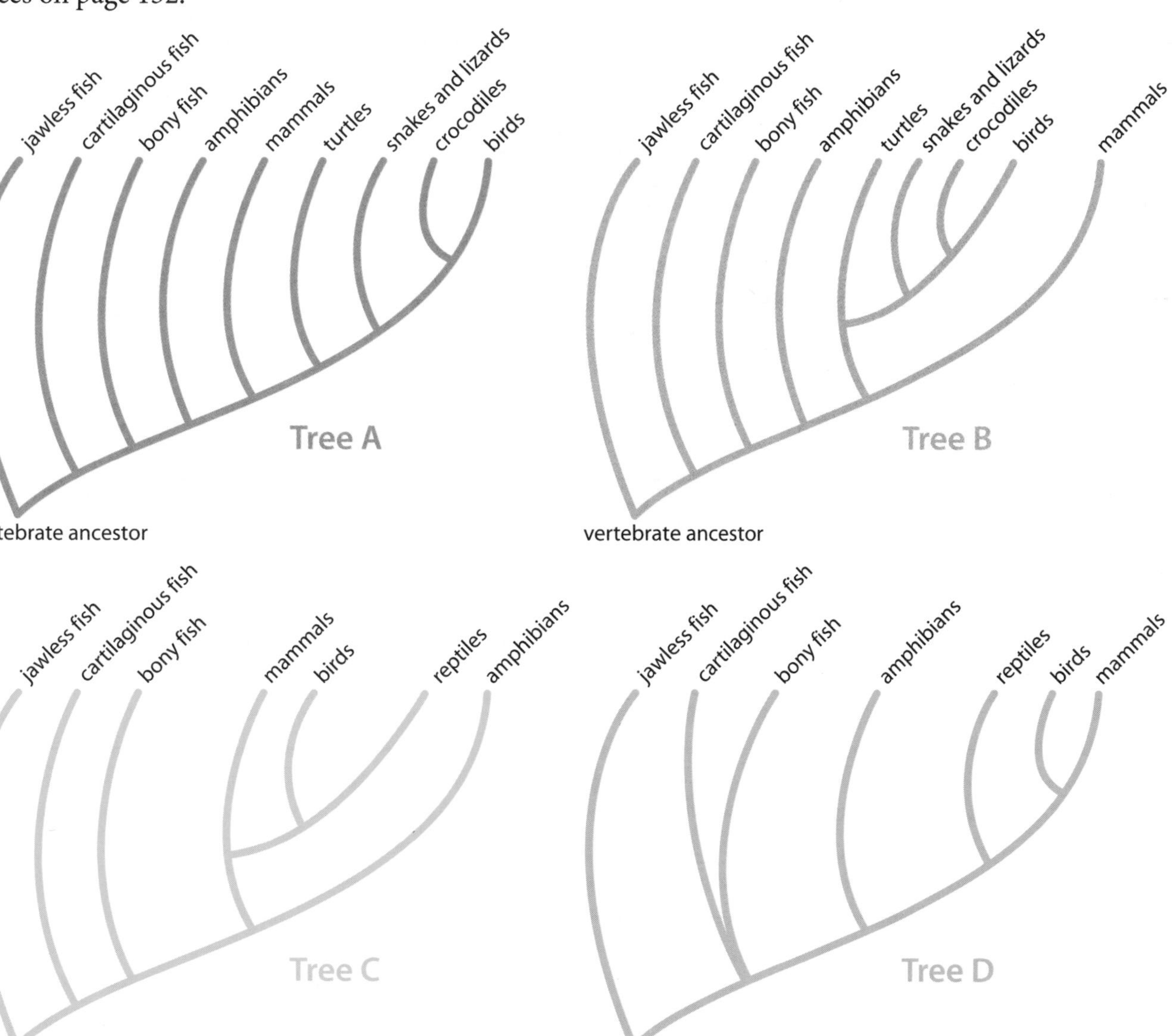

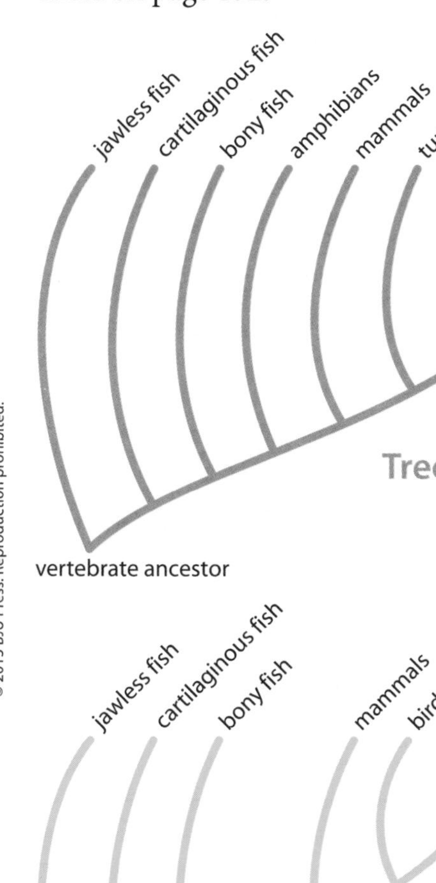

Differences Observed

name ______________________

section __________ date __________

9a Kingdoms Archaebacteria and Eubacteria

Directions

In the space provided, explain the relation between each pair of words or phrases below.

1. bacteria / cyanobacteria

____

____

____

2. nucleus / prokaryote

____

____

____

3. antibiotics / yogurt

____

____

____

4. rapid growth rate / crowded conditions

____

____

____

5. flagella / movement

____

____

____

6. bacteria / binary fission

____

____

____

7. capsule / cell wall

8. archaebacteria / eukaryotes

name____________________

section__________ date__________

9b Kingdom Fungi

Part 1

Directions

Below is a diagram of a mushroom. Around the diagram are five definitions. For each definition, write the correct term in the blank provided; then draw a line from the term to the structure on the diagram.

1. ________________________
(expanded portion that bears the gills)

2. ________________________
(structures designed for reproduction or survival through unfavorable conditions)

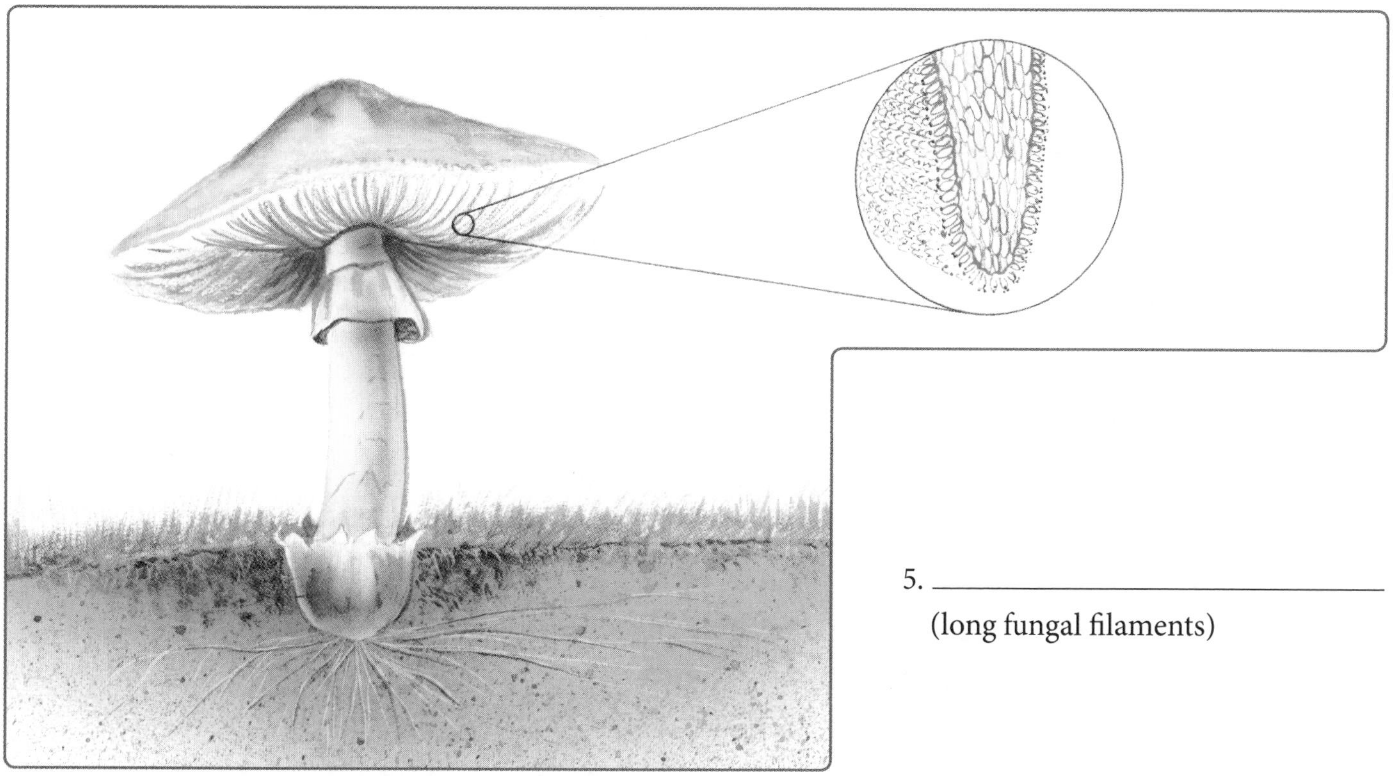

5. ________________________
(long fungal filaments)

3. ________________________
(structures on which spores are produced)

4. ________________________
(similar to a stem)

6. Two of these labeled structures occur in all fungi. What are these two structures?

____

Part 2

Directions

Write the answer to each question in the blank provided.

1. The study of fungi is called ______________________________.
2. Black bread mold and mushrooms are both made of ______________________________.
3. A(n) ______________________________ absorbs food from dead material.
4. A fungus and an alga that live as a single organism are called a(n) ______________________________.
5. The relationship described in Question 4 is a type of ______________________________ relationship.
6. ______________________________ help plant roots absorb minerals.
7. Reproductive cells formed on mushroom gills are called ______________________________.
8. Fungi and bacteria perform the important function of ______________________________.
9. Fungi digest their food by releasing ______________________________.
10. ______________________________ are a common fungal pizza topping.
11. List three human diseases caused by fungi.

    ____

    ____

12. List five products that fungi are involved in producing and that can be purchased at a store near you.

    ____

    ____

name______________________

section__________ date__________

9c Review

Directions

Match each term from List 1 with the correct kingdom in the chart below by writing the terms in the "Words from List 1" column of the chart. Then match each term from List 2 with the best kingdom–List 1 combination and write them in the "Words from List 2" column. Each term is used only once. One row is done for you as an example. Use a pencil since you may need more than one try. Only one solution will correctly match all the terms.

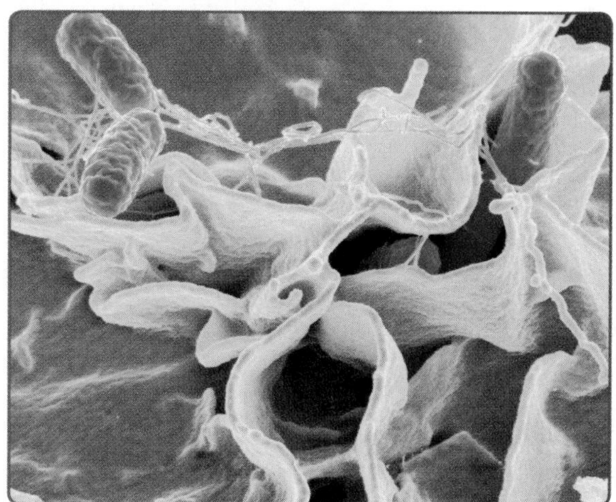

List 1	**List 2**
chloroplasts	*Amoeba*
cilia	bacteria
dinoflagellates	mold
food poisoning	no nucleus
~~mushrooms~~	oceanic food
mycorrhizae	*Paramecium*
penicillin	red tide
plankton	root association
prokaryote	*Spirogyra*
pseudopods	~~spores~~
stem rust	wheat

Kingdom	Words from List 1	Words from List 2
Archaebacteria and Eubacteria		
Protista		
Fungi	mushrooms	spores

name ______________________

section __________ date __________

9d Graphing Bacterial Growth

Goals

- ✓ Analyze data on bacterial growth rates.
- ✓ Plot data points on a line graph.
- ✓ Analyze a completed line graph.

Materials

calculator

Procedure

1. Some common bacterial species reproduce by binary fission every 20 minutes. If you started with a single bacterium and it continued dividing without any limitations, calculate how many bacteria could be produced by the end of 5 hours by filling in the total at each interval. For this exercise, assume that no bacteria died during the process. Some totals have been provided to help you check your work.

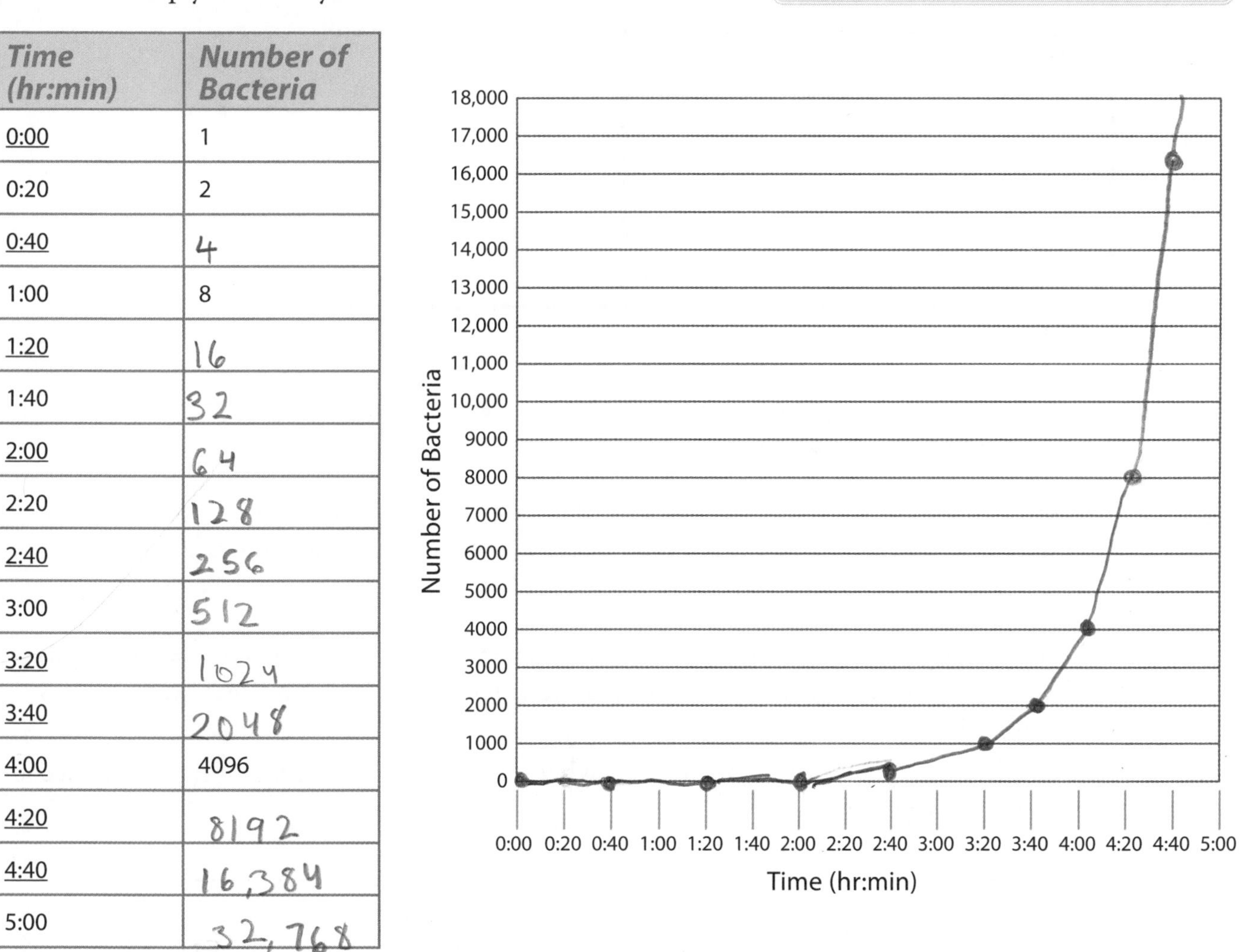

Time (hr:min)	Number of Bacteria
0:00	1
0:20	2
0:40	4
1:00	8
1:20	16
1:40	32
2:00	64
2:20	128
2:40	256
3:00	512
3:20	1024
3:40	2048
4:00	4096
4:20	8192
4:40	16,384
5:00	32,768

2. On the graph to the right of the table, plot the number of bacteria for the times underlined in the table.
3. Using the graph or the table, estimate the amount of time it took the population to reach 12,000 bacteria.

4:30 (4hrs. 30min)

4. A bacterial colony will not continue to grow beyond a certain point because some factors will limit the size of the population. What are some of those limiting factors?

availibility of food, availibility of oxygen, excessive wastes, tempratures not conducive of growth, lack of moisture

5. Below are four graphs and three descriptions. Read each description and then match it with the letter of the graph that best shows what would happen to the bacterial population. (One graph will not be used.)

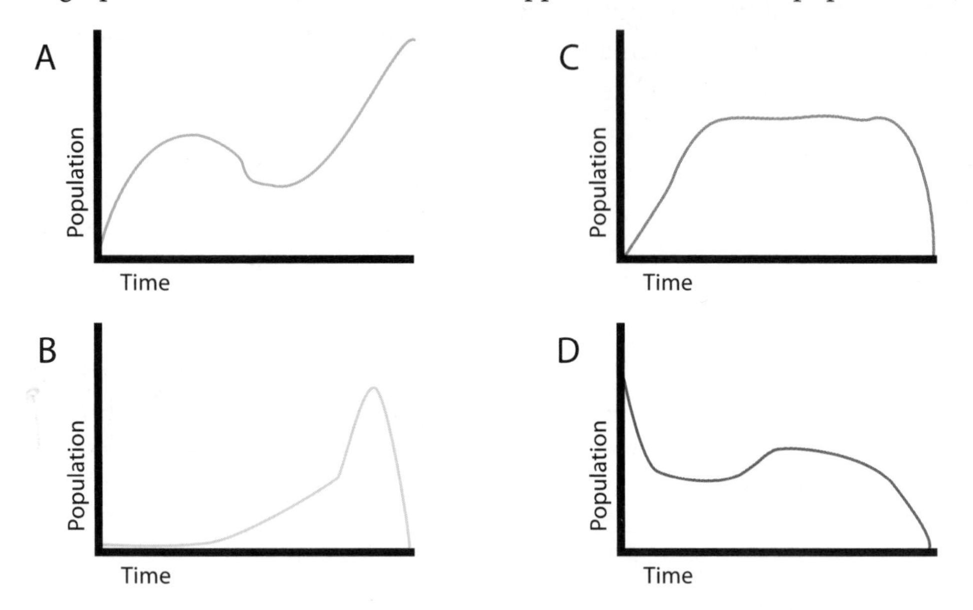

B The starting population grew slowly until extra food was provided. Then it grew rapidly for a short time until it ran out of oxygen and died.

A The starting population grew rapidly and then began to die due to lack of oxygen. The microbiologist opened the lid of the container to allow more air to get into the colony. The colony began to grow again.

C The initial population grew rapidly and then reached a point at which cells were dying as fast as they were dividing. After continuing in this balanced state for a time, excess wastes caused the whole colony to die.

6. One of the graphs from Question 5 was not used. What scenarios can you think of that might account for the results seen in this graph?

Possibly an established bacterial colony had run out of food and the bacteria were dying. Then the scientist added a small amount of food, causing them to grow again for a short time. When the food supply was used up, the colony died.

Going Beyond

Assuming no limitations on growth and no death of bacteria, use the table and graph on the previous page to calculate how long it would take the bacteria to reach one million.

6:40 (6 hrs. & 40 min.)

name ______________________

section ____________ date ____________

Class Investigation

9e Observing Protists

Procedure

1. Use a pipet to obtain a tiny sample of the amoeba culture.
2. Place the sample in the depression of your microscope slide.
3. Observe your amoeba culture under the microscope. Using low power, locate an amoeba. After you have located it, you may want to observe it under a higher power to see more detail.
4. Locate the nucleus and any vacuoles. If any of these vacuoles are changing in their size, they are most likely contractile vacuoles. Contractile vacuoles fill and empty their contents regularly.
5. Draw the basic shape of your amoeba in the first box below. Wait two minutes and then draw the basic shape of your amoeba again in the second box below.

Goals

- ✓ Observe a living amoeba.
- ✓ Learn about the structure and function of a typical protist.

Materials

cultures of living amoebas
pipets
blank microscope slides (depression, or concavity, slides are best)
cover slips
microscope

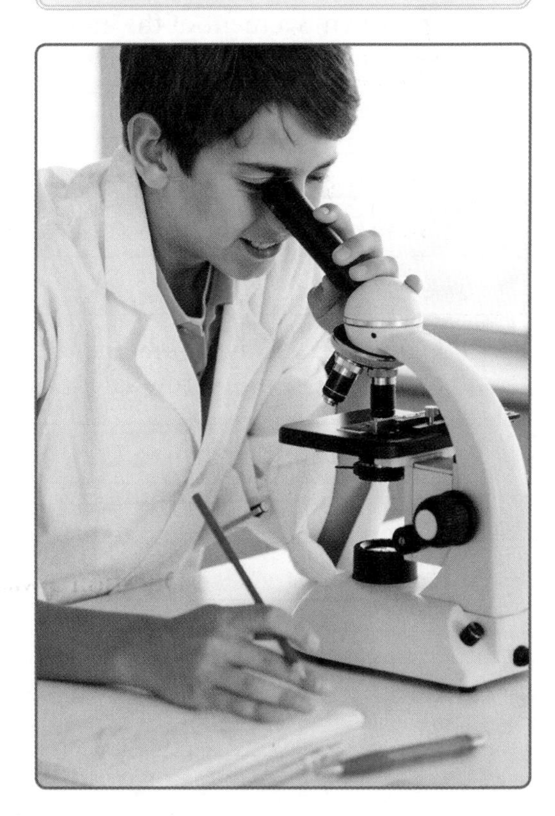

Summing Up

1. Which of the following apply to amoebas? Select one answer from each pair.

kingdom Protista ☑	kingdom Fungi ☐
prokaryotic ☑	eukaryotic ☐
protozoans ☑	algae ☐
unicellular ☐	multicellular ☑
flagella ☐	pseudopods ☑
conjugation ☑	mitosis ☐

2. Did you see your amoeba moving? If so, describe the movement.

3. How is the movement of the amoeba different from the movement of other organisms in the same kingdom?

4. Did you observe any contractile vacuoles in your amoeba? What is the purpose of a contractile vacuole?

Class Investigation

name ______________________

section ____________ date ____________

9f Examining a Mushroom

Procedure

Making a Spore Print

1. Choose a mushroom with a fully expanded cap and cut the stalk as close to the cap as possible.
2. Place the cap gill-side down on a piece of white paper. If the mushroom has pores instead of gills, lay it pore-side down.
3. Cut another cap from another mushroom and likewise place it on a piece of black paper.
4. Allow the caps to lie undisturbed for at least a day. Spores will fall out of the cap and make a pattern on the paper similar to the gill or pore pattern. Sometimes mushroom caps decompose overnight, and sometimes they are filled with insects that emerge as the cap sits overnight.

Goals

- ✓ Make a spore print.
- ✓ Observe the parts of a mushroom.
- ✓ Learn about the macrostructure and microstructure of mushrooms.

Materials

fresh mushrooms (wild or cultivated)
knife
white paper and black paper
blank microscope slides
microscope
spray shellac or hairspray (optional)
prepared slide of a mushroom, cross section (c.s.)

5. Remove the caps from the papers and observe the spore prints. What colors are your mushroom spore prints?

____

6. Are the prints the same color as the gills?

____

7. Using the point of a pencil or another sharp object, transfer a few spores to a microscope slide. Examine the spores with a microscope. Are they perfectly round?

____

8. Make a sketch of a single spore in the box below.

9. (optional) If you wish to preserve your spore print, lightly spray it with shellac or hairspray. Several light sprayings are better than one thick coat.

Observing a Mushroom

Macrostructure

1. Collect a mushroom growing in the soil, including any rootlike hyphae.
2. Examine the stalk. Sometimes a ring of tissue surrounds the stalk. This is the remnant of where the cap was attached to the stalk before the cap expanded. Does your mushroom have such a ring?

   ____

3. The stalk base in some mushrooms is expanded; in others it is the same diameter as the rest of the stalk. Is the stalk base expanded on your mushroom?

   ____

4. Mushroom caps may have either gills or pores on the lower surface. Spores are produced on microscopic structures on the gills or in the pores. Which does your mushroom have, gills or pores?

   ____

   If your mushroom has gills, are they connected to the stalk?

   ____

5. The stalk base may sit in a cup-shaped structure. Does your mushroom have such a structure?

   ____

6. Make a drawing of your mushroom in the box below. Be sure to include all the details mentioned above and any others that you may notice. Label the cap, gills, and stalk.

Microstructure

1. Examine a prepared slide of a cross section through a mushroom. You should notice the structures on the gills that form the spores.
2. Since you are observing the gills, you are looking at a cross section through the ______.

   cap ☐ stalk ☐

name ______________________

section __________ date __________

Application

10a Root and Leaf Structure

Part 1

Directions

Label the drawing below, using the terms given in the box. Write each term near the structure it names; then draw a line from each term to the proper structure.

1. What type of root system does this plant have? ______________________
2. What type of leaf venation does this plant have? ______________________
3. What type of leaf arrangement does this plant have? ______________________

Part 2

Directions

Draw another plant next to the one above but with a different type of root system, a different type of leaf venation, and a different type of leaf arrangement.

1. What type of root system does your plant have? ______________________
2. What type of leaf venation does your plant have? ______________________
3. What type of leaf arrangement does your plant have? ______________________

name ____________________

section ____________ date ____________

10b Structures and Functions of Plants

Part 1

Directions

Fill in the missing letters to complete the following statements. The circled letters form the answer to the final question.

1. The ____ ____ ____ ____ ____ L ____ is a waxy protective layer.
2. Two especially important characteristics of plant cells are ____ ____ ____ ____ W ____ ____ ____ ____ and ____ ____ A ____ ____ ____ ____ ____.
3. ____ ____ R ____ ____ ____ pressure keeps plant cells rigid.
4. Wood is made of ____ ____ ____ E ____ tissue.
5. Sugar is transported in ____ ____ ____ ____ ____ M tissue.
6. Long, tough, tapered plant cells are called ____ I ____ ____ ____ ____.
7. The outermost tissue of young plant organs is the ____ ____ ____ ____ ____ ____ M ____ ____.
8. ____ ____ ____ ____ ____ ____ ____ ____ ____ is a major component of plant cell walls.

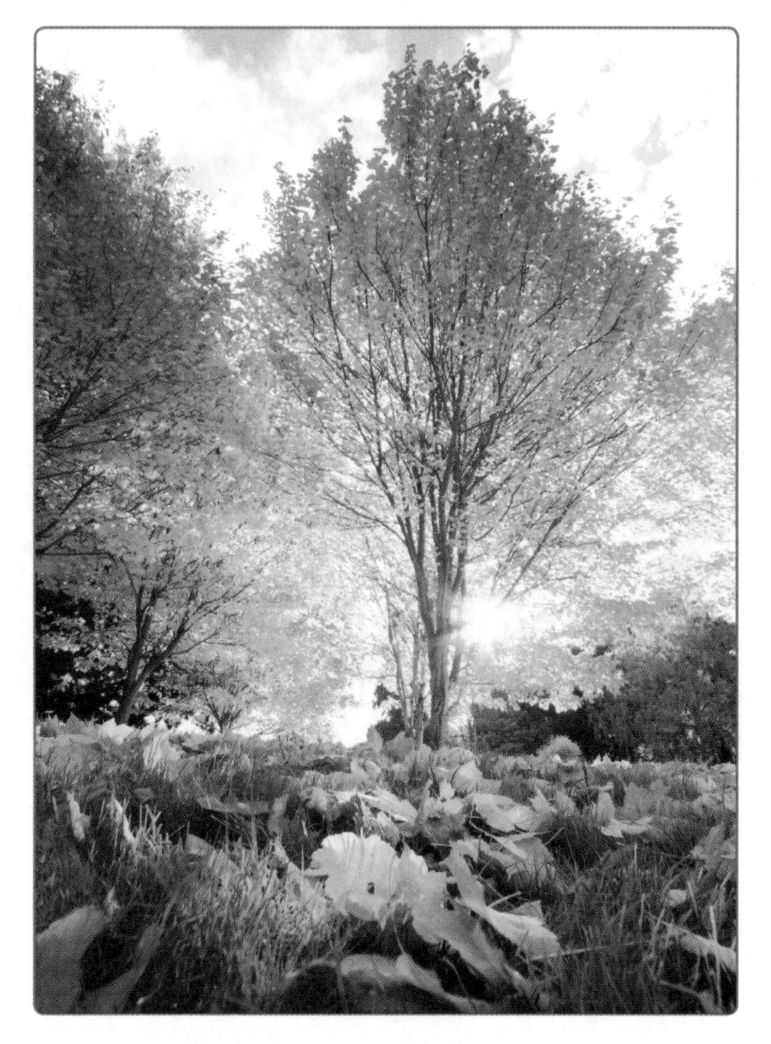

Part 2

Directions

Use the definitions to unscramble the words and write them in the blanks.

1. toro srhai	root hairs	extensions of root epidermal cells that help absorb water
2. mottasa	stomata	openings in leaves that allow gases to pass through
3. sirittrpanano	transpiration	the exiting of water through stomata of leaves
4. cellesitn	lenticels	openings in the bark of woody plants that allow gas exchange
5. poygns rayel	spongy layer	an area in a leaf containing many air spaces between cells so that carbon dioxide from the stomata can pass through
6. helpmo	phloem	a plant tissue that transports sugar solution
7. mopsirt	tropism	a plant's growth response to its environment
8. roomehn	hormone	a chemical substance made by a plant that controls its growth
9. gyexno	oxygen	the gas produced during photosynthesis
10. robcan dexdiio	carbon dioxide	the gas required for photosynthesis

Maple

Application

name ____________________

section __________ date __________

10c Photosynthesis and Leaves

Directions

Supply the missing terms based on the definitions given. Then in the cross section of the leaf, label each structure that has a line pointing to it, using the number of each term as your label. One of them is done for you as an example.

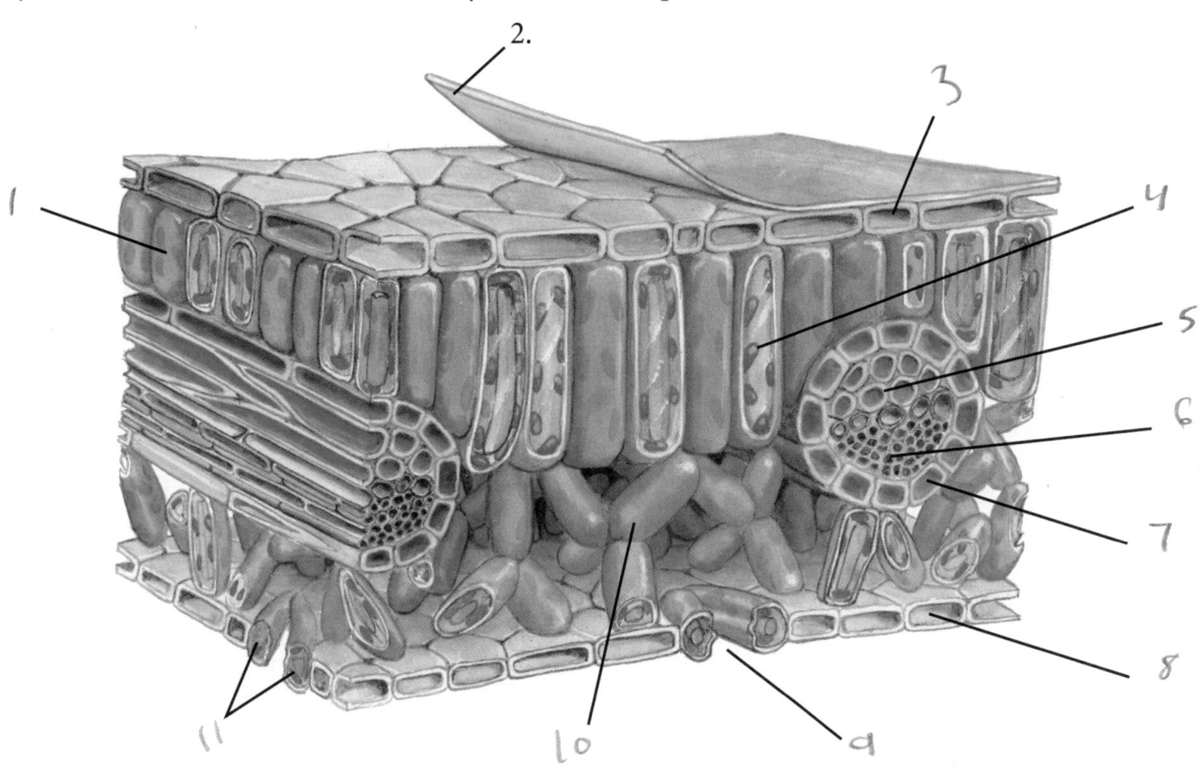

1. palisade layer
(tissue in which most photosynthesis takes place)

2. *cuticle*
(thin protective layer that makes a leaf shiny)

3. upper epidermis
(protects the top of a leaf)

4. chloroplasds
(organelle that contains chlorophyll)

5. Xylem
(brings water from the roots to a leaf)

6. phlorm
(transports sugar solution throughout a plant)

7. vasculor bundle
(supports a leaf and is composed of vascular tissue)

8. lower epidermis
(protects the bottom of a leaf)

9. stoma
(an opening for the exchange of gases)

10. spongy layer
(tissue that contains many air spaces)

11. gaurd cells
(regulate the flow of gases into and out of the stomata)

Application

name ______________________

section __________ date __________

10d Plant Anatomy Review

Directions

Read the following statements. In the space provided, write *True* if the statement is true. If the statement is false, draw a line through the word or words that make the statement false. Then in the blank, write the word or words necessary to make the statement true.

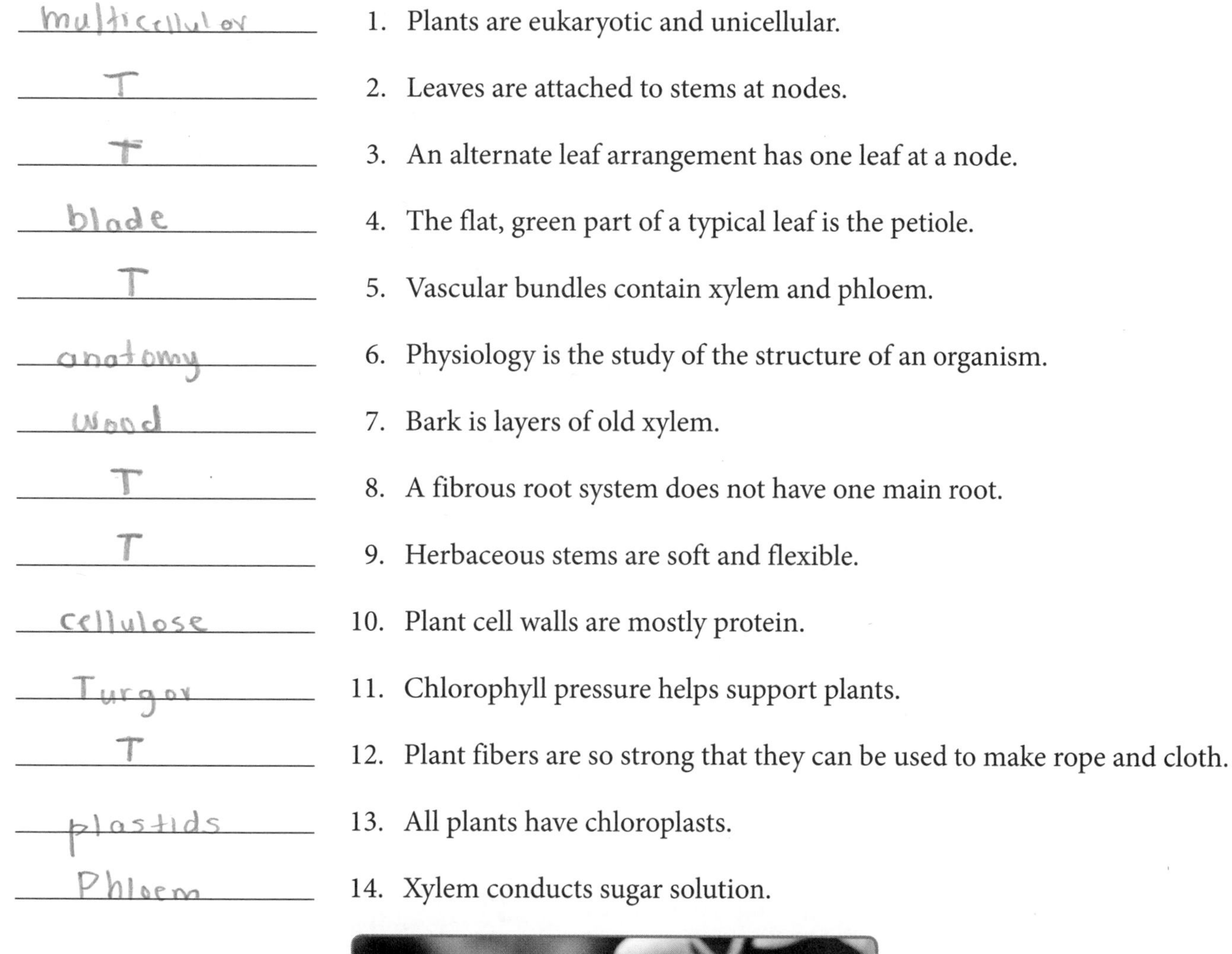

multicellular 1. Plants are eukaryotic and unicellular.

T 2. Leaves are attached to stems at nodes.

T 3. An alternate leaf arrangement has one leaf at a node.

blade 4. The flat, green part of a typical leaf is the petiole.

T 5. Vascular bundles contain xylem and phloem.

anatomy 6. Physiology is the study of the structure of an organism.

wood 7. Bark is layers of old xylem.

T 8. A fibrous root system does not have one main root.

T 9. Herbaceous stems are soft and flexible.

cellulose 10. Plant cell walls are mostly protein.

Turgor 11. Chlorophyll pressure helps support plants.

T 12. Plant fibers are so strong that they can be used to make rope and cloth.

plastids 13. All plants have chloroplasts.

Phloem 14. Xylem conducts sugar solution.

Moth orchid

name ____________________

section __________ date __________

10e Plant Physiology Review

Directions

In the spaces provided, tell how the terms in each pair are similar; then tell how they are different.

1. long-day plant / short-day plant

   similar: ____________________

   different: ____________________

2. auxin / chlorophyll

   similar: ____________________

   different: ____________________

3. guard cells / stomata

   similar: ____________________

   different: ____________________

4. lenticels / stomata

   similar: ____________________

   different: ____________________

5. palisade layer / spongy layer

   similar: ____________________

different: ____________________

____

6. starch / cellulose

similar: ____________________

____

different: ____________________

____

7. positive tropism / negative tropism

similar: ____________________

____

different: ____________________

____

8. turgor pressure / cell walls

similar: ____________________

____

different: ____________________

____

9. photoperiodism / phototropism

similar: ____________________

____

different: ____________________

____

10. transpiration / root hairs

similar: ____________________

____

different: ____________________

____

name ____________________

section __________ date __________

10f Leaf Design and Function

Part 1: The Structure of a Leaf

Procedure and Data

1. Obtain and set up your microscope.
2. Place the prepared slide of a leaf cross section on the stage of your microscope and adjust the focus.
3. Find a section of the leaf that is not damaged and that does not have a section of a vein in it.
4. Observe the structures and tissues of the leaf from the top to the bottom of the leaf. As you do this exercise, you may want to change back and forth between low and high magnification.
5. Find the following structures and tissues. For each, describe its size, shape, thickness, and other characteristics that you see.
   - Cuticle (upper)

     ____

     ____

     ____

   - Upper epidermis

     ____

     ____

     ____

   - Palisade layer

     ____

     ____

     ____

   - Spongy layer

     ____

     ____

     ____

Goals

- ✓ Observe the structures and tissues within a leaf.
- ✓ Recognize how a leaf's design aids photosynthesis.
- ✓ Observe guard cells and stomata.

Materials

microscope
prepared slide of a leaf cross section
glass slide
cover slip
eyedropper
water
leaf (geranium, philodendron, or lettuce works well)
scissors
toothpicks

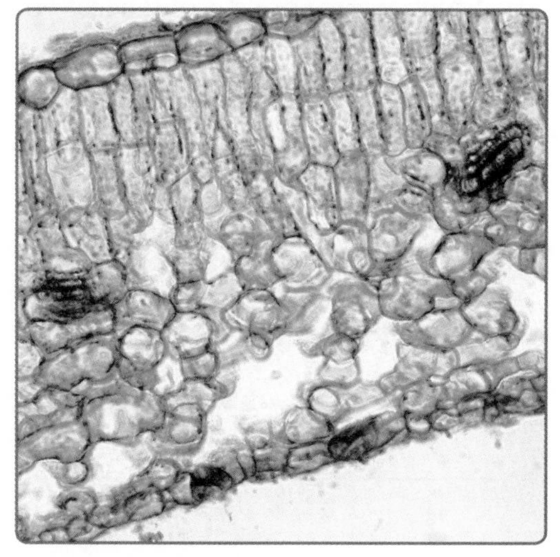

Leaf cross section, 400×

- Lower epidermis

___

___

- Cuticle (lower)

___

___

- Guard cells and stomata

___

___

6. Find a cross section of a vein. Avoid the vein that runs down the middle of the leaf and veins that are cut lengthwise.
   - What tissues do you see in the vein? How can you tell which tissue is which?

   ___

   ___

   - What is the function of a vein?

   ___

   ___

Summing Up

1. Which tissues or cells of the leaf you observed contain chloroplasts and thus carry on photosynthesis?

   ___

   ___

   ___

2. God designed the leaf to carry on photosynthesis. In what ways does the placement of the leaf's structures and tissues make the leaf ideal for carrying on photosynthesis? Tell how the requirements for photosynthesis are easily met and the products of photosynthesis easily removed because of the leaf's structure.

   ___

   ___

   ___

   ___

   ___

   ___

   ___

   ___

name ______________________

Part 2: Guard Cells and Stomata

Procedure

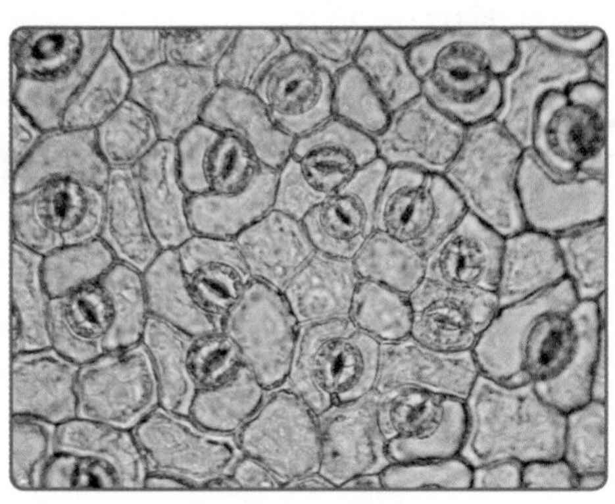
Lower epidermis of leaf, 400×

1. Obtain and set up your microscope.
2. Wash and dry a glass slide and a cover slip.
3. Place a drop of water on the slide.
4. Carefully tear a leaf, pulling away a section of the lower epidermis.
5. Being careful not to damage the epidermis, use scissors to remove the epidermis with a tiny portion of the leaf attached to it.
6. Place the epidermis and leaf portion in the water on the slide. Using toothpicks, make sure part of the epidermis is flat in the water. Do not damage the epidermis.
7. Place the cover slip on top of the water and epidermis.
8. Place the slide on the microscope stage and find the epidermis on low magnification.
9. Observe the epidermis using high power.
10. Locate guard cells and stomata.

Data

1. Check the box that indicates what you observe:
   - ☐ All the stomata are open.
   - ☐ All the stomata are closed.
   - ☐ Some stomata are open, and some are closed.
2. Describe the stomata.

   ____

   ____

   ____

3. What do the guard cells look like?

   ____

   ____

   ____

4. In the box below, draw one of the stomata you observe. Include the surrounding guard cells and a portion of the surrounding epidermal cells. Label any structures you can identify.

Summing Up

1. What is the function of the stomata?

2. What is the function of the guard cells?

3. How do you suppose the guard cells open and close the stomata?

name ______________________

section __________ date __________

10g How Much Water Is Lost During Transpiration?

Goals

✓ Observe the results of transpiration.

✓ Determine the weight of the water lost by a plant during transpiration.

Materials

potted geranium (or other plant with a single stem)
water
plastic bag
putty or modeling clay
tape or twist tie
balance

Procedure

1. Thoroughly water a geranium plant and allow the excess water to drain.
2. Place the pot in a plastic bag. Put a small amount of putty or modeling clay around the stem where you will close the bag. Close the bag around the stem, just above the soil, and use tape or a twist tie to secure the bag to the stem.
3. Weigh the plant and record its weight on the chart below.
4. Place the pot in direct sunlight or in a well-lit area of the room.
5. Weigh the plant and record its weight each day for the next four days. Record any other observations in the Notes column.

Data

Day	Weight	Weight lost	Notes
1			
2			
3			
4			
5			

Summing Up

1. Calculate the amount of weight that the plant lost each day and record the amounts on the chart.
2. What is transpiration?

____

____

____

3. On which day did the plant lose the most weight? ______________________
   Why do you think the plant lost more weight on that day?
   ____
   ____
   ____

4. On which day did the plant lose the least weight? ______________________
   Why do you think the plant lost less weight on that day?
   ____
   ____
   ____

5. How much weight did the plant lose altogether? ______________________
6. One gram of water has a volume of 1 mL; one ounce of water has a volume of ⅛ cup. What volume of water did the plant transpire? ______________________

Dutchman's breeches

name ______________________

section __________ date __________

10h Is Light Necessary for Photosynthesis?

Goals

- ✓ Determine whether light is necessary for photosynthesis.
- ✓ Determine whether the amount of light affects the rate of photosynthesis.

Preliminary Work

After reading through the Procedure section, identify the following parts of your experiment.

- Problem: Is light necessary for photosynthesis?
- Hypothesis:

  ____

  ____

  ____

- Experimental variable:

  ____

  ____

- Response variable:

  ____

  ____

- Controlled variables:

  ____

  ____

  ____

Materials

large, shallow, clear dishes (3)
test tubes (3)
ring stands (3)
clamps
water
knife
elodea
thread
nails (3)
cardboard box
lamp

Procedure

1. Fill three dishes and three test tubes with water. Carefully mount the test tubes above the dishes and upside down as illustrated in the diagram. The test tubes must be filled with water (no air in the top of the tube), and their openings must be below the surface of the water but still about 2.5 cm (1 in.) from the bottom of the dish.
2. Using a sharp knife, cut three equal lengths of elodea. Each of the elodea pieces should have the same number of leaves. Be careful not to damage the elodea's leaves as you cut the stem.
3. Tie a piece of thread to a nail. Tie the other end of the thread to the bottom end of one piece of elodea.

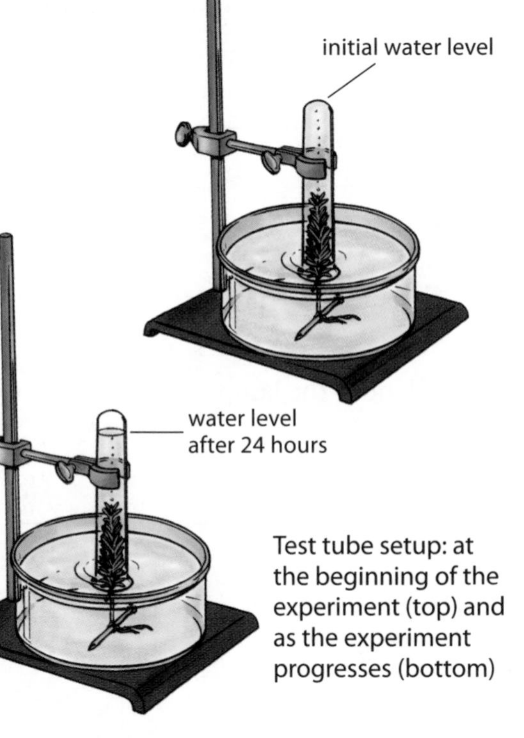

Test tube setup: at the beginning of the experiment (top) and as the experiment progresses (bottom)

4. Measure the length of your thread and elodea. With the nail on the bottom of the dish and the elodea stalk in the test tube, there should be about 5 cm (2 in.) of water-filled test tube remaining above the top end of the elodea stalk. If necessary, adjust the length of the thread by twisting the thread around the nail.
5. Place the elodea stalk inside the test tube as shown in the diagram. Do the same for the other two test tubes.
6. Place one apparatus in an area where it will receive normal room light.
7. Place a box over another apparatus.
8. Place the third apparatus in an area where you can leave a lamp shining on it overnight. The lamp should be near enough to give the elodea bright light but not close enough to heat the water.

Data

1. Half an hour after you begin the experiment, record your observations.
   - In normal room light:

     ____

     ____

   - In the dark:

     ____

     ____

   - Under the lamp:

     ____

     ____

2. Twenty-four hours after you begin the experiment, repeat your observations.
   - In normal room light:

     ____

     ____

   - In the dark:

     ____

     ____

   - Under the lamp:

     ____

     ____

name ____________________

Summing Up

1. What process was taking place in the elodea stalk to produce the results you observed in the test tubes?

    ____

2. What observations led you to this conclusion?

    ____

    ____

    ____

3. What was the gas being produced and collected at the tops of the test tubes?

    ____

4. Why do you believe that this was the substance being produced?

    ____

    ____

    ____

5. Was your hypothesis supported or falsified? ____________________

Going Beyond

You can add carbon dioxide to the water by adding baking soda. Find the amount of baking soda needed to maximize the rate of oxygen production. Use several apparatuses all exposed to the same amount of light. Be sure to keep all other conditions equal among the groups.

Bird of paradise

name ____________________

section __________ date __________

10i Gravitropism in Seedlings

Procedure

1. Place several folded paper towels on a glass plate. Place rubber bands around the glass plate and paper towels to hold the towels in place.
2. Place eight small, wet cotton balls on the paper towels; then place bean seeds in the center of each cotton ball. Be sure that the two bean seeds "face" each direction (up, right, left, or down) as indicated in the diagram. You should have two seeds facing up, two facing right, two facing left, and two facing down.
3. Slowly add a little more water to wet the paper towels.

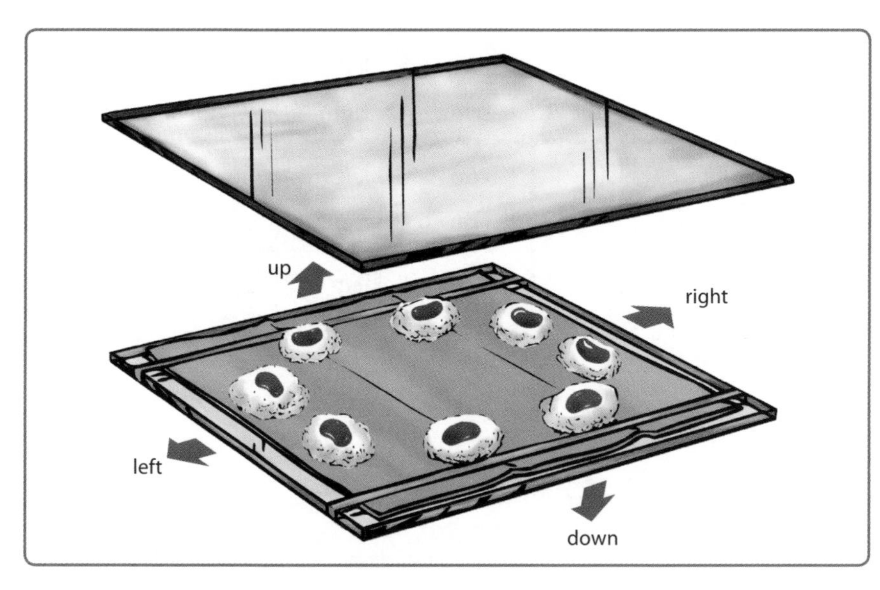

4. Place another glass plate over the top of the bean seeds and secure it with more rubber bands.
5. Using a marking pencil, draw an arrow on the top glass plate.
6. Set this assembly, with the arrow pointing up, in a dark, warm area. (The assembly should not be flat; it should be on its side with the arrow pointing up.)
7. Using an eyedropper, add water to the assembly daily.
8. Observe the bean seeds daily.
9. Once the seeds begin to grow, record their growth patterns on the chart on page 166. For each pair of bean seeds (those facing up, facing right, facing left, and facing down), record what directions the roots grow and what directions the stem shoots grow by marking an X in the appropriate box of the chart.

Goal

✓ Demonstrate and observe gravitropism in seedlings.

Materials

paper towels
glass plates (2)
rubber bands
cotton balls
bean seeds
water
marking pencil
eyedropper

Data

Date		Upward-facing beans	Right-facing beans	Left-facing beans	Downward-facing beans
	Roots	☐ up ☐ left ☐ down ☐ right	☐ up ☐ left ☐ down ☐ right	☐ up ☐ left ☐ down ☐ right	☐ up ☐ left ☐ down ☐ right
	Stems	☐ up ☐ left ☐ down ☐ right	☐ up ☐ left ☐ down ☐ right	☐ up ☐ left ☐ down ☐ right	☐ up ☐ left ☐ down ☐ right
	Roots	☐ up ☐ left ☐ down ☐ right	☐ up ☐ left ☐ down ☐ right	☐ up ☐ left ☐ down ☐ right	☐ up ☐ left ☐ down ☐ right
	Stems	☐ up ☐ left ☐ down ☐ right	☐ up ☐ left ☐ down ☐ right	☐ up ☐ left ☐ down ☐ right	☐ up ☐ left ☐ down ☐ right
	Roots	☐ up ☐ left ☐ down ☐ right	☐ up ☐ left ☐ down ☐ right	☐ up ☐ left ☐ down ☐ right	☐ up ☐ left ☐ down ☐ right
	Stems	☐ up ☐ left ☐ down ☐ right	☐ up ☐ left ☐ down ☐ right	☐ up ☐ left ☐ down ☐ right	☐ up ☐ left ☐ down ☐ right
	Roots	☐ up ☐ left ☐ down ☐ right	☐ up ☐ left ☐ down ☐ right	☐ up ☐ left ☐ down ☐ right	☐ up ☐ left ☐ down ☐ right
	Stems	☐ up ☐ left ☐ down ☐ right	☐ up ☐ left ☐ down ☐ right	☐ up ☐ left ☐ down ☐ right	☐ up ☐ left ☐ down ☐ right

Summing Up

1. What is gravitropism?

____

____

2. Did the roots of the bean seedlings exhibit positive gravitropism or negative gravitropism?

   positive ☐ negative ☐

3. Did the stems of the bean seedlings exhibit positive gravitropism or negative gravitropism?

   positive ☐ negative ☐

4. Did the way in which the seeds were positioned affect their response to gravity? If so, what were the differences?

____

____

name ____________________

section __________ date __________

11a Major Plant Groups

Directions

Use the terms from the list below to fill in the concept map showing the relationships between the terms. Words on the arrows show the relationships between terms. Each term is used only once, and there is only one correct way to use all the terms in this concept map. Three terms have already been placed on the map to get you started.

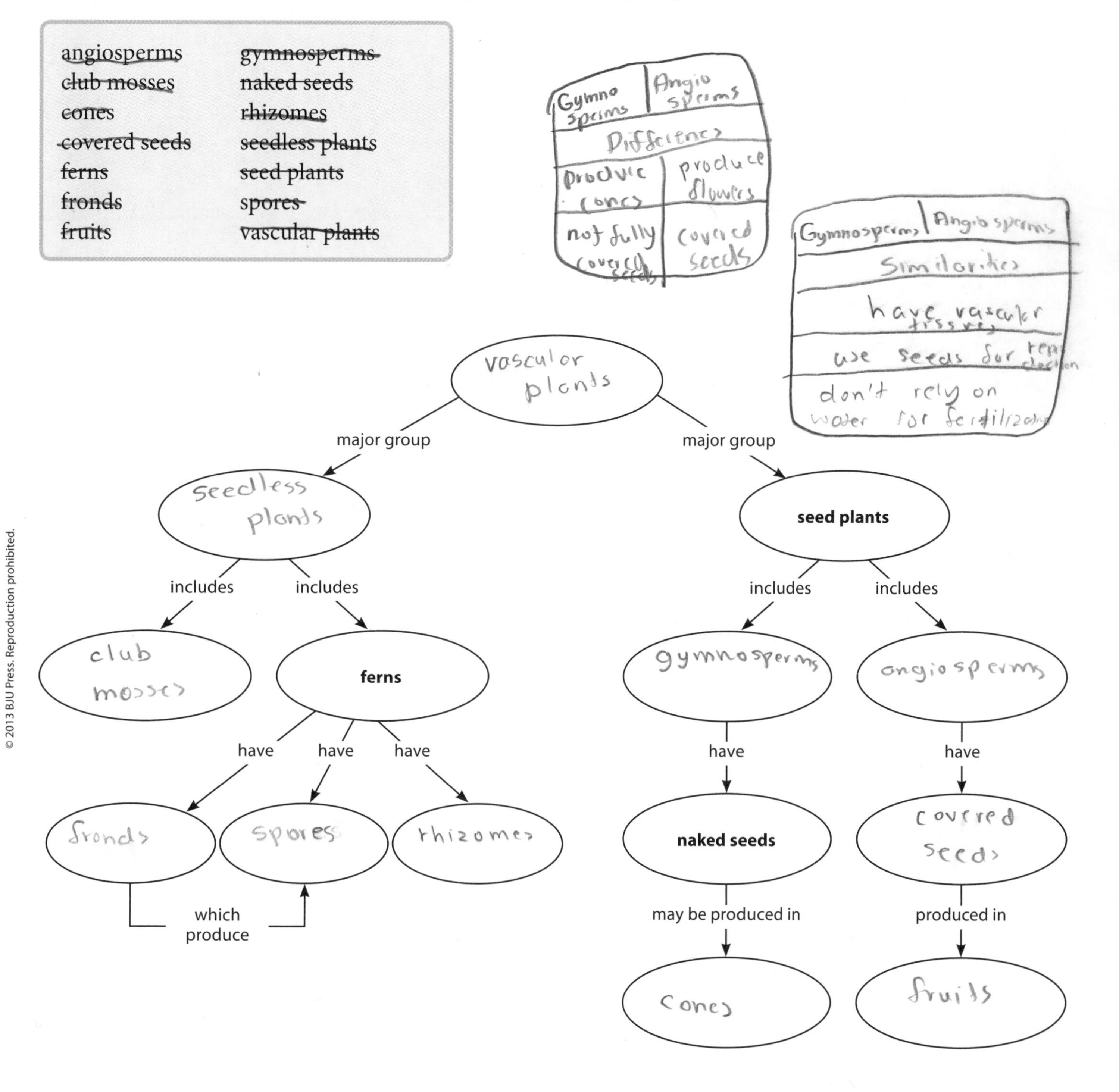

name__________

section______ date______

11b Flowers

Directions

Supply the missing terms or definitions. Then in the diagram of the flower, label each structure that has a line pointing to it, using the number of each term as your label.

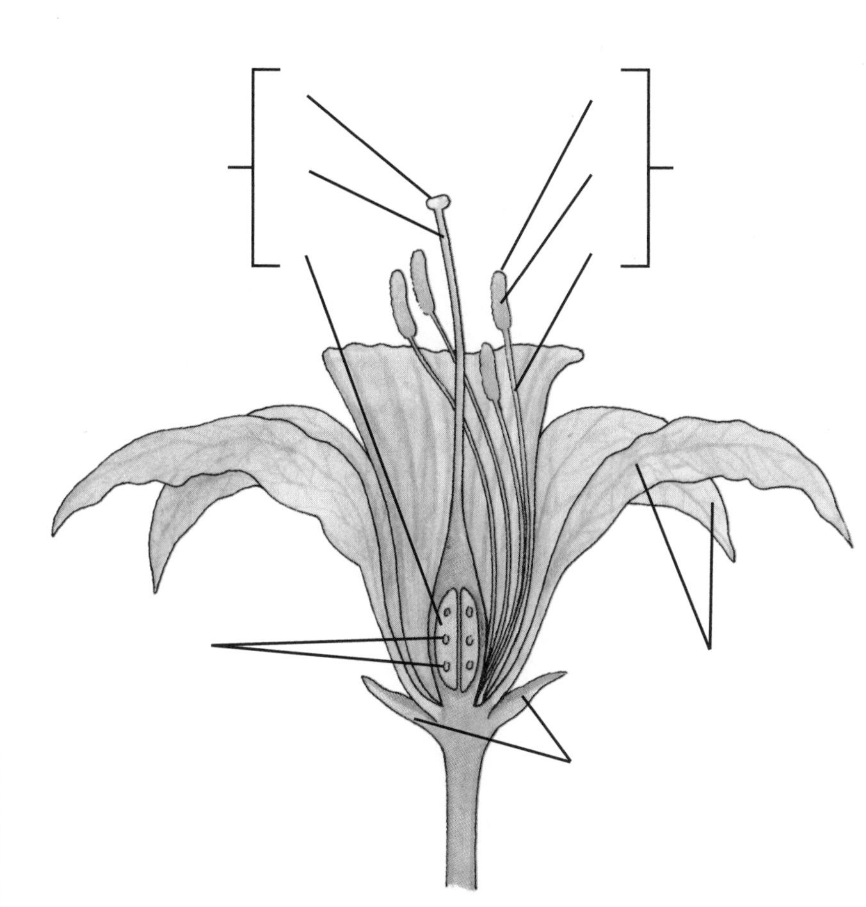

1. __________ (surface to which pollen becomes attached)
2. __________ (slender stalk supporting the stigma)
3. __________ (structure that contains the ovules)
4. __________ (female reproductive structure)
5. __________ (contains the male gametes)
6. __________ (structure that contains the pollen)
7. __________ (structure that supports the anther)
8. __________ (male reproductive structure)
9. __________ (usually the large, showy parts of flowers)
10. __________ (structures that will become seeds)
11. __________ (protect the flower while it is a bud)

name ______________________

section __________ date __________

Application

11c Pollination and Scattering Seeds

Part 1: Pollination

Directions

Number the following sentences to show the correct sequence of pollination and fertilization.

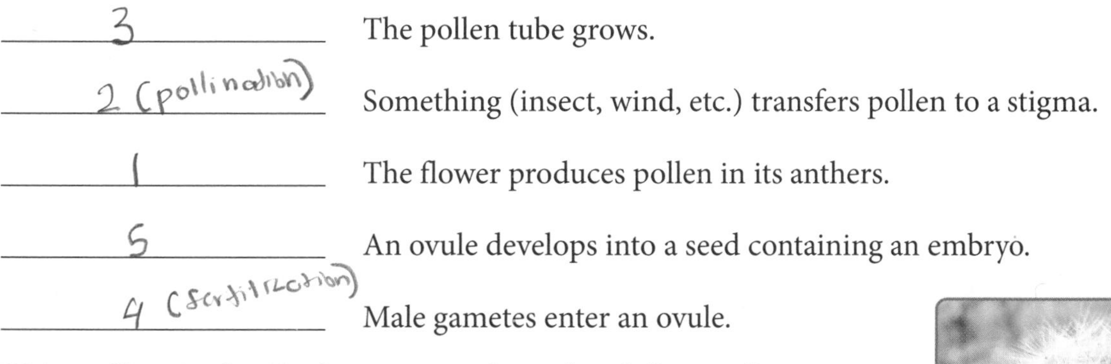

3 The pollen tube grows.

2 (pollination) Something (insect, wind, etc.) transfers pollen to a stigma.

1 The flower produces pollen in its anthers.

5 An ovule develops into a seed containing an embryo.

4 (fertilization) Male gametes enter an ovule.

Write *pollination* beside the sentence above that defines pollination.

Write *fertilization* beside the sentence above that defines fertilization.

Part 2: Scattering Seeds

Directions

Write the answer to each question in the space provided.

1. How can a bird unknowingly spread the seeds of its favorite fruit tree by eating the fruit?

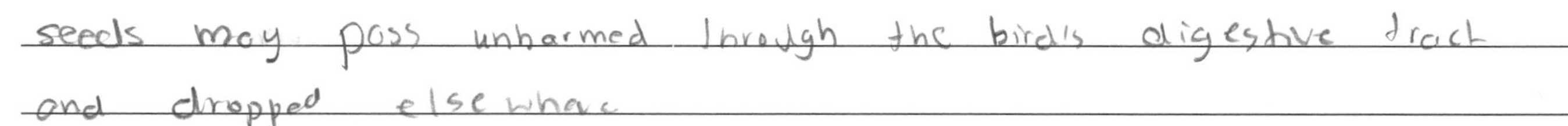

seeds may pass unharmed through the bird's digestive tract and dropped elsewhere

2. Give an example of a plant whose seeds are dispersed by wind.

dandelion; milkweed; tumbleweed

3. Give an example of a plant whose seeds are dispersed by water.

coconuts

4. Give an example of a plant that has special structures for dispersing its own seeds.

squirting cucumber & dwarf mistletoe

5. Why is it important for a plant *not* to have all its seeds accumulate in one place?

there would not be enough nutrients, water & light, for all to survive.

name ____________________

section __________ date __________

Application

11d Review

Directions

Read the following statements. In the space provided, write *True* if the statement is true. If the statement is false, draw a line through the word or words that make the statement false. Then in the blank, write the word or words necessary to make the statement true.

Spores 1. Mosses reproduce by ~~seeds.~~

true 2. Ferns have vascular tissue.

rhizoids 3. ~~Roots~~ anchor mosses to the soil and absorb water.

true 4. Fern leaves are called fronds.

fruits (or seeds) 5. Angiosperms produce ~~flowers and cones.~~

true 6. Horsetails were once used as a cleaning abrasive.

sori 7. On the lower surface of a mature fern are ~~fiddleheads~~, which produce spores.

true 8. Most mature ferns are attached to underground stems called rhizomes.

haploid 9. In the process of fertilization, ~~diploid~~ gametes combine to form zygotes.

cotyledon 10. An area of stored food in a seed is called an ~~ovule~~.

true 11. Runners, root sprouts, and leaf cuttings are all forms of asexual reproduction.

germination 12. The initial growth of a seed to form a new plant is called ~~ripening.~~

nonvascular 13. True mosses belong to the group of ~~vascular~~ plants called bryophytes.

true 14. Gymnosperms include many plants whose seeds are exposed on the scales of a cone.

fruit 15. Angiosperms are plants whose seeds are completely surrounded by ~~a flower~~.

name ______________________

section __________ date __________

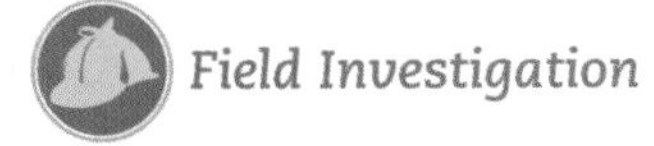

11e Moss Structures

Introduction

Mosses are classified in phylum Bryophyta. You've probably seen lots of moss plants in the shady spots of your backyard and other places. In this lab, you will observe a moss plant up close.

Goal

✓ Observe and identify the parts of an individual moss plant.

Materials

moss (collected locally)
forceps
hand lens
ruler (marked in millimeters)
microscope slide (concavity)
water
cover slip
microscope
toothpick

Procedure

1. Using forceps, grasp a single moss plant and separate it from a clump of moss. Try to find one that has a stalk and spore capsule if possible.
2. Examine your plant with a hand lens to make sure you have only one plant and not several stuck together.
3. Measure (to the nearest millimeter) the length of the structures listed in the chart below and record their lengths. If your specimen does not contain one of the structures, put a dash in that space. See Figure 11-2 on page 230 of the textbook if you are unsure of the identification of any of these parts.

Data

Structure	Length (in mm)
rhizoid	
leafy shoot	
stalk	
spore capsule	

Summing Up

1. Which parts are the hardest to identify or measure? Why?

____

____

____

2. Why are the leafy structures of the moss plant green?

____

____

3. Why are the leafy structures of the moss plant so short?

____

____

4. If your moss has a stalk and spore capsule, answer the following questions:
   - Is the color of the stalk the same as the color of the moss plant? ____________
     - If not, what might this tell you?

       ____
   - Does the spore capsule have a pointed cap on top of it? ____________
     - If the spore capsule is missing its top, what might that tell you?

       ____

Going Beyond

1. Make a wet mount to observe a single moss plant. Begin by placing one or two drops of water and the plant on the center of a microscope slide and then place a cover slip on top. A concavity (well) slide works best for this observation.
2. Using the lowest power of your microscope, position the slide so that you can clearly see a "leaf" of the moss plant. Can you identify separate cells?

   ____

   Rotate the nosepiece to the medium objective. Can you detect individual cells at this magnification?

   ____
3. Keeping the microscope on medium power, look through the eyepiece and move the slide until you are centered on the spore capsule (if present). Is there a pointed lid on the spore capsule?

   ____

   If there is a capsule, carefully remove the cover slip and crush the capsule with the tip of a toothpick. Replace the slip and reposition the slide to examine the capsule. Can you see any spores?

   ____

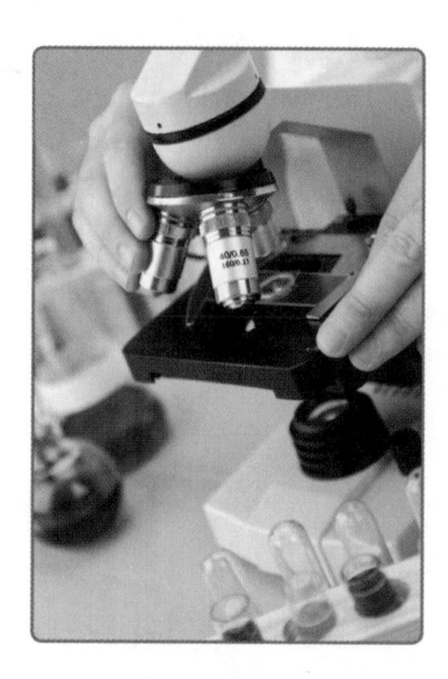

name ____________________

section __________ date __________

11f Flower Dissection

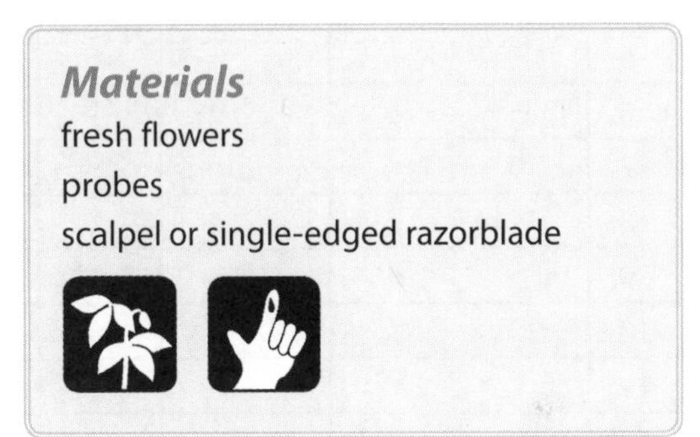

Goals

✓ Identify the parts of a flower.

✓ Observe some of the variations in flower parts.

Materials

fresh flowers

probes

scalpel or single-edged razorblade

Procedure

1. Each group in your class will be assigned a number and given a different kind of flower. As you read the following questions, record your answers in the chart on page 178. Be sure to record your answers only on the line for the number of your flower.
2. Without cutting, find as many flower parts as you can. Are any missing? Fill in your answer on the chart.
3. Count the number of flower parts asked for in the chart and record your findings. (If there are more than 25 of any one flower part, write the word *many* on the chart.)
4. Locate and examine the pistil and ovary. (In some flowers, you may find multiple pistils or ovaries.)
   - Is the ovary located above the receptacle or in the receptacle? Record your answer of *above* or *in* in the "Ovary placement" column.
   - Using a very sharp scalpel or razorblade, cut the pistil and ovary from the top to the bottom. Examine the ovary.
     - Does the ovary have a single chamber or many chambers? Record your answer on the chart.
   - Locate and examine the ovules.
     - How many ovules are there? Record your answer on the chart. (If there are more than a dozen, write the word *many* on the chart.)
     - What do ovules become? ____________________

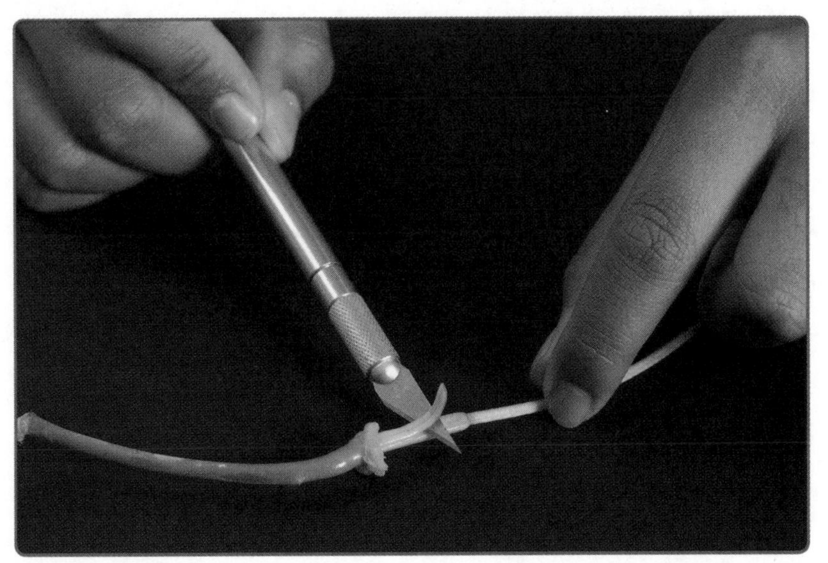

Cutting the ovary from top to bottom

Data

No.	Flower name	Missing flower parts? (yes/no)	Number of							Ovary placement*
			sepals	petals	stamens	stigmas	ovaries	ovary chambers	ovules	
1.	daffodil	yes	0	6	6	1	1	2	many	in
2.	rose	no	5	many	many	many	1	1	many	in
3.	lily	yes	0	6	6	1	1	1	many	in
4.	orchid	no	3	3	1	1	1	1	many	above
5.	tulip	yes	0	7	6	1	1	1	many	in
6.	hibiscus		3	3	6	1	many	1	many	in
7.										
8.										
9.										
10.										
11.										
12.										
13.										
14.										
15.										

**above* or *in* the receptacle

Summing Up

Go to the other groups in your class and observe the flowers they dissected. On your chart, fill in information for these flowers. Then select the correct choice for each of the following statements.

1. The organism you dissected belongs to phylum
   Anthophyta. ☐ Coniferophyta. ☐
2. The organism you dissected reproduces with
   spores. ☐ seeds. ☐
3. The organism you dissected is
   nonvascular. ☐ vascular. ☐
4. The organism you dissected is a(n)
   angiosperm. ☐ gymnosperm. ☐

name

section date

11g Factors That Affect Germination

Goals

- ✓ Determine whether seeds are alive.
- ✓ Identify the effects that various factors have on the ability of seeds to sprout and grow.
- ✓ Record observations accurately.

Materials

bean seeds
factors to be used in the experiment (See box below.)
potting soil
potting tray(s)
labels

Procedure

Your teacher will divide the class into several groups and will give each group 20 seeds. Each group will choose one of the factors from the list of suggestions below and will apply its factor to all 20 of its seeds.

1. All the groups should plant their seeds at the same time. Your teacher will plant 20 seeds that were not exposed to any factor to serve as the control group.
2. Plant the seeds in large potting trays. All seeds should be planted facing the same direction and about 1.3 cm (0.5 in.) deep in the soil. If possible, plant the seeds for the entire class in different rows of the same large potting tray.
3. Label the rows of seeds according to the factor they experienced.
4. Water the seeds enough to keep the soil moist but not too wet.
5. Place the plant trays in a warm, sunny spot.

Factors

Below is a list of factors that you can use in this experiment. Perhaps you can think of additional factors. Each group in your class should choose one factor to test.

Alcohol. Soak the seeds in rubbing alcohol for 1, 5, 10, or 24 hours. (Choose one.)
Bleach. Soak the seeds in water containing bleach for 1, 5, 10, or 24 hours. (Choose one.)
Freezing temperature. Place the seeds in a freezer for 5 minutes or for 1, 5, 10, or 24 hours. (Choose one.)
High temperature. Expose the seeds to temperatures of 300 °F, 350 °F, or 400 °F in a conventional oven for 5, 10, or 15 minutes. (Choose one combination.)
Hydrogen peroxide. Soak the seeds in hydrogen peroxide for 1, 5, 10, or 24 hours. (Choose one.)
Liquid fertilizer. Soak the seeds in water containing liquid fertilizer (at the strength recommended for lawn use) for 1, 5, 10, or 24 hours. (Choose one.)
Microwaves. Expose the seeds to microwaves in a microwave oven at a low setting for 5, 10, 15, or 30 seconds. (Choose one.)
Petroleum jelly. Coat the outside of the seeds with petroleum jelly.
Radiation. Irradiated seeds available from science supply companies are seeds that have been exposed to varying amounts of radiation.
Refrigeration. Place the seeds in a refrigerator for 5 minutes or for 1, 5, 10, or 24 hours. (Choose one.)
Sunlight. Expose the seeds to direct sunlight for 1, 5, or 10 days. (Choose one.)
Water. Soak the seeds in water for 1, 5, 10, or 24 hours. (Choose one.)
Weed killer. Soak the seeds in water containing weed killer for 1, 5, 10, or 24 hours. (Choose one.)

Data

Observe the seeds daily. Record your daily observations in a notebook. On the chart below, summarize your observations of the control group on the first line of the chart and your experimental group on another line.

On the last day of observations, your teacher will lead the class in compiling the data on the chart. Make sure you copy the information for other experimental groups onto this chart as your class discusses it.

Data for Seed Growth

Factor	Number of days for first sprout to appear	Total number of sprouts after two weeks	Average height of leaves after two weeks	Average number of leaves after two weeks	Other observations
control group					

Summing Up

1. Which factor(s) in this experiment caused the seeds to sprout quicker than those in the control group?

____

____

2. Which factor(s) in this experiment caused the seeds to sprout slower than those in the control group?

____

____

name ______________________

3. Which factor(s) caused significantly more seeds, compared with the control group, to sprout?

4. Which factor(s) caused significantly fewer seeds, compared with the control group, to sprout?

5. Which factor(s) in this experiment had little or no effect on the number of seeds that sprouted?

6. Based on your observations, do you think that the bean seeds were alive when the factors were applied to them? yes ☐ no ☐ Explain your answer.

7. Did you notice anything about the seeds before they were planted that indicated whether they were alive?

8. Why do you think the seeds in some groups did not sprout or sprouted slower than those in the control group?

9. What other significant or unusual conclusions can you make based on observations of the bean seeds that your class planted?

10. Do you think that your conclusions about bean seeds are true of seeds in general? yes ☐ no ☐ Why or why not?

11. What are some ways that this experiment and its results could have practical applications?

name ____________________

section __________ date __________

12a Sponges and Jellyfish

Directions

Read the following descriptions and decide whether a sponge or a jellyfish is being described. In the blank by each statement, write an *S* if it describes a sponge and a *J* if it describes a jellyfish. Some descriptions will have more than one answer.

_______ 1. Lacks a backbone

_______ 2. Has a body filled with pores

_______ 3. Has a hydrostatic skeleton

_______ 4. Has tentacles

_______ 5. Is a filter feeder

_______ 6. Lives mostly in oceans

_______ 7. Is classified in phylum Porifera

_______ 8. Digests food in a gastrovascular cavity

_______ 9. Can sting you with nematocysts

_______ 10. Has a skeleton made of spongin or spicules

_______ 11. Is classified in kingdom Animalia

_______ 12. Has collar cells with flagella

_______ 13. Is sessile as an adult

_______ 14. Reproduces both sexually and asexually

_______ 15. Is classified in phylum Cnidaria

_______ 16. Has radial symmetry

name______________________

section__________ date__________

12b The Planarian: A Type of Flatworm

Part 1

Directions

In the spaces below, write the words that are described by the following statements.

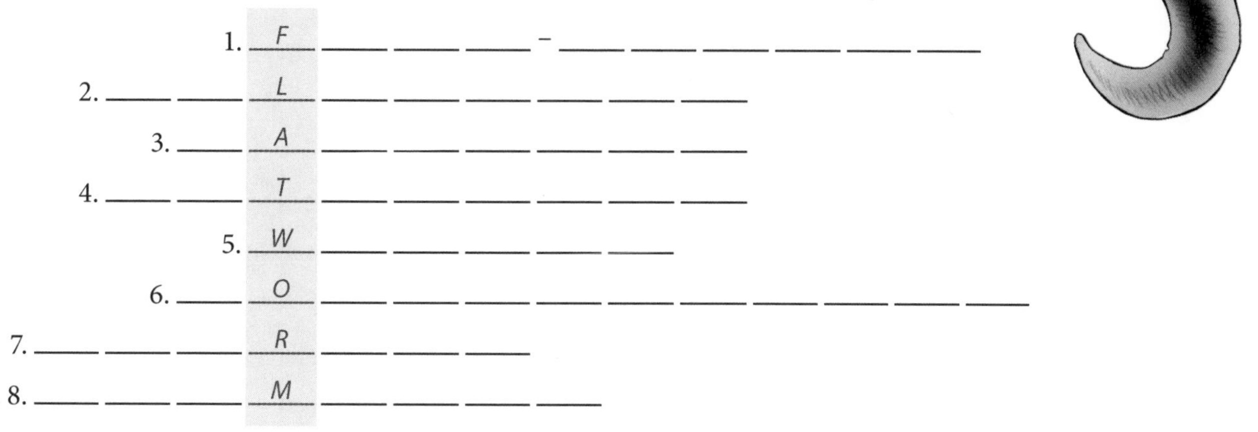

1. Not dependent on a host for survival
2. A type of body symmetry in which one side mirrors the other side
3. A simple brain
4. The long, branching cavity where digestive enzymes are secreted
5. Removed by flame cells and excretory pores
6. A type of nerve that carries impulses from one end of the body to the other
7. A muscular tube that extends through the mouth to suck in food
8. Something that causes a reaction in an organism

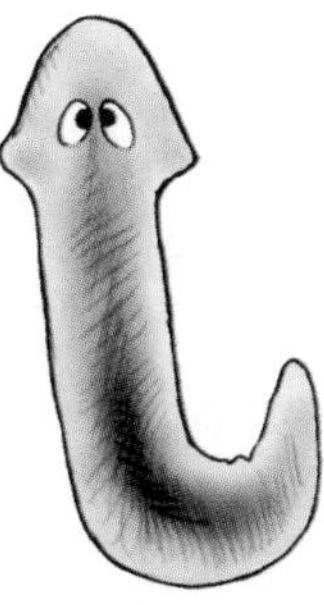

Part 2

Directions

Number the following sentences to show the correct sequence of planarian digestion.

_______ The cells inside the intestine secrete enzymes.

_______ The cells of the intestine absorb the small pieces of food, and cellular digestion begins.

_______ The planarian attacks food and pulls it through its mouth and into its intestine.

_______ Nutrients are absorbed into the tissues of the planarian from the cells of the intestine.

_______ Indigestible material is pushed out through the mouth.

_______ Enzymes break down food into small pieces.

name ______________________

section __________ date __________

12c The Earthworm

Part 1

Directions

Fill in the missing terms or definitions and then draw a line from each term to the proper structure in the drawing.

1. intestine
(______________________________________)

2. ______________________
(chamber that food is temporarily stored in)

3. pharynx
(______________________________________)

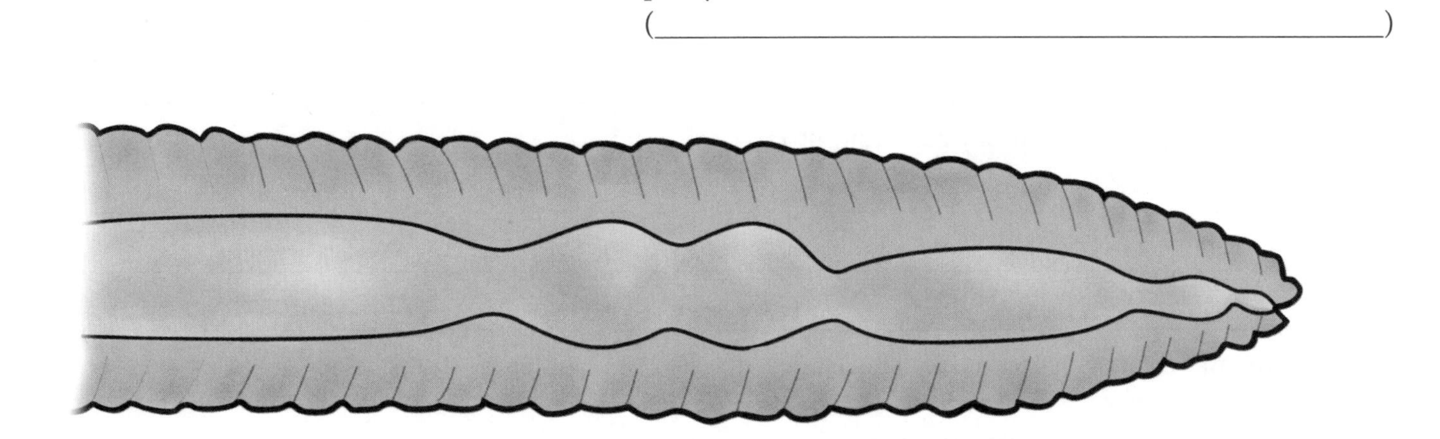

6. ______________________
(opening that allows food to enter the digestive tract)

5. esophagus
(______________________________________)

4. gizzard
(______________________________________)

Part 2

Directions

Below are several groups of terms. In each group, three of the four terms are related to one another. Draw a line through the unrelated term and then write a sentence using the remaining terms. Your sentence should show how the terms are related. (You may slightly change the form of the terms in your sentence.)

1. setae / flagella / muscles / earthworm

___

___

___

2. nerves / ganglia / impulses / cuticle

___

___

___

3. flame cells / capillaries / aortic arches / blood vessels

___

___

___

4. pharynx / esophagus / sensory receptor / crop

___

___

___

5. earthworm / leech / segmented / planarian

___

___

___

name ______________________

section ____________ date ____________

Application

12d Mollusks

Directions

Read the following descriptions and decide whether a clam, an octopus, or a snail is being described. In the blank by each statement, write a *C* if it describes a clam, an *O* if it describes an octopus, and an *S* if it describes a snail. Some descriptions will have more than one answer.

COS 1. Has a soft body

COS 2. Has suction disks

CS 3. Has one or more shells

C 4. Filters food from water

O 5. Changes color with stimulation

S 6. Is a univalve

O 7. Uses a "smoke screen"

C 8. Is a bivalve

CO 9. Has one or more siphons

COS 10. Can be eaten by humans

S 11. Has a coiled shell

O 12. Can regenerate arms

S 13. May harbor human parasites

O 14. Is in the class Cephalopoda

C 15. Has a muscular foot

S 16. Is in the class Gastropoda

name ______________________

section ________ date ________

12e Insect Life Cycles

Directions

Below are diagrams of the two types of metamorphosis commonly found in insects. On the line below each diagram, indicate which type of metamorphosis is being illustrated (complete or incomplete). Add arrows to the curved lines to show the order in which metamorphosis occurs. Then label the stages of metamorphosis on the lines provided.

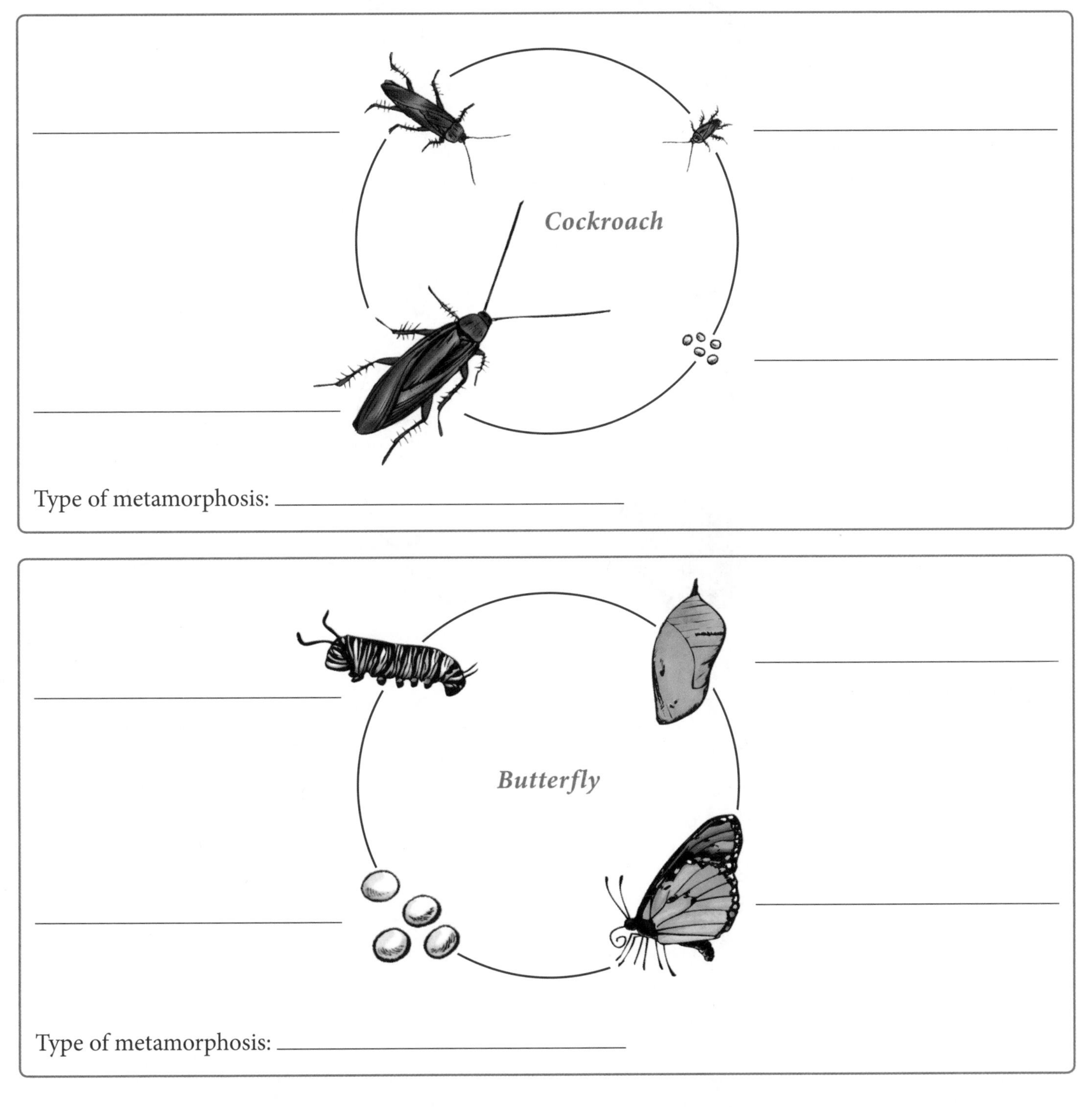

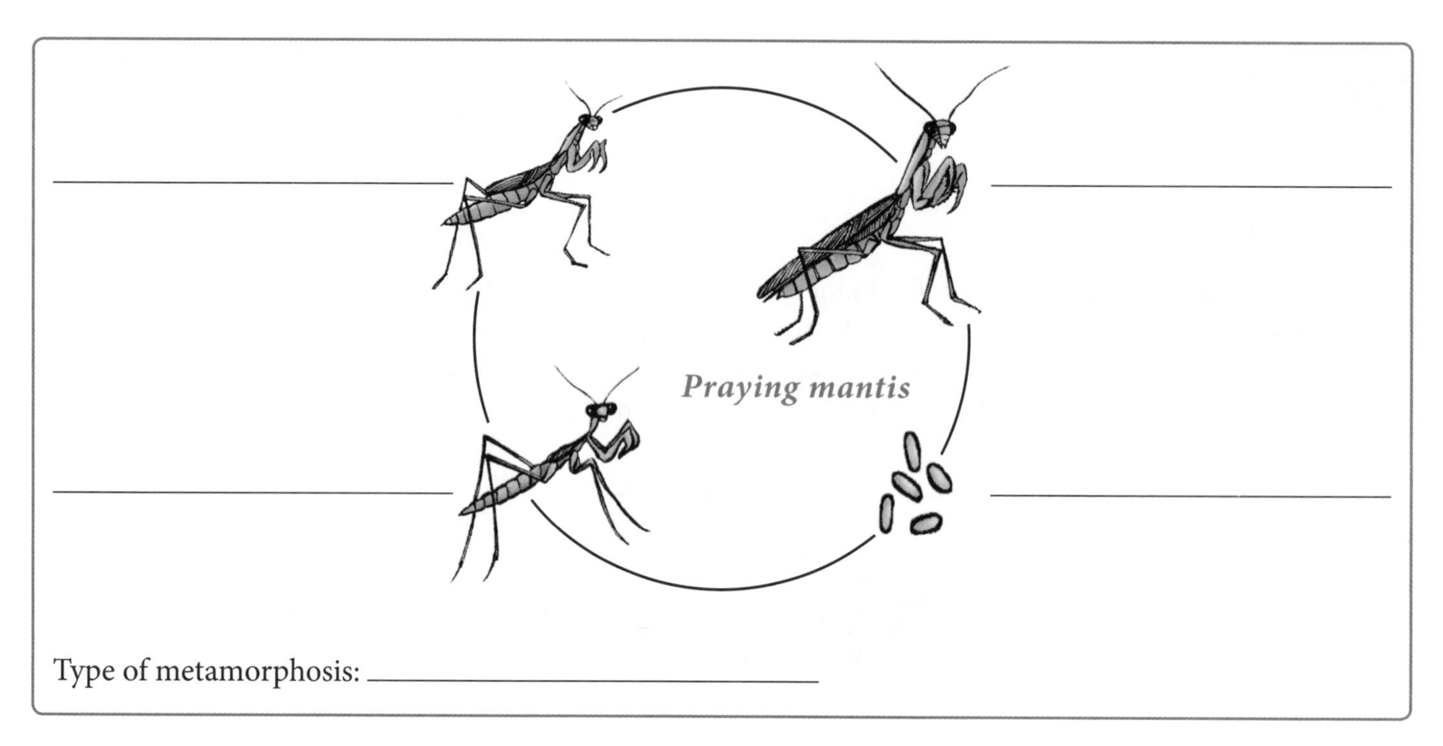

Type of metamorphosis: ____________________

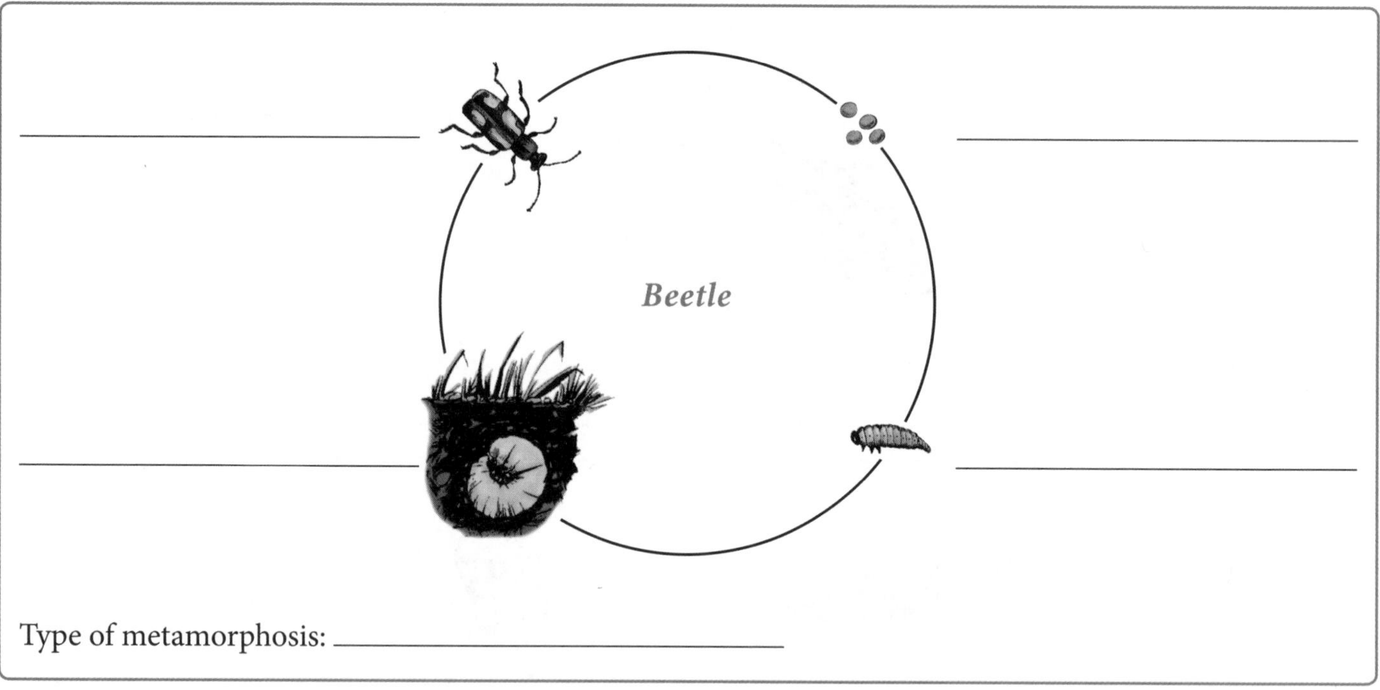

Type of metamorphosis: ____________________

name ____________________

section ____________ date ____________

12f Arthropods

Directions

In each of the following statements, draw a circle around the correct choice in the parentheses.

1. Class (Insecta / Arthropoda) has the most species of any animal class.
2. Insects have (endoskeletons / exoskeletons).
3. Eyes with thousands of small sections are called (simple / compound) eyes.
4. Spiracles are openings in a grasshopper's respiratory system that lead into the (tracheae / excretory tubules).
5. Insects that molt repeatedly and become more mature with each molt exhibit (complete / incomplete) metamorphosis.
6. Barnacles and millipedes are (insects / arthropods).
7. Insects have (six / eight) legs.
8. In (closed / open) circulatory systems, blood does not remain in blood vessels.
9. If an insect's life cycle includes a caterpillar, then the life cycle is described as (complete / incomplete) metamorphosis.
10. An arthropod's muscles are (inside / outside) its skeleton.
11. An insect's body sections include the head, (trunk / thorax), and abdomen.
12. An insect's (antennae / arteries) are sensory structures.
13. Many insecticides enter an insect's body through its (respiratory / circulatory) system.
14. A butterfly chrysalis is an example of a (larva / pupa).
15. (Centipedes / Millipedes) have one pair of legs per body segment.

Application

name ____________________

section __________ date __________

12g Review

Directions

Unscramble the words. Then match them to the clues given below.

A. lettacens ____________________

B. dilpelmie ____________________

C. texosleonek ____________________

D. bute tefe ____________________

E. pohnis ____________________

F. hidemoecrns ____________________

G. creathae ____________________

H. dopmucno ____________________

I. livesvab ____________________

J. aupp ____________________

K. ltmo ____________________

L. moelpect ratmmossihoep ____________________

M. stoh ____________________

N. tioacr aresch ____________________

O. sicpelus ____________________

P. cymenaottss ____________________

______ 1. Arthropod that usually has two pairs of legs per body segment

______ 2. A hard outer covering that supports and protects

______ 3. The long, flexible, armlike structures of an octopus

______ 4. Structures that help starfish move and hold on to things

______ 5. Breathing tubes in insects

______ 6. Clams, scallops, and mussels, but not snails

______ 7. Starfish and sea urchins

______ 8. The life cycle that includes a cocoon, chrysalis, or puparium

______ 9. The eyes of an insect

______ 10. Part of the jet propulsion system of an octopus

______ 11. To shed and replace an exoskeleton

______ 12. Resting stage of metamorphosis

______ 13. Spikes of calcium carbonate that serve as the skeleton of a sponge

______ 14. The stingers on a jellyfish's tentacles that are used for protection

______ 15. The organism that a parasite lives in

______ 16. Structures that help control an earthworm's blood pressure

name ______________________

section ____________ date ____________

Class Investigation

12h Earthworm Dissection

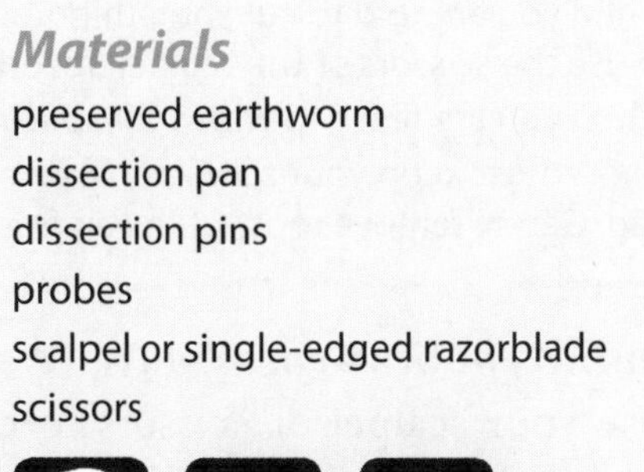

Goals

✓ Learn proper dissection techniques.
✓ Study the structures of an earthworm.

Materials

preserved earthworm
dissection pan
dissection pins
probes
scalpel or single-edged razorblade
scissors

Introduction

The earthworm is a typical member of phylum Annelida. In this lab, you will dissect a preserved earthworm. Be sure to read and follow all the directions carefully.

Procedure

Examine the earthworm's external structures.

1. Find the clitellum, the smooth enlarged area on the earthworm's body. This structure is closest to the head end of the earthworm.
2. Notice that the earthworm has many segments. Count the number of segments from the tip of the head to the clitellum.

   How many are there? 32

3. Carefully feel for the earthworm's bristles. The bristles are located on the lower side of the earthworm. Determine which surface of the earthworm is the upper surface and which is the lower surface.
   - What are these bristles called? Satae
   - What is their function? they aid in movement
4. Place the earthworm in the dissection pan; the earthworm's lower surface should be facing down.
5. Near the tip of your worm's head, put a pin through the worm and into the wax or rubber of the dissection pan. Straighten out the worm's body and put another pin somewhere past halfway along the length of the worm. (This will keep the worm from rolling when you begin to cut it.)
6. Often you can see a dark line extending down the middle of the earthworm's upper surface. This is the dorsal blood vessel. (See p. 261 of your textbook.)

Procedures and Tools for Dissection

- Never use the dissection equipment for anything other than dissection. Since this equipment can be very dangerous, do not play with it.
- Do not carve in the wax or rubber pad of the dissection pan.
- Before you begin a dissection, read the entire investigation thoroughly. In your textbook, look up pictures and diagrams of the organism you will be dissecting.
- Reread the directions before you begin to cut.
- Be sure that you have identified the proper structure(s) before you cut.
- When you are told to cut something but are not told which tool to use, you must decide whether to use the scissors or the scalpel (razorblade).
- When you are finished with your specimen, wrap it in a paper towel and place it in the trash can.
- If you must keep your specimen overnight, wrap it in a wet paper towel and place it in a plastic bag. Gently remove most of the air from the bag and tightly close it.

Open the earthworm's body.

1. Use your scalpel or scissors to cut a small slit (1 mm long) behind the clitellum.
2. Insert the point of your scalpel or scissors into the slit and cut an opening along the middle of the earthworm's back all the way to the tip of its head. (If you are using a scalpel, use only the tip of the scalpel to cut). Cut just to the side of the dorsal blood vessel. You can see the dorsal blood vessel if you lift the cut edge of the body wall with your probes. Be sure you are cutting only the body wall and none of the internal organs.
3. Carefully pull apart the sections of the body wall. Note the partitions inside the body. These partitions separate the inside of the earthworm's body. Use a probe or the tip of your scalpel to break apart these partitions.
4. Pull the body walls back; insert pins through the body walls and into the wax or rubber of the dissection pan. Place the pins into segments 5, 10, 15, 20, and 25.
5. The earthworm's reproductive structures are light-colored masses in segments 9–12. (Locations for the particular structures may vary somewhat. The segment numbers given in this lab tell the approximate locations.) The reproductive structures lie over the aortic arches, which are dark-colored structures. (See p. 261 of your textbook.) Carefully remove the reproductive structures but do not destroy the aortic arches, the dorsal blood vessel, or the digestive system structures beneath.

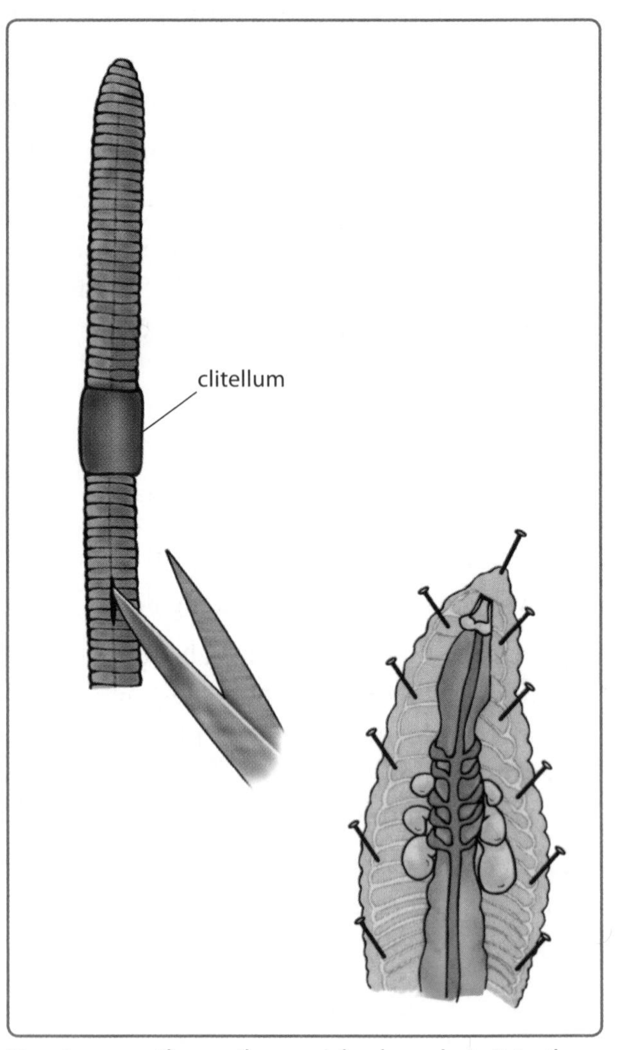

How to open the earthworm's body and pin it to the dissection pan

name ____________________

Locate the circulatory system structures.

1. Find all the aortic arches. They are located near segment 10. The aortic arches come in pairs, one on each side of the earthworm.
   - How many pairs of aortic arches are there? 5
   - What is their function? blood pressure
2. Locate the dorsal blood vessel in segments 20–25. Then move the intestine carefully to one side and locate the ventral blood vessel.
   - The dorsal blood vessel pumps blood in which direction? front
   - The ventral blood vessel pumps blood in which direction? back
3. What type of circulatory system does the earthworm have? open ☐ closed ☒
   Describe this type of circulatory system.

   blood never leaves blood vessels.

Locate the digestive system structures.

Give a range of segments in which each of the following organs are located and describe their functions.

1. pharynx

   segments 4-5; sucks in food

2. esophagus

   segments 6-14; passes food from the pharynx to the crop

3. crop

   segments 15-16; stores food temporarily

4. gizzard

   segments 17-18; grinds food

5. intestine

   segments 19-anus; performs chemical digestion and absorption

name ______________________

section __________ date __________

Research Investigation

12i Other Sponges, Jellyfish, and Worms

Goal

✓ Compare different types of sponges, jellyfish, and worms.

Materials

encyclopedia, other reference materials, or online sources

Procedure

The table below lists some other examples of the invertebrates studied in Chapter 12. Use encyclopedias or other sources to find the information needed to complete the table. Some of the more difficult answers have been provided.

Animal	Phylum	Symmetry (radial / bilateral)	Parasite (yes / no)	Type of food
1. red beard sponge		none (asymmetrical)		
2. Portuguese man-of-war		bilateral		
3. box jellyfish (sea wasp)				
4. anemone				
5. brain coral				
6. liver fluke		bilateral		
7. marine flatworm (turbellarian)				small marine organisms
8. hookworm				
9. vinegar eel		bilateral		
10. leech				
11. bearded fireworm				
12. lugworm				
13. fan worm (feather duster worm)		bilateral		

name ____________________

section __________ date __________

12j Butterfly Metamorphosis

Introduction

Metamorphosis is the change in body form an insect goes through as it develops. In this lab, you will observe the stages of complete metamorphosis in the painted lady butterfly.

Goals

- ✓ Observe the stages of complete metamorphosis.
- ✓ Learn about the life cycle of a butterfly.

Materials

painted lady butterfly larvae*

containers for growing larvae and hatching butterflies

suitable food source

*This investigation is written for use with the painted lady butterfly (*Vanessa cardui*), a small, common butterfly that is available from science supply companies. If you use another species of butterfly, you may need to alter the directions.

Procedure and Data

Raise the larvae.

1. Place several larvae in a container with a suitable food source. In the wild, these caterpillars would pull the edges of a leaf together, with themselves inside, and would then begin eating the leaf. If you have purchased your caterpillars, they probably have come with a food source. Thistles are a favorite food of painted lady caterpillars.
2. Place the container in a well-lit, warm area. The caterpillars should not be in direct sunlight, and the temperature should not go above 25 °C (77 °F).
3. Observe your caterpillars daily and record your observations on a separate sheet of paper. Note things such as changes in size, shape, and activity.
4. After a time of feeding and growing, the caterpillars will climb to the top of the container and hang from it. They will then each form a chrysalis.

Observe the chrysalises.

1. How many days did you observe the caterpillars before the first one formed a chrysalis?

   ____

2. Describe the shape, size, color, and other characteristics of the chrysalises.

   ____

   ____

3. How many days did you observe the caterpillars before the last one formed a chrysalis?

   ____

4. Take the chrysalises and place them in a larger container.

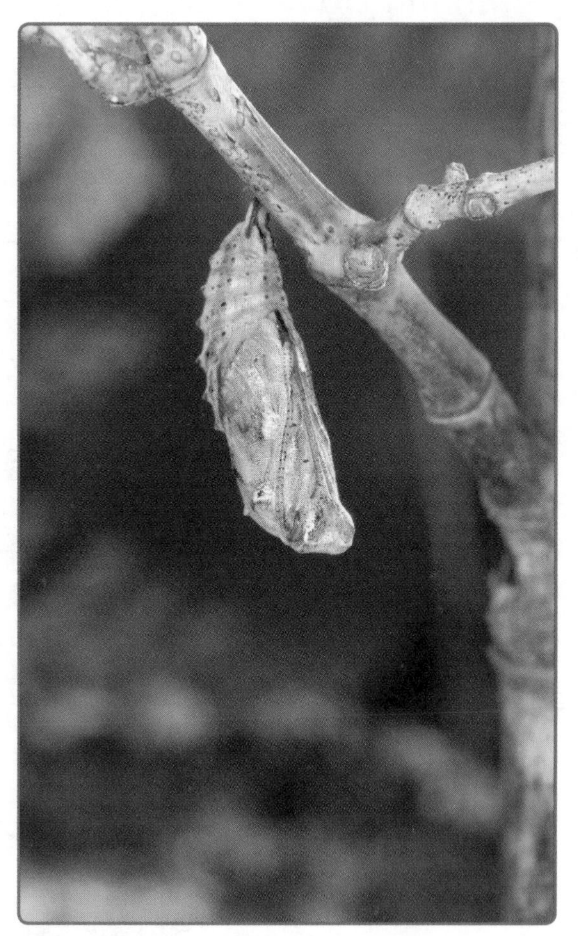

Chrysalis of the painted lady butterfly

5. How many days did you observe the chrysalises before any adults emerged?

____

6. Once an adult comes out, observe the other chrysalises carefully. Try to observe a butterfly emerging from a chrysalis. On a separate sheet of paper, describe the process. Tell what part of the butterfly came out first, how long the butterfly took to come out, and how long it was out before it tried to fly.

Raise the adults.

1. The adults will feed on a weak sugar solution placed in a bottle with a wick of paper towel sticking out of it.
2. Place leaves, stems, or seedlings of mallow or hollyhock in with the butterflies. If these materials are supplied for them, the adults will mate and begin to lay eggs on the plant leaves within about a week.
3. The eggs are small, light green balls with lines on them. They will hatch in about a week.

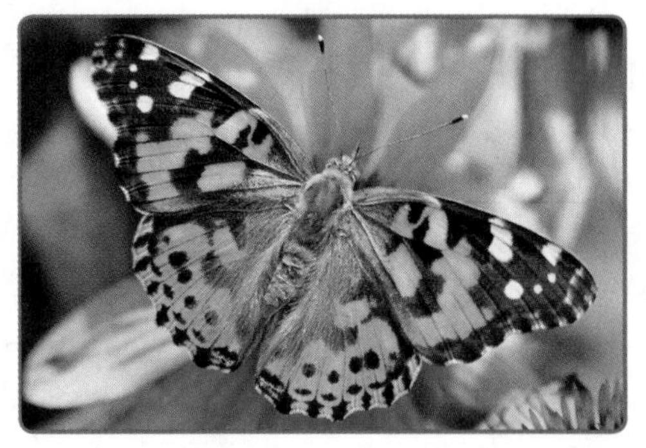

Adult painted lady butterfly

Summing Up

1. What did you learn about butterfly metamorphosis that you did not know before?

____

____

____

____

____

____

2. Which observation was the most fascinating to you? Why?

____

____

____

____

____

____

name ______________________

section ____________ date ____________

13a Endothermic vs. Ectothermic

Directions

Below are listed statements that relate to being endothermic or ectothermic. In the space by each description, write *EN* if it relates to endotherms or *EC* if it relates to ectotherms.

EC 1. Include amphibians

EN 2. Include birds

EC 3. Change body temperature based on surroundings

EN 4. Can be active regardless of temperature

EC 5. Cannot control body temperature by internal means

EC 6. Include fish

EC 7. Include insects

EN 8. Include mammals

EN 9. May have fur or feathers

EN 10. May sweat

EN 11. Do not change body temperature based on surroundings

EC 12. Include reptiles

EN 13. May pant for cooling

EC 14. Include worms

EN 15. Require more energy from food

Application

name____________________

section__________ date__________

13b Vertebrate Digestive System

Directions

Supply the missing terms or definitions. Then in the diagram of the vertebrate digestive system, label each structure that has a line pointing to it, using the number of each term as your label.

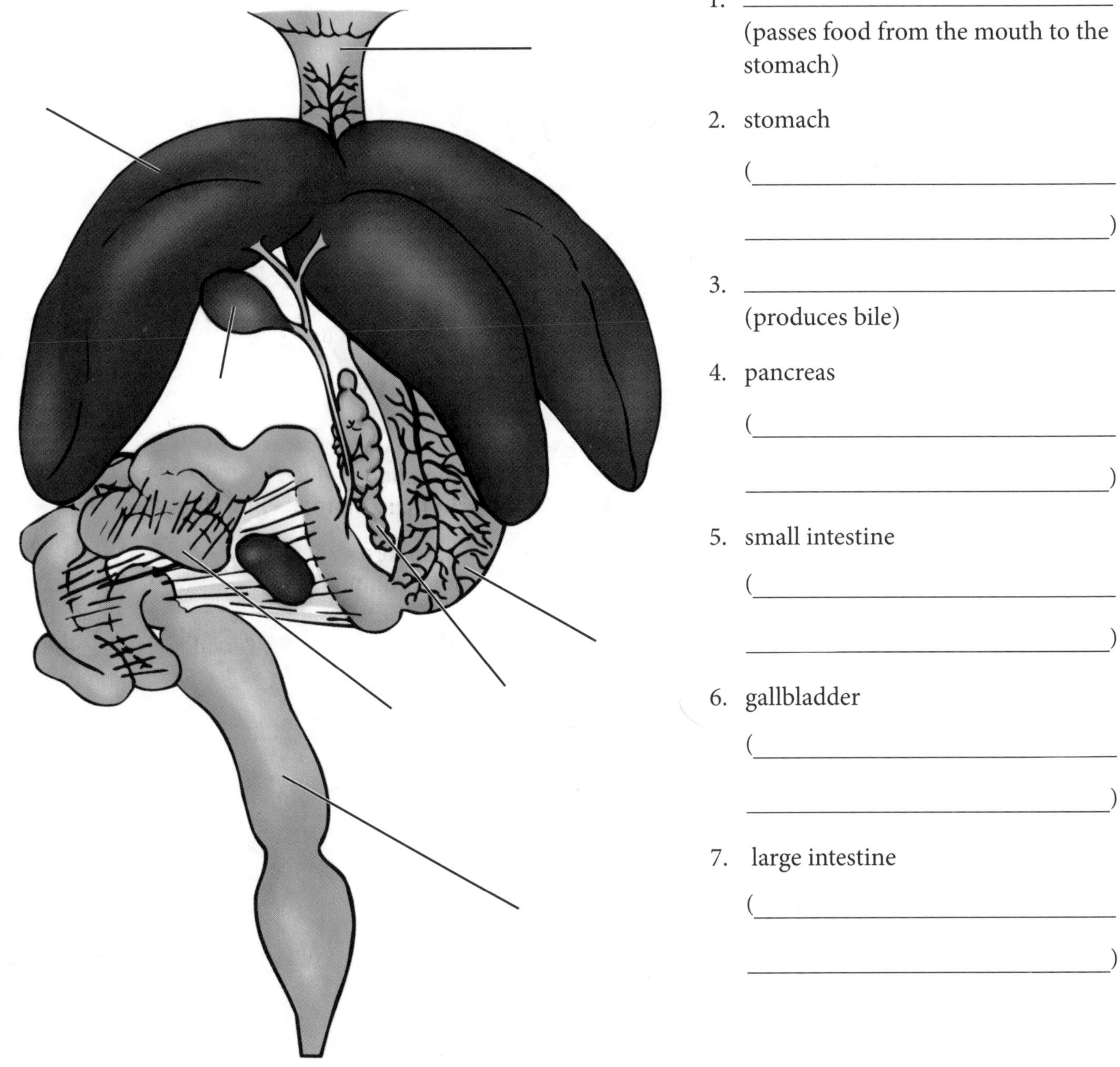

1. ____________________
   (passes food from the mouth to the stomach)
2. stomach
   (____________________
   ____________________)
3. ____________________
   (produces bile)
4. pancreas
   (____________________
   ____________________)
5. small intestine
   (____________________
   ____________________)
6. gallbladder
   (____________________
   ____________________)
7. large intestine
   (____________________
   ____________________)

name ______________

section ______ date ______

13c Body Systems in Vertebrate Animals

Directions

Choose the answer that best completes each of the following statements. Then use the letters of your answers (*A*, *B*, *C*, or *D*) and the key above the map on page 211 to plot a trail on the map. If all your answers are correct and you correctly plot the trail, your trail will end in the state that answers the question below the map.

A 1. The air chambers inside an animal's body where blood can get oxygen and give off carbon dioxide are

A. lungs. C. nephridia.
B. spiracles. D. flame cells.

C 2. Blood vessels that take blood to the heart are called

A. capillaries. C. veins.
B. arteries. D. aortic arches.

B 3. A thin layer of muscle that separates the chest chamber from the abdomen in many animals and in humans is the

A. mesoderm. C. ventricle.
B. diaphragm. D. air sac.

C 4. A fluid that carries food, oxygen, wastes, and other substances throughout the body is

A. bile. C. blood.
B. protein. D. urine.

C 5. Blood containing little oxygen is

A. yellow. C. red.
B. blue. D. clear.

B 6. The central nervous system includes the brain and

A. skull. C. sensory receptors.
B. spinal cord. D. sensory organs.

D 7. A structure between two heart chambers that allows blood to go only one way is a(n)

A. artery. C. vein.
B. capillary. D. valve.

B 8. Blood that carries an abundant amount of oxygen is

A. deoxygenated. C. unoxygenated.
B. oxygenated. D. dark red.

D 9. Spinal nerves branch off the

A. vertebrae. C. muscles.
B. brain. D. spinal cord.

A 10. The normal process of moving air into and out of the lungs is called

A. breathing. C. coughing.
B. sneezing. D. swallowing.

D 11. Blood vessels that take the blood away from the heart are called

A. atria. C. capillaries.
B. veins. D. arteries.

D 12. The respiratory structures that have capillaries close to their surfaces to exchange oxygen and carbon dioxide in water are

A. lungs. C. air sacs.
B. tracheae. D. gills.

A 13. Tiny blood vessels that allow substances to pass between the blood and body tissues are called

A. capillaries. C. arteries.
B. veins. D. aortic arches.

D 14. Bile aids in the digestion of

A. minerals. C. proteins.
B. carbohydrates. D. fats.

A 15. The kidneys connect to the urinary bladder through the

A. ureters. C. small intestine.
B. urethra. D. spleen.

D 16. Blood that has had most of its oxygen given to the body's cells is

A. diluted. C. dissolved.
B. oxygenated. D. deoxygenated.

B 17. The number of chambers in a fish heart is

A. one. C. three.
B. two. D. four.

D 18. Undigested food leaves the digestive tract through the

A. kidneys. C. urinary bladder.
B. small intestine. D. anus.

B 19. When food leaves the stomach, it normally moves to the

A. esophagus. C. gallbladder.
B. small intestine. D. liver.

name ____________________

C 20. The structures that filter wastes from the blood in vertebrates are the

A. flame cells.
B. urethras.
C. kidneys.
D. urinary bladders.

Key

If the answer to a statement is *A*, draw a line 5° northward from your last stopping point.
If the answer to a statement is *B*, draw a line 5° southward from your last stopping point.
If the answer to a statement is *C*, draw a line 5° eastward from your last stopping point.
If the answer to a statement is *D*, draw a line 5° westward from your last stopping point.

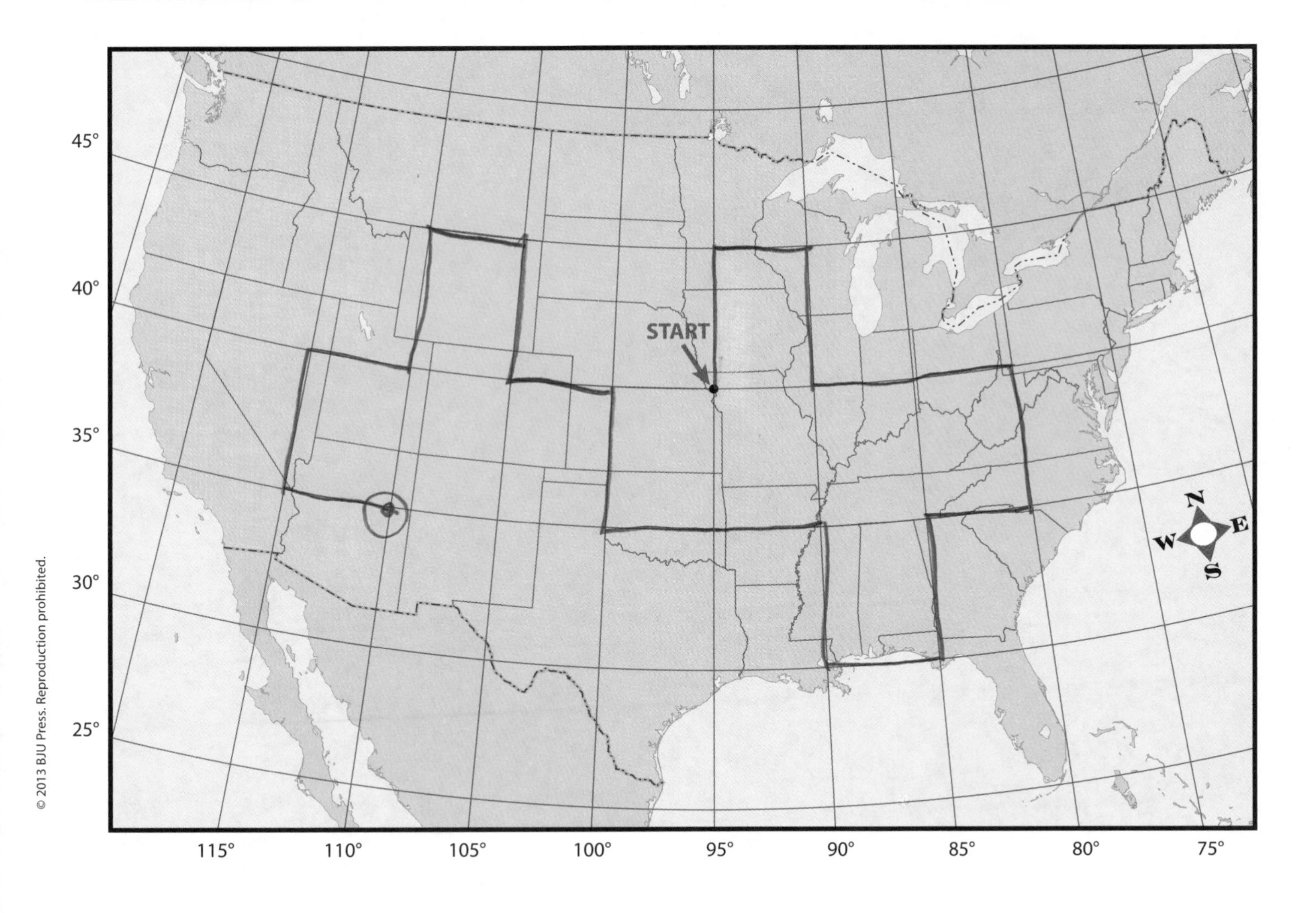

Which state has the largest number of venomous reptile species? Arizona

name ______________________

section ____________ date ____________

Application

13d Fish, Amphibians, and Reptiles

Part 1: Fish

Directions

Read the following statements. In the space provided, write *True* if the statement is true. If the statement is false, draw a line through the word or words that make the statement false. Then in the blank, write the word or words necessary to make the statement true.

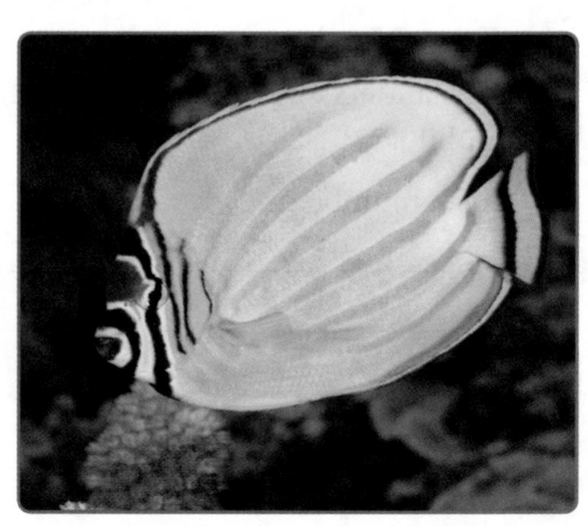

________________ 1. Fish are invertebrates.

________________ 2. Fish are ectothermic.

________________ 3. A fish's scales are shed as the fish grows larger.

________________ 4. The lateral line is sensitive to vibrations in the water.

________________ 5. A fish has a three-chambered heart.

________________ 6. The lamprey is a jawless fish.

________________ 7. Sharks do not have swim bladders.

________________ 8. Sharks and rays are bony fish.

________________ 9. Fish have an open circulatory system.

Part 2: Amphibians

Directions

Choose the best word from the list below to complete each sentence, and write the word in the blank provided. Each word may be used once or not at all.

Appalachian	double	hibernation	moist	tailed
Asian	dry	incisors	single	tailless
back	estivation	maxillary	skin	
coastal	front	metamorphosis	spiracles	

1. The name *amphibian* means "________________ life."
2. The process that changes an amphibian from a gilled organism to a lunged organism is called ________________.
3. Amphibians must return to ________________ places to lay their eggs.
4. ________________ is a period of inactivity during hot, dry spells.

5. Frogs and toads are ______________________ amphibians.
6. A frog's tongue is attached to the ______________________ of its mouth.
7. Frogs have ______________________ and vomerine teeth.
8. Salamanders and newts are ______________________ amphibians.
9. Most amphibians can exchange gases through their ______________________.
10. The ______________________ region has the most salamander species.

Part 3: Reptiles

Directions

Write your responses in the spaces provided.

1. Why do reptiles not have to return to water to lay their eggs?

____

____

2. What sensory organ do humans have that snakes do not? ______________________
3. Are most snakes venomous or nonvenomous? ______________________
4. Why are snakes capable of eating prey larger in diameter than themselves?

____

____

5. How can a large alligator approach its prey and yet be almost completely hidden?

____

____

6. How do sea turtles, tortoises, and terrapins differ?

____

____

7. Below is a photo of an American alligator and one of an American crocodile. Label each correctly.

______________________ ______________________

name ______________________

section ____________ date ____________

13e Fish Respiration Rates

Goals

- ✓ Observe the respiration of a fish.
- ✓ Determine the effects of temperature on the respiration rate of a fish.

Introduction

Many factors may affect the respiration rate of fish. In this lab, you will conduct an experiment to determine the effects of temperature on the respiration of fish.

Materials

live fish
small aquarium
thermometer
plastic bags
hot water
ice cubes

Procedure

1. Place a live fish in a small aquarium. The water in the aquarium should be the same as the water the fish is accustomed to. Do not use tap water unless it is well water or it has been dechlorinated. Place a thermometer in the aquarium.
2. Locate and observe the operculum. The *operculum* is the flap that covers a fish's gills. The fish moves this flap back and forth to cause water to circulate over its gills. In the gills, gases are exchanged between the water and the blood.
3. Carefully count the number of times the operculum beats in 15 seconds. Multiply this number by four to find out how many times the operculum beats in one minute. Repeat the observation four times. Record your findings in the table on page 216.
4. Place several cups of hot water in a plastic bag and close it tightly. Slowly, without disturbing the fish, lower the bag into the aquarium. Wait for the aquarium water to increase five degrees. Then slowly remove the bag of hot water. Repeat your observations of the operculum's movements, and record your findings in the table. In the "Other observations" column, record any observations you make at this temperature that are different from those at the previous temperature.
5. Place several ice cubes in a plastic bag and close it tightly. Slowly, without disturbing the fish, lower the bag into the aquarium. Wait for the aquarium water to cool five degrees below the original temperature. You may need to replace the ice. Slowly remove the bag of ice. Repeat your observations of the operculum's movements, and record your findings in the table. In the "Other observations" column, record any observations you make at this temperature that are different from those at the other temperatures.
6. Let the aquarium water return slowly to its normal temperature.

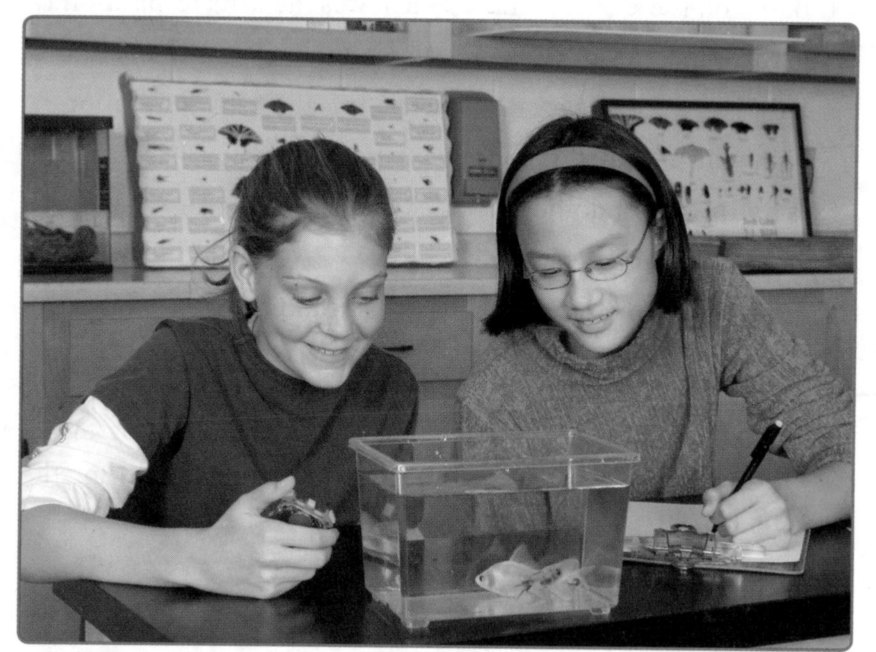

Data

Fish Respiration Data						
Temperature of water	Number of beats in one minute					Other observations
	First count	Second count	Third count	Fourth count	Average beats per minute	
Room temperature	72	80	64	56	68	
Hot	80	68	88	84	80	
Cold	56	72	68	60	64	

Summing Up

1. When was the fish's operculum the most active?
   high temperature ☒ room temperature ☐ low temperature ☐
2. When was the fish's operculum the least active?
   high temperature ☐ room temperature ☐ low temperature ☒
3. How did the rate of operculum beats compare to the amount of activity of the fish?
   The faster the operculum beads the more active it is and vice versa.
4. Based on these observations, when was the fish's respiration rate the highest?
   high temperature ☒ room temperature ☐ low temperature ☐
5. Based on these observations, when was the fish's respiration rate the slowest?
   high temperature ☐ room temperature ☐ low temperature ☒
6. Is this fish an endothermic or ectothermic animal?
   endothermic ☐ ectothermic ☒
   Explain how the results of this investigation support your answer to Question 6.
   The results show that the respiration of a fish changes due to external changes. This means that it is ectothermic.
7. On a separate sheet of paper, draw a bar graph representing the average beats per minute at each temperature. Label your graph properly.

name ____________________

section __________ date __________

13f Frog Dissection

Goals
- ✓ Identify the organs of a frog.
- ✓ Prepare for studying human organs by studying frog organs.

Materials
preserved frog
latex gloves (optional)
dissection pan
dissection pins
forceps
probe
ruler
scalpel
scissors
thin straw

Introduction

The frog is a typical member of class Amphibia. In this lab, you will dissect a preserved frog. Be sure to read and follow all the directions carefully. You may find Section 13D in your textbook helpful as you complete this lab.

Procedure

Examine the frog's external structures.

1. Feel the frog's skin. Describe the texture.

   Smooth and slippery

2. Remove a small section of skin from the frog's back. Look on the underside of the skin and notice the blood vessels there. Why would the frog's skin need to have a rich supply of blood?

   exchanges gasses through skin.

3. Find the following structures: eyes, mouth, nostrils, and tympanic membranes.
4. Notice the difference in size between the frog's forelegs and its hind legs.
   - How long are the forelegs? 2.25
   - How long are the hind legs? 6.5
   - Do you think this difference in size has anything to do with the different ways the frog uses its legs? yes ☒ no ☐
   - What is the function of the forelegs?

     support
   - What is the function of the hind legs?

     jumping

Examine the frog's mouth.

1. Open the mouth of the frog and notice the grooves and ridges along the edge of the jaws. These grooves and ridges allow the mouth to close tightly. Why does the frog's mouth need to close tightly?

   breathes by swallowing air if did not close tightly would not breath.
   - Does the frog have lips? yes ☒ no ☐
2. Move your finger along the upper jaw and feel the frog's tiny teeth.
   - What are these teeth called? maxillary teeth
   - How does the frog use them? hold prey
3. Locate the frog's vomerine teeth at the front of the roof of the mouth.

4. Gently pull the tongue until it extends from the frog's mouth.
   - Where is the tongue attached?

     front of the mouth
   - How is the free end of the tongue shaped? notched
   - Normally when the frog is alive, a part of the tongue is sticky. Why is this characteristic important to the frog?

     to chach insects and prey

Open the frog's body cavity.

1. Place the frog on its back in the dissection pan.
2. Beginning above the anus, place the scissors to the left of the whitish or reddish line that runs down the middle of the frog.
3. Break through the body wall with the point of the scissors and cut toward the mouth. Make sure to cut only the skin and muscles.
4. Continue cutting until you reach the frog's neck region. You will have to cut through the bone in the chest region.
5. Make additional perpendicular cuts across the top and bottom of the first cut. Pull back the cut sections and pin them to the dissection pan.
6. If you find obvious clusters of dark eggs, you have a female frog that was ready to reproduce. Carefully remove these eggs and set them aside without destroying any of the surrounding organs.

How to open the frog's body cavity

Examine the frog's heart.

1. Describe what the heart looks like.

   triongluor red muscle
2. Cut the heart in half, slicing off the front half with the scalpel, so that there is a front half and a back half.
   - How many chambers does the frog's heart have? 3
   - What is the function of an upper chamber?

     recieves blood
   - How many lower chambers does the frog's heart have? one
   - What is the function of a lower chamber?

     pumps blood

Examine the frog's lungs.

1. To help locate the lungs, open the frog's mouth and place a thin straw through the opening that leads to the trachea. Gently blow through the straw. As the lungs fill with air, they will become more noticeable to you.
2. Where are the lungs in relation to the heart? behind heart
3. When the frog was alive, how did air enter its lungs?

   forced air into lungs

name ______________________

Examine the frog's digestive system.

1. Liver
   - Where is the liver located in relation to the heart?

     each side of heart
   - What color is it? reddish brown
   - What does the liver produce? bile
2. Gallbladder
   - The gallbladder is a small, greenish sac located between the lobes (sections) of the liver.
   - What is the function of the gallbladder?

     stores bile
3. Esophagus
   - To find the esophagus, open the frog's mouth and place a probe into the hole leading to the digestive system.
   - Describe the esophagus.

     short tubular
4. Stomach
   - Move the left lobe of the liver to find the stomach.
   - What color is the stomach? pink
   - Does it feel hard or soft? hard
   - What is the function of the stomach?

     digestive enzymes
5. Small intestine
   - The small intestine is the small, tubular organ continuing from the stomach.
   - Cut the tissues that hold the small intestine in place, but do not cut the small intestine.
   - How long is the small intestine? long
   - What color is it? pink
   - What does the small intestine do to the food that the frog eats?

     digest absorbs food

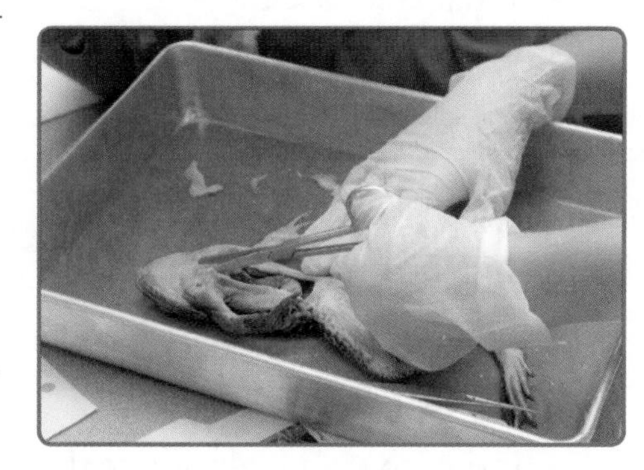

6. Large intestine
   - The large intestine is a larger tubular organ that continues from the small intestine.
   - How long is the large intestine? ______________________
   - Give two differences (other than length) between the large and small intestines.

     thicker, darker than small intestine

7. Pancreas
   - The pancreas is a yellowish organ that is thin and flat. It is located in the thin membrane that is attached to the stomach and the small intestine. (You may have difficulty locating this organ.)
   - What does the pancreas produce?

     insulin and enzymes

Remove the frog's digestive system.

1. Cut across the esophagus and the lower section of the large intestine. Carefully lift and remove the digestive system out of the body cavity. The remaining half of the heart will come with the digestive system.
2. Cut open the stomach and look inside.
   - Is there any food in the stomach? yes ☐ no ☐
   - If so, can you recognize any of it? yes ☐ no ☐
   - If so, what did you find?

     ______
3. Rinse out the stomach and study the stomach's muscular walls.
   - How do these walls help digestion?

     ______

Examine the frog's excretory and reproductive systems.

1. Kidneys
   - The kidneys are oval organs that are positioned against the body wall of the frog's back.
   - How many kidneys does the frog have? two
   - What color are they? reddish brown
   - What do the kidneys do?

     filter wastes
2. Urinary bladder
   - The urinary bladder looks like a small, deflated balloon at the bottom of the body cavity.
   - What does the urinary bladder store? urine
3. Reproductive structures
   - If the frog is a male, locate the testes. These are two small organs attached near the kidneys.
   - If the frog is a female, locate the ovaries. If there were large masses of dark eggs filling the body cavity, you removed the ovaries when you removed the eggs. Ovaries with few or no eggs, however, are located near the kidneys.

Cleanup

When you complete this investigation, if your teacher informs you that you will be doing a study of the frog's nervous system, carefully wrap the preserved frog in moist paper towels and place it in a plastic bag. Otherwise, you can wrap it up in a paper towel and discard it in the trash.

name ______________________

section ____________ date ____________

Application

14a Birds

Directions

Complete the crossword puzzle.

Across

2. Much energy and ____________ must be available to muscles during flight.
4. Birds have wings and ____________.
5. When a bird inhales and exhales, its ____________ are filled with oxygen-rich air.
6. Usually birds build nests and ____________ their eggs.
8. The ____________ is a food-storage organ.

Down

1. Birds with ____________ beaks probably eat meat.
3. Birds' lightweight bones are reinforced by a ____________ structure.
7. Birds must ____________ their eggs regularly so that they develop normally.

Application

name ____________________

section __________ date __________

14b Mammals

Directions

Use the terms from the list below to fill in the concept map showing the relationships between the terms. Words on the arrows show the relationships between terms. Each term is used only once, and there is only one correct way to use all the terms in this concept map. Three terms have already been placed on the map to get you started.

~~eggs~~	marsupials	placentas
~~hair~~	milk	platypus
horse	monotremes	pouches
mammals	opossum	~~umbilical cords~~
mammary glands	placental mammals	

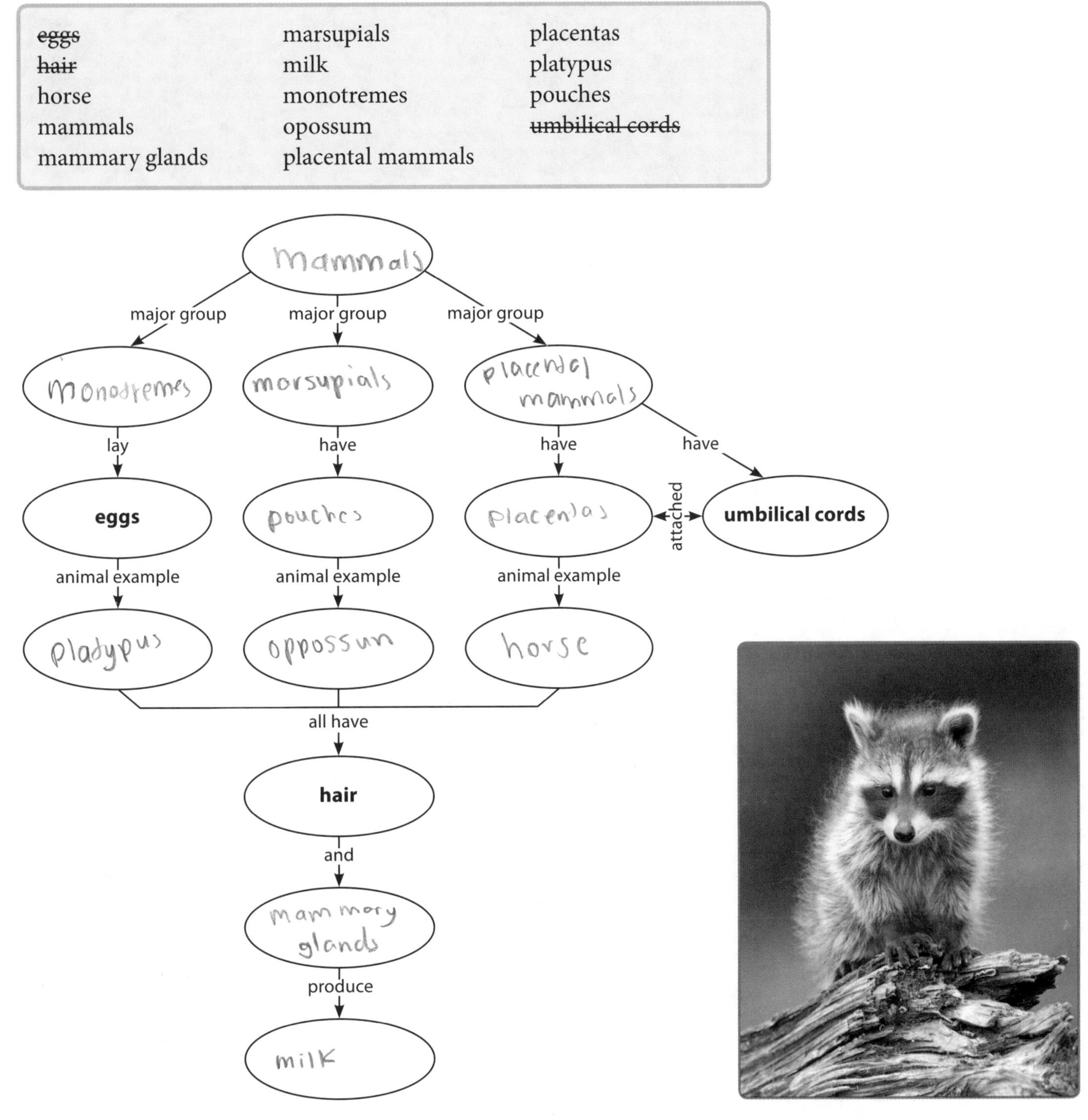

name ____________________

section __________ date __________

14c Review

Directions

Below each pair of terms, tell how the terms are similar; then tell how they are different.

1. air sacs / lungs

   similar:

   ____

   ____

   different:

   ____

   ____

2. mammals / birds

   similar:

   ____

   ____

   different:

   ____

   ____

3. yolk / egg white

   similar:

   ____

   ____

   different:

   ____

   ____

4. incisors / canines

   similar:

   ____

   ____

   different:

   ____

   ____

5. monotremes / marsupials

   similar:

   ___

   ___

   different:

   ___

   ___

6. placenta / mammary glands

   similar:

   ___

   ___

   different:

   ___

   ___

7. hair / milk

   similar:

   ___

   ___

   different:

   ___

   ___

name ____________

section ________ date ________

14d Conserving Body Heat: Wool vs. Down

Goal

✓ Compare the effectiveness of wool (fur) and down (feathers) as insulators.

Materials

containers (cups or glasses) with lids that have a hole (3)
wool (fur)
down (feathers)
thermometers (3)
freezer

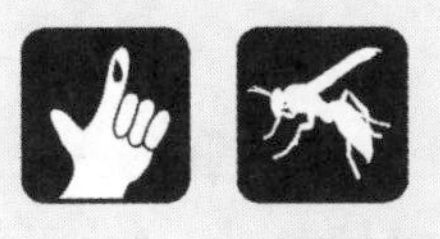

Procedure

1. Fill one container with wool and another with down. The containers should have equal amounts of the materials to be tested. Label the containers *Wool* and *Down*. Label a third empty container *Control*.
2. Put lids on all three containers, and insert a thermometer through the hole in each lid. The thermometers should be positioned so that the thermometer bulb is about midway in the container. Do not allow the thermometer bulbs to touch the bottom or sides of the containers.
3. Before taking your first temperature reading, form your hypothesis about the experiment.
   - Which container do you think will cool the least in 25 minutes? wool
   - Which container do you think will cool the most in 25 minutes? down
4. On the table below, record the starting temperatures of all three containers. Then put all three in the freezer. (Note: All three should be at approximately the same starting temperature.)
5. At five-minute intervals, record the temperatures of all three containers.

Data

Temperature Data

Time	Control (°C)	Down (°C)	Wool (°C)
start	20	20	20
5 minutes	12	17	16
10 minutes	6	10	11
15 minutes	-1	6	7
20 minutes	3	4	5
25 minutes	2	3	3

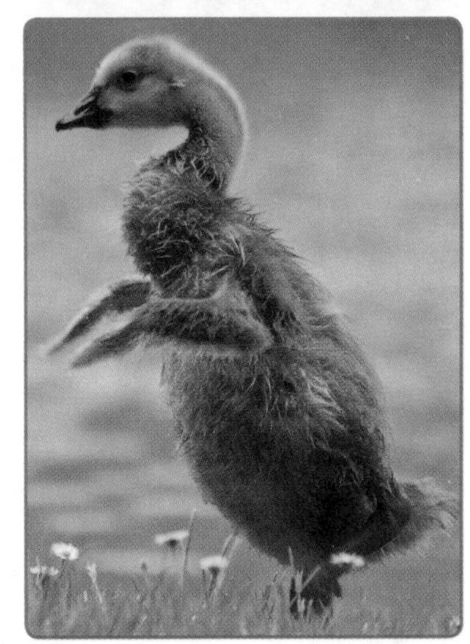

Summing Up

1. What was the experimental variable in this experiment? ______
2. Which container had the greatest temperature change from start to finish? ______
3. Which container had the smallest temperature change from start to finish?

   ______
4. Was your hypothesis correct? ______
5. Which container had the greatest temperature change during a five-minute interval?

   ______
6. What do you think would have happened if you had left the lid off the control container?

   ______
7. If you had left the lid off the control container and put the lids on the two experimental containers, could you have reached a reliable conclusion? Why or why not?

   ______

   ______
8. Are down and wool insulators? How do you know?

   ______

   ______
9. Which of the materials tested in this experiment is the best insulator? ______
10. What do down and wool do for endothermic animals?

    ______

    ______
11. Explain how down and wool could be a disadvantage for endothermic animals.

    ______

    ______

name ____________

section ________ date ________

14e Observing Feathers and Hair

Goals

- ✓ Compare types of feathers.
- ✓ Observe the fine structure of feathers and hair.

Materials

contour (wing or tail) feather
hand lens
microscope
ruler with millimeter markings
down feather
prepared slide of animal hairs (3 different kinds of animals)

Procedure

Observe a contour feather.

1. Bend the contour feather gently. Is it stiff? ____________
2. Examine the quill. Is it solid or hollow? ____________
3. Separate some barbs from the other barbs. Can you refasten them? ____________
4. Separate a barb and examine it with a hand lens or microscope.
   - What can you see on the barb? ____________
   - Why do you think these are important? ____________
5. Measure your feather.
   - How long is your feather? ________ mm
   - How long is the vane of your feather? ________ mm
   - How wide is the vane at its widest point? ________ mm
   - Is the vane of equal width on either side of the central shaft? ____________
6. Does your feather have differences between the upper and lower surfaces? ____________
7. In the box below draw a section of the contour feather as seen with your hand lens or microscope. Show the smallest details that you are able to see.

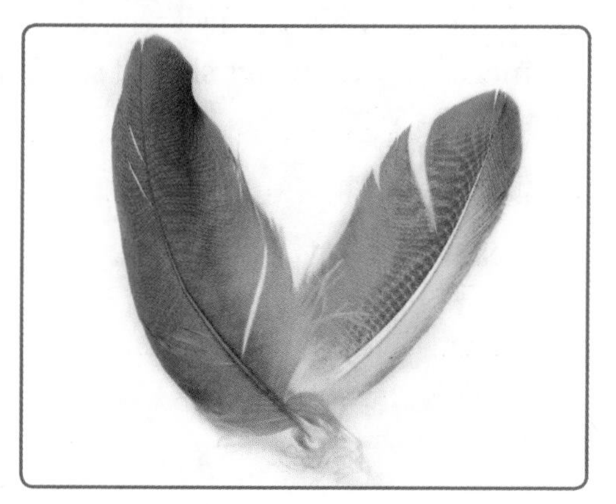

Observe a down feather.

1. Is the down feather stiff? ______
2. Can you fasten the barbs together? ______
3. In the box below draw the down feather as seen with your hand lens or microscope. Show the smallest details that you are able to see.

Observe a microscope slide of preserved animal hairs.

1. Describe what the hairs look like as seen through a microscope.
______
2. In the box below draw the microscopic views of the hairs of three different animals. Your drawings should show how the animal hairs differ.

Summing Up

1. Which do you think are most important in flight, contour feathers or down feathers?
______
2. Down feathers have a different structure from contour feathers. How does the different structure of a down feather relate to its function?
______
______
3. Why do hairs not need to hold together like contour feathers do?
______
4. What do the different types of animal hair that you observed have in common?
______

name ______________________

section __________ date __________

14f Man vs. Beast

Goal

✓ Discover what the Bible says about the similarities and differences between humans and animals.

Materials

Bible

Procedure

1. Read each Scripture passage, looking for what it teaches us about humans and animals.
2. Fill in the table with what you learn from each passage.

Scripture	Humans	Animals
Genesis 1:24–28; 2:19–22		
Genesis 9:2–6		
Psalm 8:4–9		
Proverbs 12:10		

Summing Up

1. What did you learn about how humans and animals are alike?

____

____

____

____

2. What did you learn about how humans and animals are different?

____

____

____

____

____

____

____

____

name ______________________

section __________ date __________

15a Innate and Learned Behaviors

Part 1: Types of Behaviors

Directions

Answer the following questions in the space provided.

1. How are reflexes and instincts similar?

2. How are reflexes and instincts different?

3. What do you think would happen to an animal if its reflexes and instincts did not function properly?

4. Give an example of a learned behavior taught to an animal by man.

5. Give two examples of learned behaviors that animals might acquire in the wild, apart from man.

Part 2: Animal Behaviors in Scripture

Directions

Each of the Scripture passages listed in the table below mentions or describes an animal doing something. Complete the table by naming each animal, describing what each does, and writing whether each action is innate or learned. You may need to do some research to find out whether a behavior is learned or innate.

Passage	Animal	Action	Innate or learned?
Genesis 24:11			
Exodus 23:28		attacking people	
Deuteronomy 22:10			
	ass (donkey)		
Deuteronomy 28:42			innate
Deuteronomy 32:11			
Esther 6:8		carrying a rider	
Matthew 15:27			
Luke 13:34			
John 10:4	sheep		
John 18:27			
2 Peter 2:22			
Revelation 9:5			innate
Revelation 19:17–21	fowls of the air		

The Brazen Serpent, Benjamin West, P.R.A., from the Bob Jones University Collection

This painting graphically shows an Old Testament example of God's using the innate behavior of an animal to accomplish His purposes. Use a Bible concordance to figure out what book and chapter is depicted here.

____

Application

name ______________________

section ____________ date ____________

15b Animal Behavior Review

Directions

Read the following examples and choose from the list below which types of behavior are being described. If the behavior is innate, tell whether the innate behavior is an instinct or a reflex. Some examples may have more than one answer.

A. innate behavior—instinct

B. innate behavior—reflex

C. intelligent behavior

D. learned behavior

_______ 1. When given the proper materials, a bird kept isolated for its entire life builds a nest typical of its species.

_______ 2. During dinner, a dog sits under the chair of the family member who often gives it bites of food.

_______ 3. After watching the older lions in its pride, a lion cub stalks its first prey.

_______ 4. A monkey uses a long stick to get food that is beyond its reach.

_______ 5. When a bird becomes cold, its feathers stand up and it begins to shiver.

_______ 6. A guard dog attacks a prowler who comes into the yard but does not attack its owner when he enters the yard.

_______ 7. A honeybee collects pollen from flowers to produce honey.

_______ 8. A honeybee stings your foot when you step on it while walking barefoot across a lawn.

_______ 9. When frightened, a de-scented pet skunk raises its tail and turns its back to the thing that frightened it.

_______ 10. At a security checkpoint, dogs sniff travelers' bags. When a dog smells drugs, it barks and claws at the bag.

_______ 11. After twenty tries, a rat can run the maze in less than one-third of its original time.

_______ 12. Screeching loudly, a mockingbird swoops down toward you as you walk by the tree where its nest is.

name ______________________

section ____________ date ____________

15c Animal Reproduction

Part 1: Meiosis, Gametes, and Fertilization

Directions

In the space provided, describe the difference between the terms given.

1. ovaries / testes

____

____

____

2. eggs / sperm

____

____

____

3. gametes / zygotes

____

____

____

4. fertilization / meiosis

____

____

____

5. haploid / diploid

____

____

____

Part 2: External and Internal Fertilization

Directions

In each of the following statements, draw a circle around the correct choice in the parentheses. On the lines provided, explain why the incorrect choice is not acceptable.

1. (Male / Female) salmon produce milt.

2. Salmon reproduce by (spawning / nesting).

3. A baby animal develops within an egg during a period known as (incubation / gestation).

4. When egg and sperm are united inside the female's body, (internal / external) fertilization takes place.

5. (Yolk / Albumen) is the primary stored food that a developing chick will use to grow.

6. An eggshell has tiny pores to allow (water / gases) to pass through.

7. Crocodiles incubate their eggs by (heating them with rotting plants / sitting on them).

8. The umbilical cord carries (amniotic fluid / blood).

name ______________________

section ____________ date ____________

15d Animal Reproduction Review

Directions

All the scrambled words listed below deal with sexual reproduction in animals. Using the definitions as clues, unscramble the words and write them in the blanks.

	Scrambled	Answer	Definition
1.	teelanxr	external	the union of an ovum and a sperm outside an animal's body
	tetiiaifoznrl	fertilization	
2.	tilm	milt	fluid containing fish sperm
3.	butoiicnna	incubation	the period of growth inside an egg
4.	lenntira	internal	the union of an ovum and a sperm inside a female parent
	eilafzrtotiin	fertilization	
5.	tetogansi	gestation	the period of time an embryo spends inside the womb
6.	yomber	embryo	an unborn organism
7.	balnume	albumen	an egg white
8.	geg	egg	(1) a zygote enclosed by a shell or (2) the female gamete
9.	nnomia	amnion	the fluid-filled sac around an embryo
10.	liilcuamb	umbilical	the structure with blood vessels connecting an embryo to its mother
	rdoc	cord	
11.	getaprnn	pregnant	the condition of an animal with an unborn offspring
12.	wpasginn	spawning	the external fertilization carried on by a fish
13.	remsp	sperm	the gametes produced by males
14.	okly	yolk	stored food that an unhatched chick uses to grow
15.	yavor	ovary	the organ that produces ova
16.	rayammm	mommory	the structures that produce milk for a newborn
	danlgs	gland	
17.	ritbh	birth	the normal end of pregnancy
18.	caatelnp	placenta	the structure that is attached to the wall of a uterus and provides nourishment and oxygen for an embryo

name ______________________

section ____________ date ____________

15e Myrmecology: The Study of Ants

Goals

✓ Become familiar with ants.

✓ Observe relationships within an ant colony.

Introduction

A *microcosm* is a small area that simulates the situation in a larger area. Scientists often use microcosms to study organisms, such as ants. Myrmecologists (MUR mih KAHL uh jists), scientists who study ants, use ant microcosms called formicariums to study ant behavior. Why are there so many strange names for things about ants? The Greek word for "ant" is *murmek*, and the Latin word for "ant" is *formica*.

A formicarium is a thin, clear container that people use to observe the actions of ants. If the container were thick, the ants would construct their tunnels in the middle of the sand or dirt and you would not be able to see them. You can build a formicarium or purchase a specially designed one.

Materials

ant microcosm chamber
sand
water
ants
food (corn flakes, wheat or barley seeds, or small potato slices)
eyedropper

1. Fill the chamber about halfway with sand or some other medium.
2. Add water so that the sand is moist but not soggy.
3. Obtain your ants.
   - You can collect your own ants by placing a stick in front of a group of ants, letting them crawl up the stick, and then placing them in your microcosm. You can also dig up an anthill and collect a mass of ants all at once, perhaps even a queen. If you collect your own ants, collect them from only one colony. If you put ants from different colonies in your formicarium, they will kill each other.

Myrmecology Notes

A normal ant colony has female workers and a queen. Each day, the queen lays hundreds of eggs that develop into the workers that build and protect the colony. Usually once a year the queen lays eggs that develop into males and other queens. The males and potential queens have wings, and they fly away from the colony. They mate in the air and then land. Once on the ground, they soon lose their wings and the males die. The new queens then establish new colonies.

The ants in your ant microcosm are most likely all workers. The queen usually remains deep underground, and you would need to dig carefully to obtain her. If you purchased your ants, you will not have a queen because shipping queens is illegal. (It has been made illegal to prevent unwanted ants from being introduced to various parts of the country. Workers alone cannot produce a new colony.) Even without a queen, though, the ants in your colony will still carry on most of their normal functions. This is possible because their actions and reactions are not regulated by a queen. What are the ants' actions and reactions based on?

Ant workers, if properly cared for, can live for a year in a formicarium. For various reasons, however, they often live for only a few months.

- You can buy ants from a science supply company. Carefully put your ants in the formicarium. Be ready with sticks and other devices to direct the ants into the chamber. Placing a paper funnel in the opening of the ant chamber often works well to direct the ants into the chamber. Do not injure the ants.

4. Place a piece of food in the chamber. A tiny portion of a corn flake is good to use.

Procedure and Data

Care for your ant colony.

1. Add several drops of water (more if your formicarium is large) every two or three days.
2. Add a small piece of food every three or four days. The major problem with keeping ant microcosms is overfeeding. If you put in too much food, it will begin to rot and will cause the ants to die. If food is not consumed before it begins to mold, remove the food. Removing the food can be difficult if the ants have taken their food deep into the colony. The best solution is to feed the ants very small amounts. If the ants ignore the food you introduce, do not feed them for several days.
3. Keep your formicarium in a well-lit area, but do not put it in direct sunlight or in very strong light. The strong light will cause the temperature inside to rise so high that it will kill the ants.
4. Keep your formicarium steady. If you must move it, do so carefully and slowly. Ants and their tunnels are sensitive to movement.

Observe your ant microcosm often.

Observe the various activities occurring in your ant microcosm, and record your observations. Although you may want to observe the formicarium several times a day, record your observations only once or twice a day. Make your recorded observations at the same time every day. Use the questions below when making your observation record.

- What are the ants doing? Where are they tunneling? Where are they stacking sand? Where are their chambers built?
- As they work on various projects, ants will work in large groups, in small groups, or sometimes alone. Indicate the size of the group that is working on each ant project you observe.
- What do the ants do with the food?
- What do the ants do when water is introduced?
- Are all the ants working? Where are the ones that are not working? Is there any physical difference between those that are working and those that are not?
- When an ant dies, what do the other ants do?

Summing Up

After you have observed the ant microcosm for several weeks, write a brief summary of what you saw the ants do. Include your observations of the ants' reactions.

name

section date

15f An Animal's Response to Its Environment

Goal

✓ Observe and categorize an animal's reactions to stimuli in its environment.

Materials

an animal in its natural environment

All animals constantly respond to their environment. We may not always be able to determine what stimulates the responses. Often, however, we can determine what the animal is responding to if we observe carefully and think about our observations.

Find some active animal in a large area. A squirrel in a yard or park, a dog in a yard, a bird near a bird feeder, a rabbit in a meadow, or a zoo animal in a large enclosure would be good to observe. If you cannot observe an animal in a large space, you can use an active animal in a smaller space: a fish in an aquarium or a bird, chameleon, guinea pig, or hamster in a cage. Observe the animal for three five-minute periods. These five-minute periods should each be separated by several minutes.

While you are watching the animal, observe the animal's reactions to stimuli. For each observation, record both the stimulus and the reaction. To do this, you may need to use an audio recorder, a video recorder, or a friend or two to record your observations. Animals will not wait for you to write down notes. You may want to have a friend record his own observations of the animal at the same time. You could then compare notes and compile a more accurate list of the animal's reactions.

Compile your list of reactions on a separate sheet of paper. Then indicate whether each reaction was a reflex, an instinct, a learned behavior, or an intelligent behavior. Compute the percentage of each type of reaction.

Personal Investigation

name ______________________

section ____________ date ____________

15g Sexual Reproduction: Means of Amazing Variation

Goal

✓ Illustrate the variety in offspring that results from sexual reproduction.

Materials

none

Introduction

Sexual reproduction offers one clear advantage that asexual reproduction (or cloning) does not offer—variation. Organisms produced by sexual reproduction are similar to, but not exactly like, their parents. In Chapters 6 and 7 of your textbook, you can read about how this variation occurs. In this investigation you are going to verify that animals produced by sexual reproduction can have certain characteristics that are different from their parents.

Procedure

Observe the cat family pictured below.

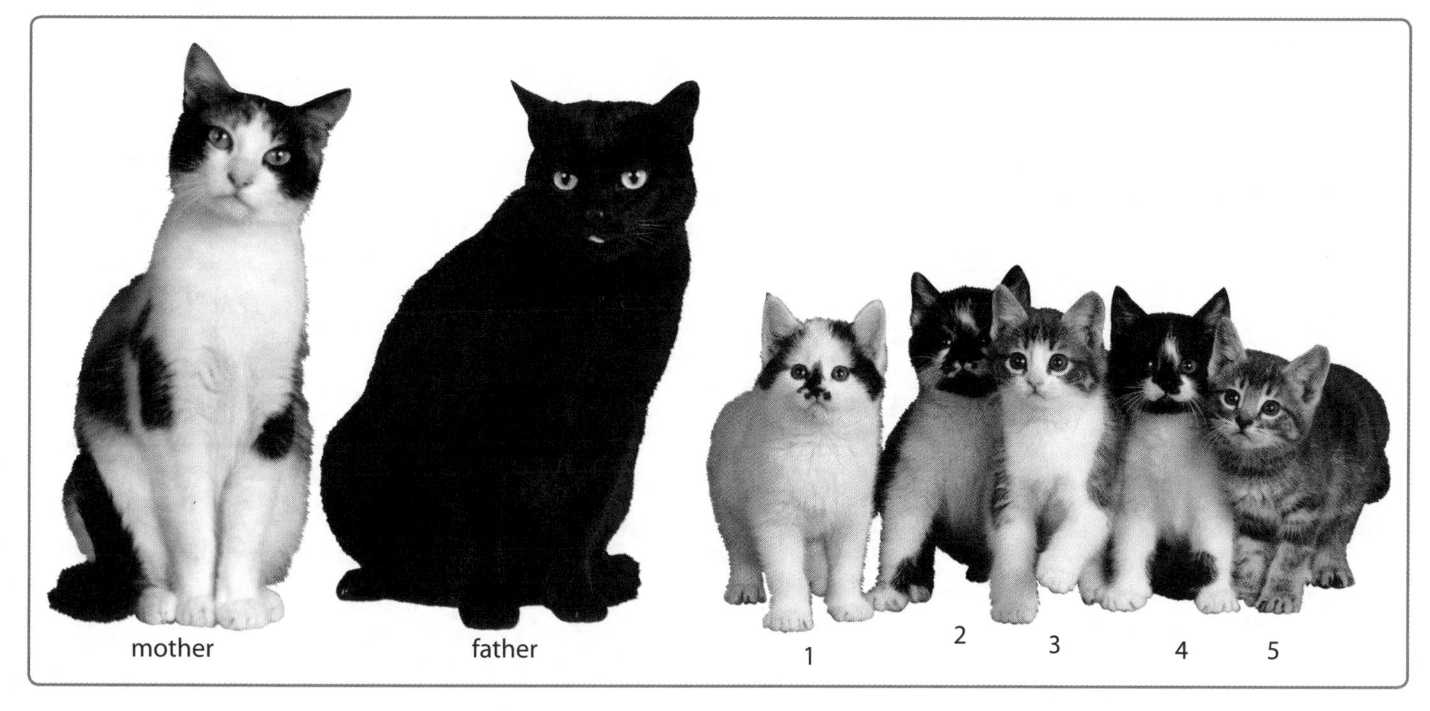

Describe the fur coat pattern of each animal.

mother ______________________________

father ______________________________

offspring #1 ______________________________

offspring #2 ______________________________

offspring #3 ______________________________

offspring #4 ______________________________

offspring #5 ______________________________

1. How many of the offspring had fur coat patterns identical to the mother's or father's? ____________
2. How many different kinds of fur coat patterns were found in the litter? ____________
3. How many different kinds of fur coat patterns were demonstrated by the parents? ____________
4. If the offspring were genetically identical to one parent, would the pattern of their fur coats be different from that parent? ____________

Summing Up

1. Other than fur coat pattern, list five traits in which wild animals could vary from their parents.

2. How could having different patterns of fur coats help an animal species survive for thousands of years?

3. Why would *not* having variation be harmful to a species?

name ____________________

section __________ date __________

15h Animal Reproduction Worksheet

Goal

✓ Compare the various ways that animals reproduce.

Materials

encyclopedia, other reference books, or online sources

Procedure

Data Interpretation

Use the data in this table to answer the questions below. Questions 4–7 may require additional outside research.

Animal name	Length of incubation or gestation	Live bearer or egg layer?	Number of eggs or young at one time	Parental care provided?
black widow	14–30 days	eggs	200–750	yes (eggs)
blue crab	14 days	eggs	1 million–3 million	yes (eggs)
brown pelican	30 days	eggs	1–4	yes
emperor penguin	63 days	eggs	1	yes
emperor scorpion	7–9 months	live	15–40	yes
Gila monster	4–12 months	eggs	3–13	no
largemouth bass	3–7 days	eggs	2,000–43,000	yes
lined sea horse	21 days	eggs	250–600	yes (eggs)
lobster	11–12 months	eggs	5,000–10,000	yes (eggs)
orangutan	7–8 months	live	1	yes
prairie dog	28–32 days	live	2–10	yes
snapping turtle	3–4 months	eggs	25–80	no
Surinam toad	3–5 months	eggs	60–80	yes (eggs)

1. Which egg layer has the longest incubation period? ____________________
2. Which organism produces the greatest potential number of offspring? ____________________
3. Which organism has the shortest gestation or incubation period? ____________________
4. What might account for the wide range in number of possible eggs laid by the largemouth bass?

____

____

5. How does a scorpion mother care for her offspring?

____

____

6. What is unusual about the egg development of the Surinam toad?

____

____

7. What might account for the 30-day variation in hatching time for snapping turtle eggs?

___

___

Data Research

Use encyclopedias, other reference books, or reliable online sources to find the information needed to complete the table. Some answers have been provided.

Animal name	Length of incubation or gestation	Live bearer or egg layer?	Number of eggs or young at one time	Parental care provided?
Asian elephant			1	
bald eagle		eggs		
box turtle	7–12 weeks or over winter			
bullfrog				
cottontail rabbit		live		
guppy				no
robin				

Summing Up

1. What is the difference between incubation and gestation?

___

___

___

2. Which of the animals above do you think has the most unusual reproduction? Why?

___

___

___

3. What type of care might an animal provide for its young?

___

___

___

___

___

___

name ______________________

section __________ date __________

16a Ecosystems

Part 1

Directions

Listed below are three common relationships in ecosystems. Below the list are some examples of relationships in ecosystems. In the blank by each example, write the letter of the relationship that is being described. You will use each letter more than once.

Common Relationships in Ecosystems

A. Organisms affect other organisms.

B. Abiotic factors affect organisms.

C. Organisms affect abiotic factors.

B 1. To keep from becoming too hot, a lizard spends the hottest part of the afternoon in the shadow of a rock.

C 2. A groundhog digs tunnels in the soil.

A 3. A squirrel scampers up a tree, sits on a limb, and begins eating a pecan.

C 4. The roots of a tree have grown into the cracks of a rock. As the roots continue to grow, the rock slowly crumbles.

C 5. A leech attaches itself to a turtle's flipper and obtains a meal of blood.

B 6. Birds navigate their migrations by the stars.

A 7. A snake swallows a rat.

B 8. Warm soil and abundant moisture trigger seeds to sprout.

C 9. When it rains, the plants growing on a hillside prevent the water from running down the hill quickly and carrying soil with it.

B 10. A year of drought causes an oak tree to produce fewer acorns than normal.

Part 2

Directions

In the spaces provided, describe the difference between the terms in each pair.

1. ecosystem / habitat

2. abiotic environment / biotic community

3. intensity of light / duration of light

4. humus / substrate

5. evaporation / precipitation

6. runoff / groundwater

name ____________________

section __________ date __________

16b The Water Cycle

Directions

In the illustration below, draw arrows to show the water cycle. One arrow has been provided for you. Then use the terms from the box to label the illustration by writing the correct term in the numbered blank that matches the corresponding number on the diagram.

clouds	stream
evaporation	transpiration
groundwater	water entering plant roots
precipitation	water seeping through the ground
runoff	water table

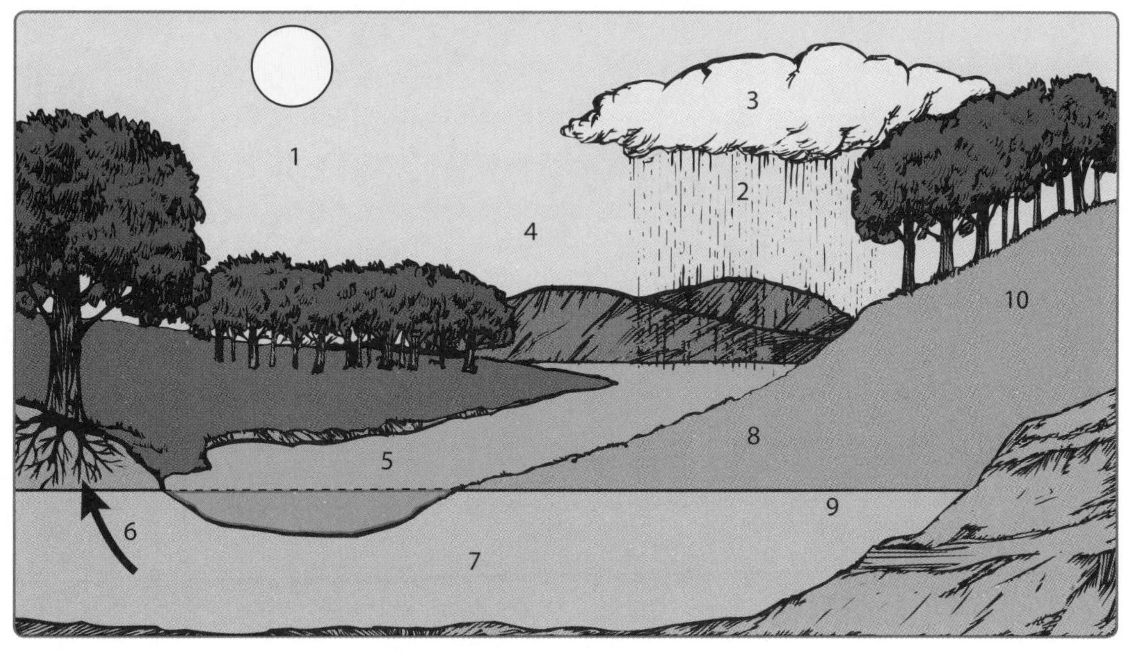

1. ____________________
2. ____________________
3. ____________________
4. ____________________
5. ____________________
6. ____________________
7. ____________________
8. ____________________
9. ____________________
10. ____________________

name____________________

section__________ date__________

16c Succession on a Volcano

Directions

In each of the following statements, draw a circle around the correct choice in parentheses. On the lines provided, explain why the incorrect choice is not acceptable.

1. The plants and animals that lived on Mount Saint Helens in Washington before its 1980 eruption included pine and fir trees, grouse, foxes, hares, deer, bobcats, bears, and mountain lions. Populations of these organisms made up the (biotic community / abiotic environment) of Mount Saint Helens.

2. When Mount Saint Helens erupted in 1980, almost all living things on the mountain were destroyed. This is an example of the (biotic community affecting the abiotic environment / abiotic environment affecting the biotic community).

3. In some areas, all life was destroyed. But within a few months of the eruption, some plants, such as pearly everlasting and fireweed, were found growing in these areas. They had sprouted from windblown seeds. Such plants are examples of (pioneer organisms / climax vegetation).

4. Pine and fir seedlings could not grow on the fresh volcanic surface of Mount Saint Helens because they require soil. Several generations of other plants would be needed to build the soil for pines to grow. The soil building that is still going on at Mount Saint Helens is an example of the (abiotic environment affecting the biotic community / biotic community affecting the abiotic environment).

5. As the soil is built, the first plants give way to other plants. If not hindered by more eruptions, pine and fir trees will once again grow on Mount Saint Helens. These predictable changes in the biotic community are called (succession / evolution).

____

____

____

6. The biotic community surrounding Mount Saint Helens immediately before the 1980 eruption was not a climax community. It was still recovering from an 1857 eruption. A forest community of hemlocks and firs is the climax community for the mountains in that area. If no more eruptions occur, Mount Saint Helens will probably reach its climax community (before / after) the year 2103.

____

____

____

7. The appearance of pine trees on Mount Saint Helens does not represent the final climax community because other major species changes (will still occur / will not occur).

____

____

____

Mount Saint Helens in (a) 1980, (b) 1984, and (c) 2004

name ____________________

section __________ date __________

16d Rhythms in the Ecosystem

Directions

All the scrambled words listed below deal with rhythms in the ecosystem. Using the definitions as clues, unscramble the words and write them in the blanks.

1. hthymrs ____________ changes that take place regularly
2. alnoesas ____________ occurs at a certain time of the year
3. tunrlacno ____________ active at night
4. danicrica ____________ rhythms that happen every 24 hours
5. dlruian ____________ active during the day
6. rodycnam ____________ a period of inactivity
7. odtrmna dbu ____________ a bud that is not growing
8. nilesepnra ____________ plants that grow year after year
9. nnaauls ____________ plants that grow and die within a year
10. nrebhiatoni ____________ winter dormancy in some animals
11. globicoila ckclo ____________ the internal mechanism that controls rhythms in many organisms

name ____________________

section __________ date __________

16e Review

Part 1

Directions

Record your responses in the spaces provided.

1. List the major factors of the abiotic environment that are found in most ecosystems.

2. List several materials that are cyclic in an ecosystem. Why is it essential that these materials cycle in an ecosystem?

3. Choose an ecosystem. How does your choice qualify as an ecosystem?

4. List several factors of the abiotic environment that are significant in the ecosystem you chose in Question 3.

5. List several populations that are found in the ecosystem you chose in Question 3. Indicate which of these populations are producers and which are consumers.

6. What are the differences between a winter-resident bird, a summer-resident bird, and a permanent-resident bird?

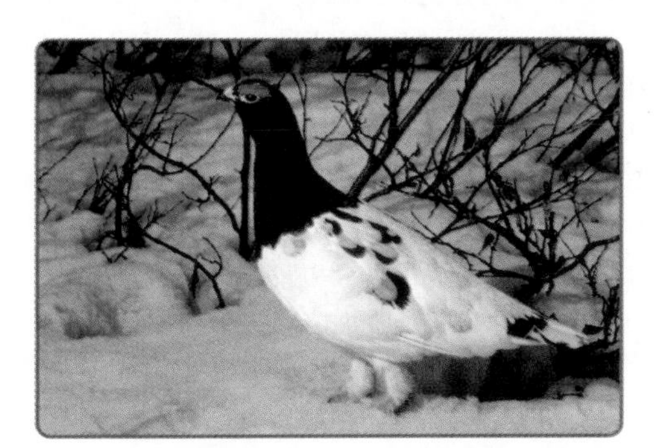

Part 2

Directions

Match the terms with the choice that best fits them. Each choice will be used once, and there is only one way in which all choices can be used correctly.

A. abiotic environment
B. biogeochemical cycles
C. biotic community
D. circadian rhythms
E. ecosystem
F. habitat
G. limiting factors
H. niche
I. population
J. seasonal rhythms
K. succession
L. water cycle

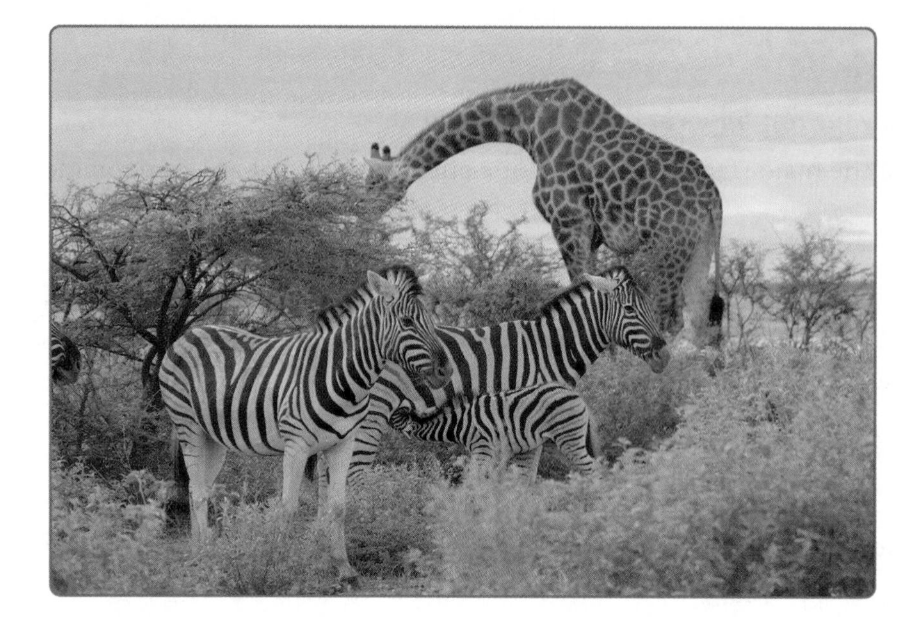

E 1. abiotic environment and biotic community

F 2. where an organism lives

D 3. nocturnal and diurnal

A 4. light, temperature, and water

C 5. producers and consumers

H 6. what an organism does

L 7. evaporation and precipitation

K 8. pioneer species and climax community

b 9. carbon, oxygen, and nitrogen

G 10. limit the growth or existence of a species

J 11. hibernation and dormancy

I 12. all the individuals of the same species in an area

name ____________________

section __________ date __________

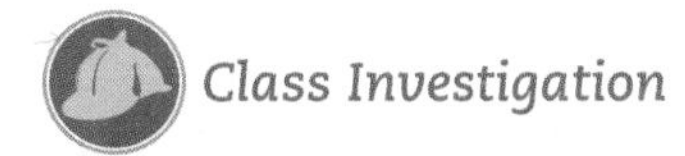

16f The Biotic Community of the Soil

Goals

- ✓ Collect and identify the organisms in a soil sample.
- ✓ Demonstrate that a wide variety of organisms live in soil.

Introduction

Thousands of different kinds of organisms live in the soil. In this lab, you will study a sample of topsoil to get an idea of the variety of living things that exist there. As you see the many organisms in a small soil sample, imagine how many there are in your entire backyard!

Materials

sample of topsoil
large funnel
wire screen (¼ in. mesh)
ring stand and iron ring
small jar or 250 mL beaker
isopropyl alcohol (optional)
incandescent light bulb (60–100 watts)
hand lens or stereomicroscope
nutrient agar plate or slice of bread (optional)

Procedure

1. Collect about 1 L (1 qt) of topsoil. Especially include any organic debris on the surface. Thoroughly decomposed wood works well. Avoid areas that have been treated with insecticide, such as lawns, or recently cultivated areas, such as gardens. Forest soil is excellent for this investigation.
2. Assemble a Berlese funnel. This is a large funnel with a wire screen set inside it that is used to remove tiny organisms from soil samples. Support the funnel with a ring stand and iron ring as shown in the illustration. The wire screen should be cut or bent into a disk that fits the funnel about halfway down the fluted portion.
3. Place part or all of your soil sample on the wire screen in the Berlese funnel. Place the portion of the soil that has the most organic material (leaves, stems, twigs, etc.) on the screen first. It will help keep the remainder of the soil from falling through the screen. The soil layer should be about 5 cm deep.
4. Position the funnel over a jar or beaker containing isopropyl alcohol to collect the organisms that fall through. You may substitute water for alcohol, but some organisms may then escape.
5. Suspend an incandescent light over the funnel about 4 in. above the soil. Leave the light on for about 24 hours. Organisms in the soil will burrow deeper to avoid the drying heat and light. As they do, they will fall through the screen and into the collection jar or beaker.
6. Many of the organisms are small, so you should use a hand lens (or stereomicroscope) to observe the collected organisms. Identify and count the organisms. Your teacher will help you identify them. Record your observations in the table on the next page.
7. (Optional) Put a small amount of soil on a nutrient agar plate or on a piece of bread moistened with water. Incubate this in a warm, dark area for 1–2 days. Observe the organisms that grow and include your observations in the table on the next page.

Data

Type of Organism	How Many?	Notes and Observations

Summing Up

1. What types of organisms did you find in your soil sample?

____

____

2. What type of organism was most numerous in your soil sample?

____

3. If you did the optional soil incubation, what types of organisms did you find?

____

____

   - Could there be more of these organisms in the soil than the larger organisms? _______________

4. Do you think there may be organisms in your soil sample that you did not find? _______________
   - If so, what kinds of organisms?

____

____

Going Beyond

Repeat your observations using soil samples from different areas (a meadow, a swamp, a riverbank, deeper in the ground, etc.). Record your findings and determine what differences in the biotic community of the soil exist between these areas.

Field Investigation

name ____________________

section __________ date __________

16g Backyard Ecosystems

Goal
✓ Identify components of the abiotic environment and the biotic community in an ecosystem.

Materials
natural ecosystem

Introduction

An ecosystem is a limited area in which living and nonliving things interact. Thus a backyard, a school yard, or a park is an ecosystem. Each of these areas has a biotic community (made up of various populations of living organisms) and an abiotic environment (made up of nonliving factors). You observe these ecosystems every day. But what specific organisms and factors make up these ecosystems?

Procedure

Choose a limited area and list various factors of its abiotic environment. Be sure to include factors that people control. For example, mowing the lawn, watering, and adding fertilizer or pesticides are all abiotic environmental factors that are not natural to an area but are important parts of an ecosystem.

List the populations that make up the biotic community of the ecosystem you are studying, and be as specific as possible. In other words, do not just list "birds"; list the specific kinds of bird populations in the ecosystem, such as "robins." Include both the animal populations and the plant populations. Be sure to list both large organisms and small ones, such as earthworms and ants. Also keep in mind that some populations, such as grasshoppers and daffodils, may be out of season. Do not forget that if pets use the area, they are also a part of the ecosystem, even though they may be in it only sometimes.

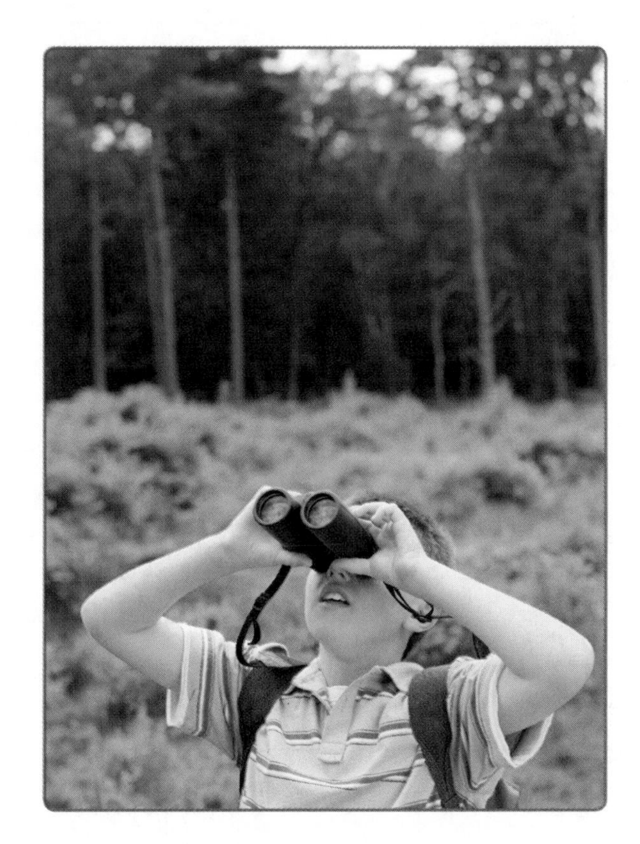

Data

Abiotic Environment	*Biotic Community*

Application

name ____________________

section __________ date __________

17a Energy Exchange Between Organisms

Directions

Using the food chain examples given below, label each level of the ecological pyramid with the proper organism. The organisms in the food chain examples are in alphabetical order. Then answer the questions to the left of the pyramid. Sometimes you may need to write *none* in the blank.

Food chain A: clover, hawk, rabbit

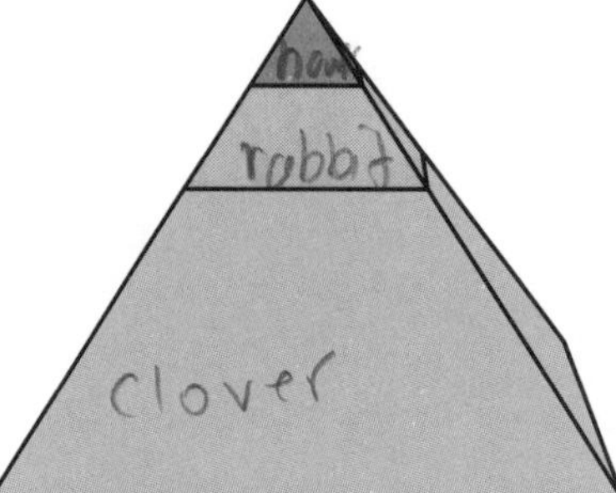

1. Name the producer(s) in this food chain. clover
2. Name the consumer(s) in this food chain. hawk, rabbit
3. Name the decomposer(s) in this food chain. none
4. Name the herbivore(s) in this food chain. rabbit
5. Name the carnivore(s) in this food chain. hawk
6. Which population in this food chain contains the most of the original energy? clover
7. Which population in this food chain contains the least of the original energy? hawk
8. Give an example of a predator-prey relationship in this food chain.

   hawk (predator) and rabbit (prey)

Food chain B: frog, grasshopper, snake, wheat

1. Name the producer(s) in this food chain. wheat
2. Name the consumer(s) in this food chain. frog, grasshopper, snake
3. Name the decomposer(s) in this food chain. none
4. Name the herbivore(s) in this food chain. grasshopper
5. Name the carnivore(s) in this food chain. frog, snake
6. Which population in this food chain contains the most of the original energy?

   wheat
7. Which population in this food chain contains the least of the original energy?

   snake
8. Give an example of a predator-prey relationship in this food chain.

   snake (predator) and frog (prey)

name ____________________

section __________ date __________

17b Bible Creatures and Their Food Chain Positions

Directions

Below is a list of Scripture references. For each one, find the animal mentioned and write its common name in the "Name" column. In the next pair of columns, check whether the animal is an herbivore or a carnivore. In the final three columns, check all the terms that apply to that animal. (Some animals will have more than one role.)

The Heavenly Shepherd, Bartolomé Esteban Murillo, from the Bob Jones University Collection

		(Choose one.)		(Choose all that apply.)		
Reference	**Name**	**Herbivore**	**Carnivore**	**Prey**	**Predator**	**Scavenger**
Exodus 8:2						
Exodus 10:4–5						
Leviticus 11:6						
Numbers 21:9						
Deuteronomy 8:15						
1 Samuel 17:15						
1 Kings 20:36						
1 Kings 21:23						
Job 39:27–30						
Proverbs 21:31						
Proverbs 30:28						
Isaiah 27:10						

name ____________________

section __________ date __________

17c Food Webs

Directions

Draw arrows to represent the flow of energy between the organisms in the food web illustrated below. One arrow has been drawn for you as an example. Then on the blank by each organism, place one letter from Column 1, telling whether the organism is a producer (P) or a consumer (C). If the organism is a consumer, place a letter from Column 2 beside the *C*, telling which kind of consumer the organism is. Any animals that help decompose dead material are detritus feeders. These were covered in Chapter 9 on page 189.

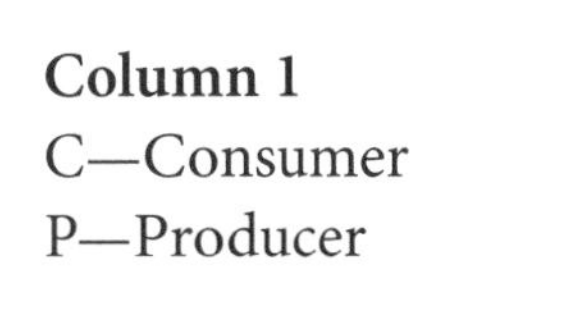

Column 1
C—Consumer
P—Producer

Column 2
C—Carnivore
D—Decomposer
H—Herbivore
O—Omnivore
T—Detritus feeder

Food Web of a Meadow

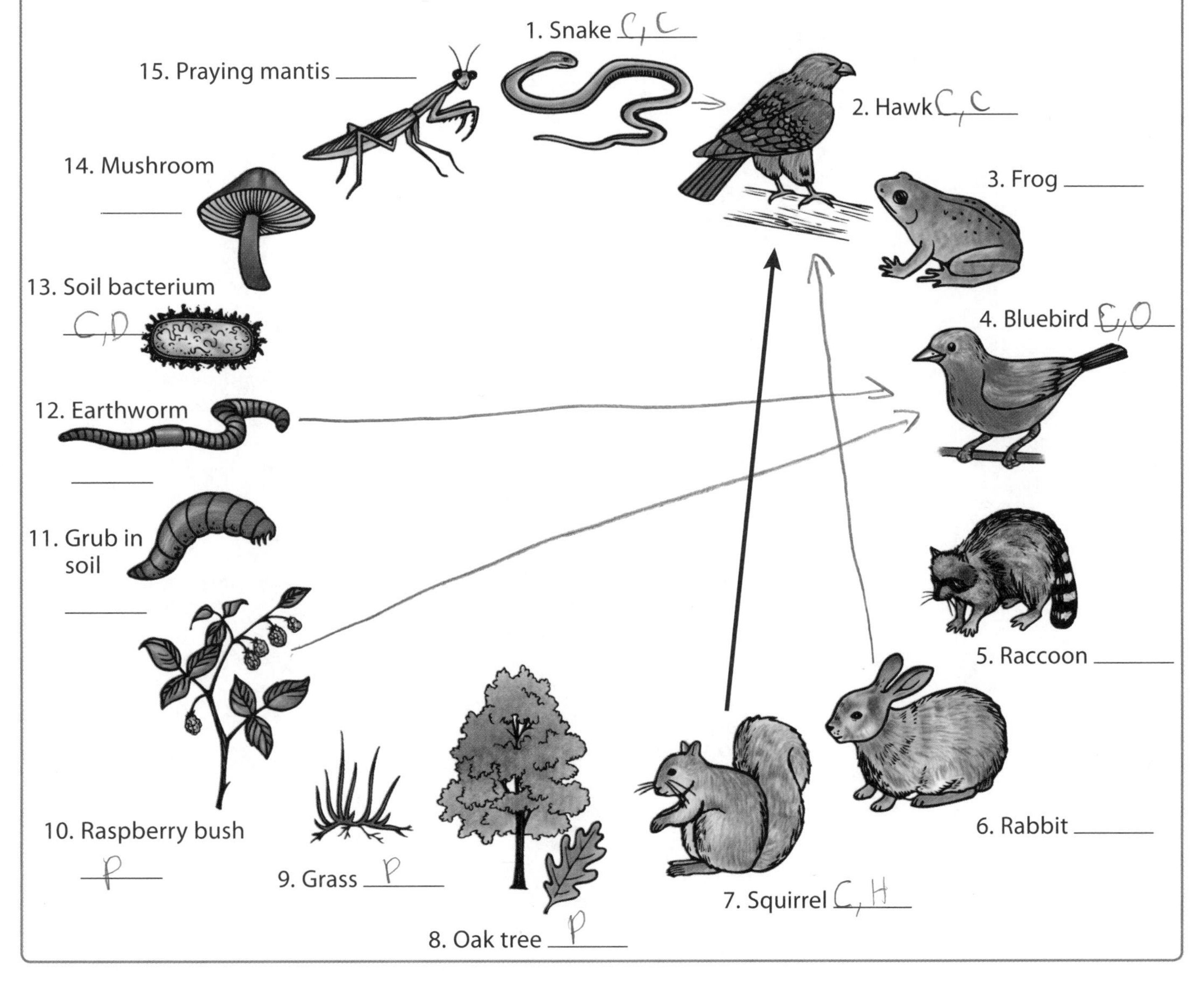

name ______________________

section ____________ date ____________

17d Organism Relationships

Directions

Identify each of the examples below with the correct organism relationship from the box. Write the letter of your answer in the blank. Each answer may be used more than once.

A. Camouflage
B. Commensalism
C. Competition between animals of the same species
D. Competition between plants of the same species
E. Competition between populations
F. Couple that is mated for life
G. Decomposer and its food
H. Independent organism
I. Mimicry
J. Mutualism
K. Parasite and host
L. Predator and prey
M. Scavenger and its food
N. Social organisms in a group
O. Warning coloration

_______ 1. A lion attacks and kills a zebra.

_______ 2. Vultures clean up the remains after the lion has finished eating the zebra.

_______ 3. In Africa, both white rhinoceroses and zebras graze on the grasses in their habitat.

_______ 4. Because the praying mantis looks like a branch when it sits still, insect-eating birds often do not see it as they search for food.

_______ 5. Mushrooms grow on a rotting stump along the bank.

_______ 6. Cattle egrets are birds that follow rhinoceroses across the African plains. The birds catch insects that are disturbed by the rhino's movements across the ground. The rhinos are unaffected by the birds.

_______ 7. A green katydid is hidden in the plants along the water's edge.

_______ 8. Several kinds of ticks may live in the fur of grazing mammals on the African plains.

_______ 9. The red-billed oxpecker bird picks the ticks off grazing mammals' backs and eats them.

_______ 10. A group of honeybees work to build their hive.

_______ 11. The skunk's black and white stripes warn other animals to stay away from it.

_______ 12. A spider spins its web far away from other spiders.

_______ 13. A bird builds its nest in a pine tree.

_______ 14. A mosquito lands on your arm and begins to feed on your blood.

_______ 15. Weeds invade a flower garden.

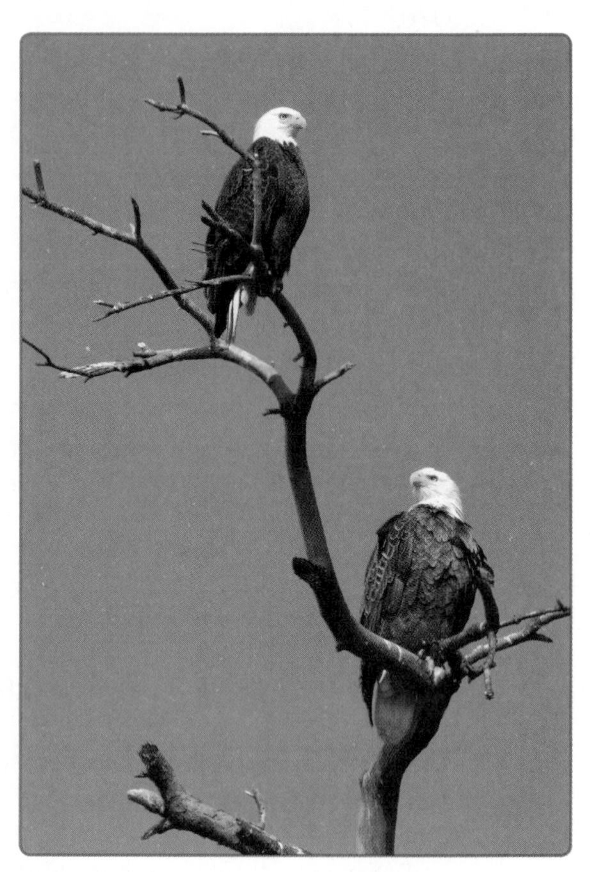

_______ 16. The highly venomous coral snake has yellow, black, and red stripes. The harmless scarlet king snake has similar colors of stripes, but in a different order. Predators that avoid the coral snake also avoid the scarlet king snake.

_______ 17. A dragonfly swoops after a mosquito.

_______ 18. A crayfish nibbles on a dead fish in shallow water.

_______ 19. Two male wolves fight for dominance in the pack.

_______ 20. Water lilies cover the surface of one end of the pond, and their leaves overlap.

_______ 21. Bald eagles have spectacular courtship rituals, after which they remain together until one of them dies.

_______ 22. A honeybee gets a meal of pollen from a rose flower and in the process helps spread the pollen to other areas.

_______ 23. A line of ants goes from their hill to the edge of the pond.

name ______________________

section ___________ date ___________

17e Your Food Chain

Goal

✓ Determine your position in various food chains.

Materials

none

Introduction

Humans are consumer organisms. Every time you eat, you are a link in a food chain. But what food chains are you involved in? To find out, you will record the foods you eat during an entire day. You may need to divide some of the foods into their various parts. For example, you should consider a sandwich made of bread, cheese, and ham as bread, cheese, and ham—not simply a sandwich.

Procedure

Determine which organisms your food came from and which link you are in the food chain. List the organisms that are involved in the food chain for each of the foods you ate.

The first link in a food chain, of course, is the producers. If you eat plants or plant products, you are the second link in the food chain (an herbivore). If you eat meat or animal products (such as milk or cheese), you are functioning as a carnivore and are the final link (hopefully) in a three- or four-link food chain. By eating some foods, you may become the last link in a four- or five-link food chain.

Put a *2* in the "I Am Link #" column if you were the second link in a particular food chain, a *3* if you were the third, and so on. A sample has been entered for you.

Food I Ate	I Am Link #	Other Organisms in the Food Chain
roast beef	3	grass, steer
sweet potato	2	sweet potatoe plant
cat fish	4	smaller fish; insects, aquatic plants
egg	3	grain; chicken

1. From your list of foods, what might an herbivore eat?

____

____

____

____

____

2. From your list of foods, what might a carnivore eat?

____

____

____

____

____

name ____________________

section __________ date __________

Class Investigation

17f Overcrowding

Introduction

Many different factors can affect the growth of a population. One factor is overcrowding. In this lab, you'll observe the effects of overcrowding on the growth of bean seedlings.

Goal

✓ Observe the effects of overcrowding on bean seedlings.

Materials

flowerpots, about 10 cm (4 in.) in diameter (2)
potting soil
bean seeds, presoaked (33)

Procedure

1. Fill the pots with potting soil to about 2.5 cm (1 in.) below the rim. Do not add any fertilizer or plant food to the soil.
2. Plant 3 bean seeds in one pot and 30 in the other pot. Cover the seeds with 1 cm (0.4 in.) of soil. Water each pot thoroughly and set them in a warm, well-lit area where they will have identical conditions (temperature, light).
3. Record the date you planted your seeds: ____________
4. Regularly water the pot with 3 seeds with enough water to keep the soil moist but not soggy. The pot with 30 seeds should be watered with the same amount of water as the first pot, regardless of how much water it appears to need.
5. Once the seeds sprout, do not move the pots. If some seedlings in the crowded pot get more light than others, that is a consequence of overcrowding and should not be changed.

Data

1. Observe the pots daily. When the seeds sprout, begin recording your observations on the table below. In the columns that ask for observations about the sprouts, record data about the height, color, number of leaves, and general condition of the plants.

Bean Seed Data

Date	Pot with 3 seeds		Pot with 30 seeds	
	Number of sprouts	Observations	Number of sprouts	Observations
4	0		0	
6	0		0	
7	0		0	
10	0	moved outside	0	moved outside
12	1		3	
14	2	1st sprout 3" tall	4	all about 1" tall
17	2	5" & 3" tall	12	tallest = 5"; avg = 2"
18	2	6" & 3½" tall	12	4 = 5"; 4 = 3" tall; 4 less than 2"
		✯ 100% grew		✯ 40% grew

2. After you have completed your observations for a week or two, unpot the seedlings and carefully remove the soil from them. Do this by putting the seedlings in a large dish of water and gently moving them.
3. Record your observations of the differences between the root systems of the plants in the two pots.

___

___

___

4. As an alternative to Steps 2 and 3 above, you could allow the seedlings to grow for four to six weeks before making your final observations. Depending on a number of factors, the seedling differences may be more obvious after an extended time period.

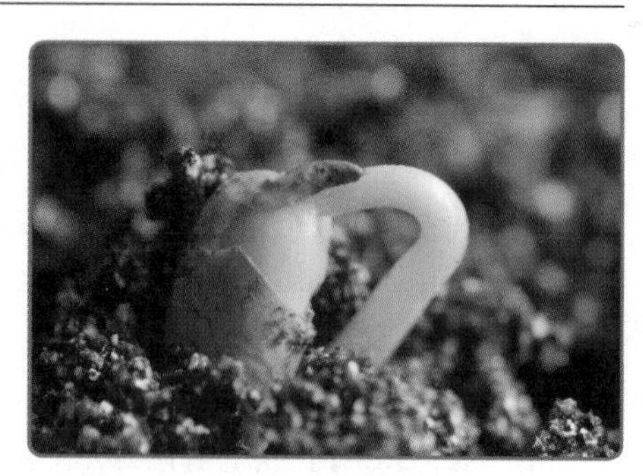

Summing Up

1. Write a paragraph comparing the bean sprouts in the two pots, giving their similarities and differences.

___

___

___

___

___

___

___

___

___

___

___

___

2. Why did the seeds in one pot do better than the seeds in the other pot?

___

___

___

3. The bean seeds in the pot with 30 seeds illustrate which type of relationship among organisms?

___

4. What is a limiting factor? What was a major limiting factor for the bean seed population?

___

___

Class Investigation

name ____________________

section __________ date __________

17g Lichens

Goal

✓ Observe the mutualistic relationship of lichens.

Materials

field guides
lichen specimens
eyedropper
glass slide
probes
cover slip
microscope
prepared microscope slides of lichens

Procedure

Obtain and identify lichen specimens.

1. Using field guides, find the types and locations of lichens that are common in your area.
2. Obtain samples of several different lichens. Be sure to obtain permission from the people who own the land where you collect your specimens. Be careful not to destroy other things while you collect specimens.
3. Using field guides, try to identify your specimens. If field guides are not available, at least classify them according to their form (crustose, foliose, or fruticose—see the photos below).
4. Bring your specimens to class.

Observe the various lichen specimens.

In the table below, describe five of the lichen specimens brought into class. From the person who collected each specimen, find out where the lichen came from, and include that information in your description. In the "Type" column, write *C* for a crustose lichen, *F* for a foliose, or *T* for a fruticose.

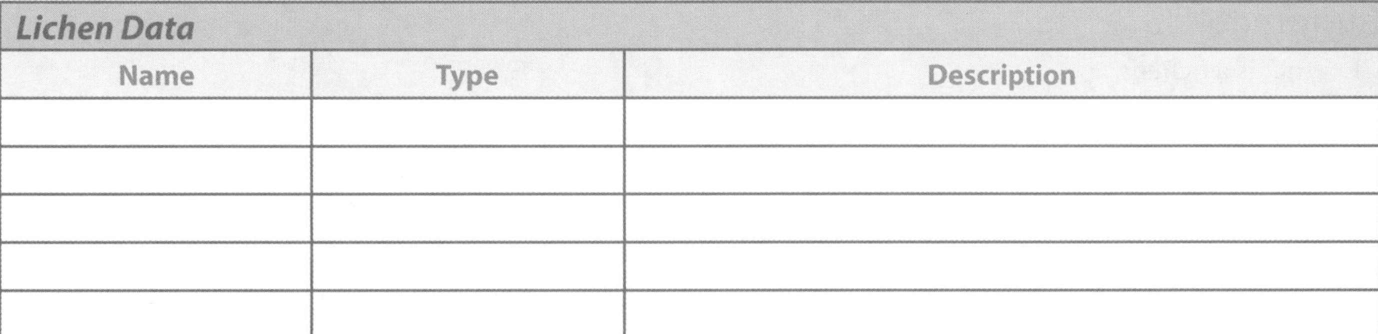

Lichen Data

Name	Type	Description

Crustose lichen

Foliose lichen

Fruticose lichen

Prepare a slide of a lichen and observe it through a microscope.

1. Place a tiny piece of a lichen in a drop of water on a glass slide.
2. Using two probes, tear the lichen into small shreds. This process is called teasing.
3. Place a cover slip on top of the teased lichen.
4. Observe this slide through a microscope.
5. Describe what you see.

Observe a prepared slide of a cross section of a lichen.

1. Focus the microscope on the prepared slide of a lichen.
2. Find the cells of the algae and fungi.
3. Describe what you see.

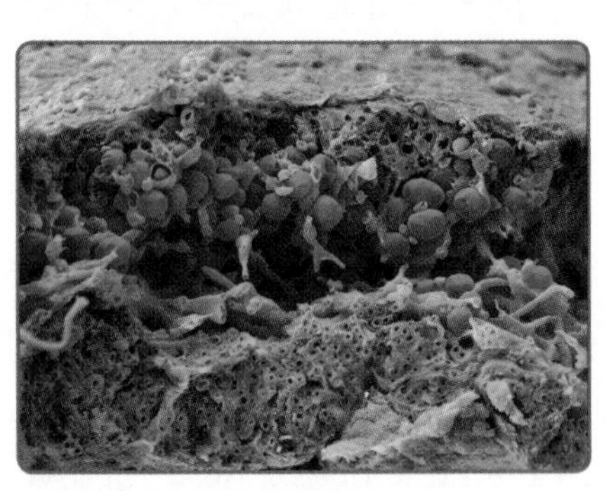

Cross section of a lichen

Summing Up

1. What is a lichen?
2. How does a lichen exhibit mutualism?
3. Why can lichens grow in places where other organisms cannot grow?

Field Investigation

name ______________________

section ____________ date ____________

17h Observing Relationships

Goal

✓ Observe the relationships among organisms in a natural environment.

Materials

none

Introduction

Organisms are constantly interacting with each other. With even a casual observation of a natural setting, you can see dozens of interactions if you know what to look for.

Procedure

The relationships discussed in Chapter 17 of your textbook are listed below. Beside each of these relationships is a point value. Go to a beach, a field, a forest, a meadow, or some other natural area where you can observe both plants and animals. In the table on the next page, record the places, dates, and times that you made your observations. List the names of the organisms involved in each relationship you observed. In the "Type of relationship" column, record the number of the correct relationship from the list below. For example, a skunk exhibits warning coloration, so if you saw a skunk, you would write *15* in this column.

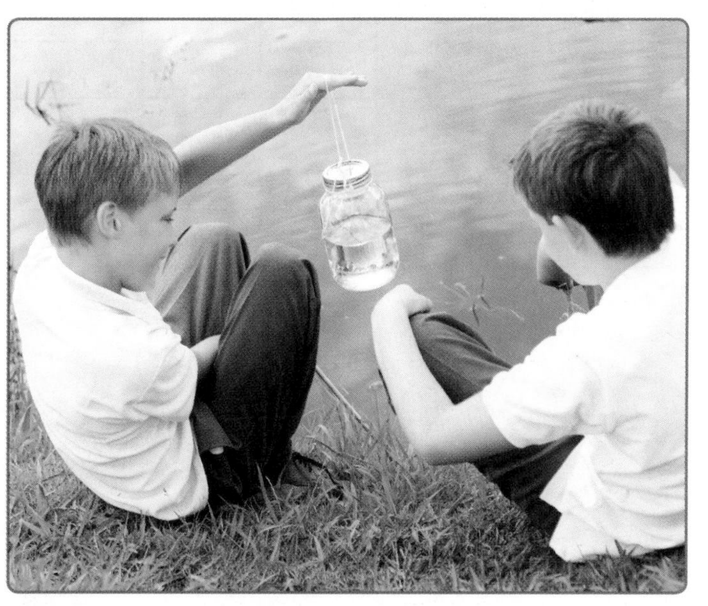

In the "Point value" column, list the number of points that your observation is worth (or, your teacher may assign points to this column during grading). For each kind of relationship listed below, no more than five examples may be counted. See Application 17d, "Organism Relationships," for some examples of the types of relationships that you might observe.

Relationships

1. Competition between plants of the same species (1 point)
2. Decomposer and its food (1 point)
3. Independent organism (1 point)
4. Predator and prey (2 points)
5. Competition between animals of the same species (3 points)
6. Competition between populations (3 points)
7. Social organisms in a group (3 points)
8. Camouflage (4 points)
9. Couple that is mated for life (4 points)
10. Scavenger and its food (4 points)
11. Commensalism (5 points)
12. Mimicry (5 points)
13. Mutualism (5 points)
14. Parasite and host (5 points)
15. Warning coloration (5 points)

Observations of Organism Relationships

Place	Date	Time	Names of organisms	Type of relationship	Point value
					total points =

Application

name ____________________

section __________ date __________

18a Natural Resources

Part 1: Renewable and Nonrenewable Resources

Directions

Below is a list of natural resources. By each resource, write an *R* if it is a renewable resource or an *N* if it is a nonrenewable resource.

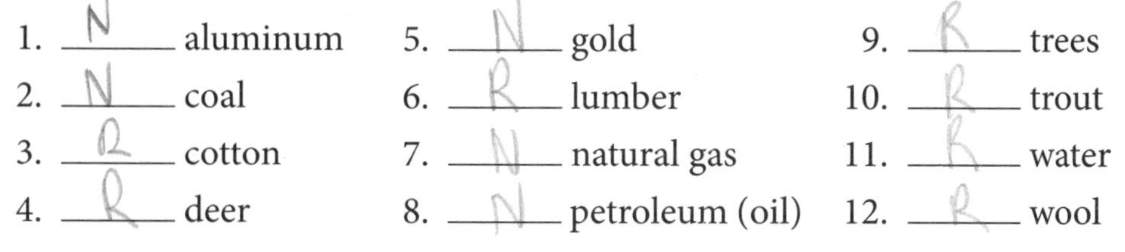

1. N	aluminum	5. N	gold	9. R	trees
2. N	coal	6. R	lumber	10. R	trout
3. R	cotton	7. N	natural gas	11. R	water
4. R	deer	8. N	petroleum (oil)	12. R	wool

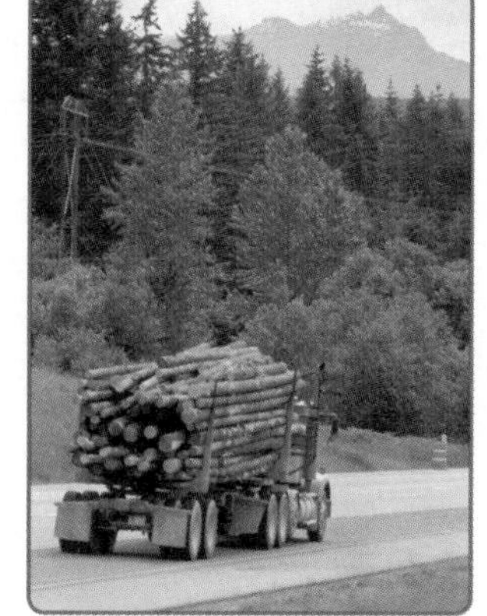

These logs are going to a paper mill.

Part 2: Agriculture and the Soil

Directions

Below are several groups of terms. In each group, three of the four terms are related to one another. Draw a line through the unrelated term and then write a sentence using the remaining terms. Your sentence should show how the terms are related. (You may slightly change the form of the terms in your sentence.)

1. agriculture / livestock / crops / legumes

____

____

2. fertilizer / harvest / land grants / productivity

____

____

3. humus / irrigation / depletion of minerals / soil productivity

____

____

4. soil / humus / legumes / nitrogen

____

____

5. depletion of minerals / fertilizer / legumes / irrigation

____

____

6. crop rotation / field / crop / fertilizer

____

____

Application

name________________

section________ date________

18b Man's Role in the Ecosystem

Part 1: Populations

Directions

All the scrambled words listed below deal with populations. Using the definitions as clues, unscramble the words and write them in the blanks.

1. xpnoeenaitl ohwtgr	__________ __________	A constant rate of increase
2. trraethib	__________	The rate at which individuals are born into a population
3. namhu tiopnlaupo	__________ __________	The number of people living on the earth at one time
4. pupoailnot inrcasee	__________ __________	A condition that occurs when the birthrate of a population is greater than the death rate
5. brtnaoio	__________	The killing of an unborn child
6. dthea rtea	__________	The rate at which individuals in a population die
7. nopitlaoup crdeaese	__________ __________	A condition that occurs when the death rate of a population is greater than the birthrate
8. ueiaaathns	__________	The killing of very old or very sick people
9. yasdmdoo	__________	A supposed future time when man will destroy the earth by abusing it
10. srvacnontioe	__________	The careful use of natural resources

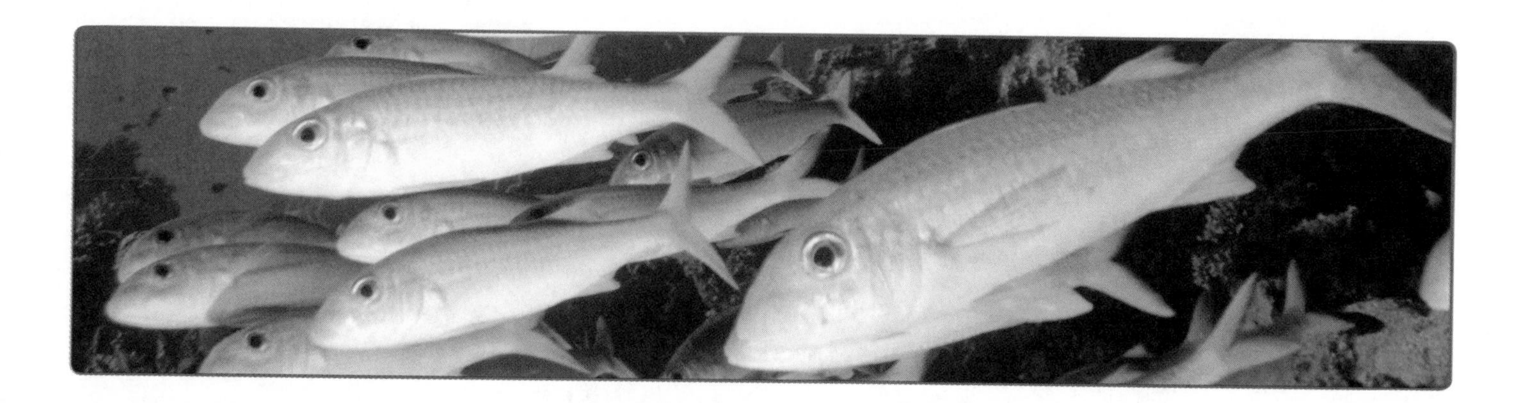

Part 2: Pollution

Directions

Fill in the missing letters to complete the following statements about pollution. The circled letters form a phrase that completes the sentence at the bottom.

1. By law, many ___ ___ (___) ___ ___ ___ ___ E ___ ___ are made of recycled paper.
2. Gases and tiny particles form the major components of ___ (___) ___ P ___ ___ ___ ___ ___ ___ ___ ___.
3. (___) ___ ___ ___ U ___ compounds are the second most abundant type of air pollutant.
4. Today aluminum is cheaper to ___ (___) ___ Y ___ ___ ___ than to mine.
5. Solid unwanted or unusable materials are called ___ R ___ (___) ___.
6. The final stage of sewage treatment that removes chemicals from the water is called ___ ___ ___ (___) ___ ___ R ___ treatment.
7. The two major types of pollutants are substance pollutants and (___) ___ ___ R ___ ___ pollutants.
8. Unwanted products that are potentially harmful to man or the environment are called ___ ___ Z ___ ___ ___ ___ ___ ___ (___) A ___ ___ ___ ___.
9. One of the most abundant components of air pollution is the deadly gas ___ (___) ___ B ___ ___ ___ ___ ___ ___ X ___ ___ ___.
10. Chemicals and heat released into streams and lakes are common forms of ___ ___ T ___ (___) ___ O ___ ___ ___ ___ ___ ___ ___.
11. Substances that the environment can recycle are called ___ ___ ___ (___) ___ ___ R ___ ___ ___ ___ ___ ___ substances.
12. A solid, liquid, or gas may be a ___ ___ B (___) ___ ___ ___ ___ ___ pollutant.
13. Although too much pollution can be bad, not all pollution is (___) A ___ ___ ___ U ___ to an environment.
14. A place where trash has layers of soil placed over it is called a ___ ___ N (___) ___ ___ ___ ___ ___ ___ ___ ___ ___ ___ L ___.
15. An area where cities used to dispose of trash was the city ___ U ___ (___).

Christians should use the earth's resources with ___ ___ ___ ___ ___ ___ ___ ___ ___ ___ ___ ___ ___ ___ ___ rather than abuse them.

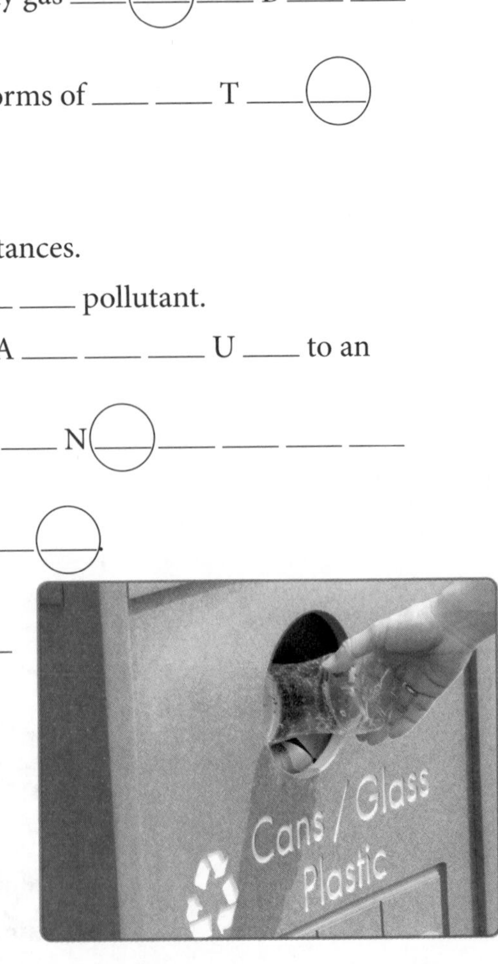

name ______________________

section ____________ date ____________

18c Estimates

Introduction

The population of the world is a topic of great interest to politicians, scientists, and many others. To properly prepare for future needs, it is important to have accurate predictions on how many people might be on the earth in future years. There are many attempts to use these estimates to influence decision making. Sometimes these arguments use misleading statistics on how population increases might cause the loss of certain natural resources. In this exercise, you will plot population data on a graph and then estimate what the world population might be at several points in the future.

Goals

- ✓ Understand how estimates are made.
- ✓ Estimate future world population levels.
- ✓ Recognize the factors that affect the accuracy of estimates.

Materials

none

Procedure

1. Using the population figures from 1950 to 2010 that are given to you in the tables on the next page, plot each point on the graph below. Since the graph provides horizontal lines only for every billion, you will need to estimate where to place each data point. For instance, if the figure for a certain year is 6.5 billion, you should mark it halfway between the 6 and the 7. A figure of 4.2 should be about two-tenths of the way between the 4 and the 5.
2. After you have plotted the values from 1950 to 2010, connect the points to form a continuous line.
3. Next, extend your line as far as 2035, attempting to follow the direction the line is heading. If your original line seems to be a straight one, you might want to use a ruler or other straight edge to complete it. If your line seems be curving, you should probably sketch it freehand.

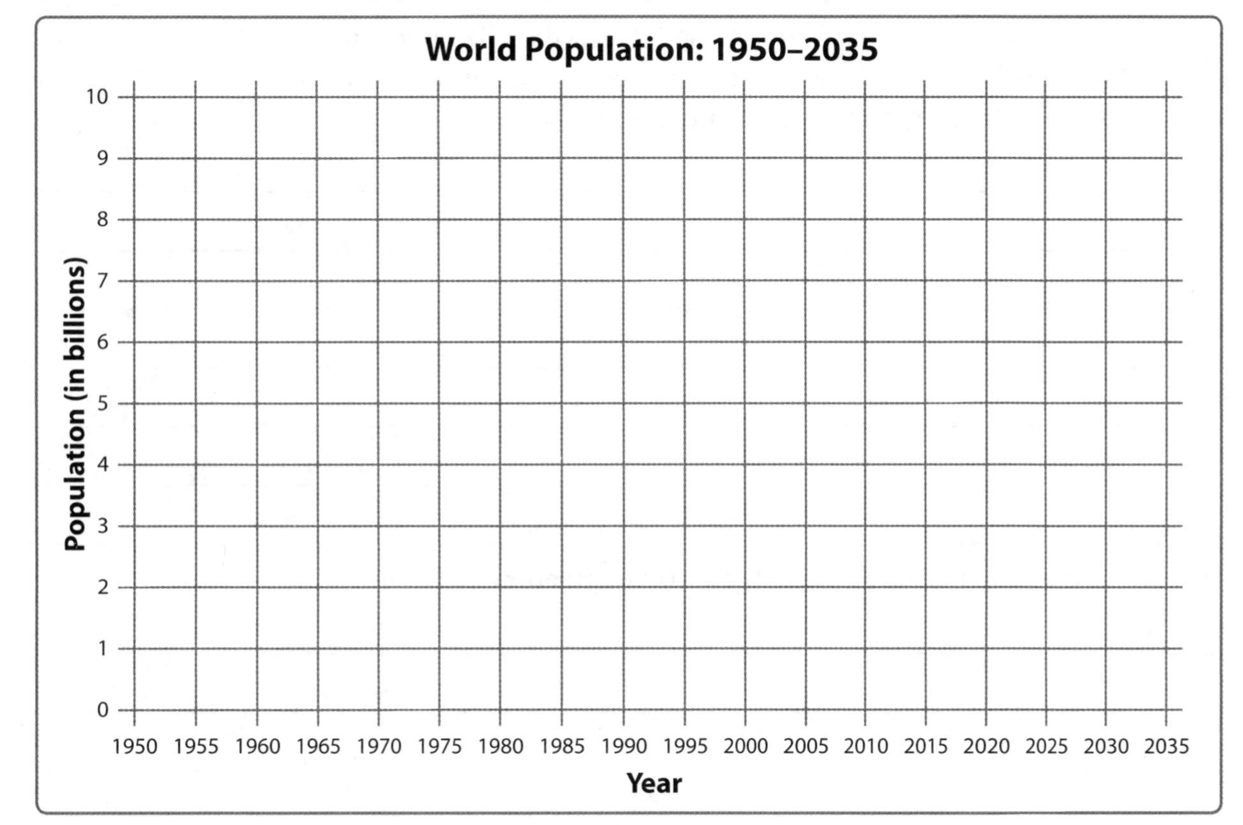

4. Based on your line estimate, record your estimates for the world population for the years 2015–2035 in the table below. Here is a hypothetical example: if your estimated line for the year 2020 crosses the point at 9.5 billion, you would enter "9.5" in the table for the year 2020.

Year	Approximate world population in billions
1950	2.6
1955	2.8
1960	3.0
1965	3.4
1970	3.7
1975	4.1
1980	4.5
1985	4.9
1990	5.3

Year	Approximate world population in billions
1995	5.7
2000	6.1
2005	6.5
2010	6.8
2015	
2020	
2025	
2030	
2035	

5. Based on your graph, answer the following questions:
   - To the nearest year, when did the world's population reach 4 billion? __________
   - When did it reach 6 billion? __________
   - What was the approximate population in 1987? __________
   - What was the approximate population in 2004? __________
   - When did it reach 7 billion? __________

Going Beyond

1. Suppose you had to find out if the world population increased at the same rate from 2000 to 2005 that it did from 1960 to 1965. How would you find the answer? (Hint: The following formula may help you: percentage of increase = [(present value – past value) ÷ past value] × 100%.)

2. What factors will influence the rate at which the world population increases?

name ____________________

section __________ date __________

18d Recycling Paper

Introduction

Recycling materials is one way that we can be good stewards of the resources God has given us. In this lab, you will model the recycling of paper.

Goals

✓ Demonstrate how paper is recycled.
✓ Make recycled paper.

Materials

wood frame
mesh screen (window screen)
staple gun and staples
paper to be recycled (newspaper)
blender
water
large dishpan
piece of cloth (or blotting paper)
large sponge
heavy object such as a phone book (optional)
clothes iron (optional)

Procedure

1. Obtain the screen frame provided by your teacher. It should be smaller than the dishpan.
2. Cut or tear an amount of paper equal to a two-page spread of a newspaper into squares that are approximately 2 cm (1 in.).
3. Place the torn paper into a blender with 1000 mL (1 qt) of water, and blend it until it becomes a cloudy liquid rather than wet, stringy bits of recognizable paper (15–30 seconds). This recycles the paper back into pulp.
4. Pour the pulp into the dishpan. Continue making pulp until the dishpan is filled to within 8 cm (about 3 in.) of the top.
5. Stir the pulp in the dishpan with your hands. You may need to add water if the pulp seems thick.
6. Hold the screen frame with both hands (screen side toward you). In one motion, lower it vertically into the pulp in the dishpan and then position it horizontally in the pulp. (See diagram.)
7. Holding the screen frame horizontally, lift it straight up out of the pulp. Wiggle the frame slightly while lifting to evenly distribute the pulp on the screen. A layer of pulp will be deposited on the screen. Steps 6 and 7 should take 10–30 seconds, depending on how much pulp is in the water and how thick you want your paper to be.
8. Allow the screen to drain over the dishpan for 15–30 seconds. You may tilt it slightly to help the water drain.
9. Lay a piece of cloth over the screen frame, and then flip the frame and cloth upside down. (The layer of pulp should be between the cloth and screen.)
10. Press down on the screen with the sponge to absorb water from the recycled piece of paper.

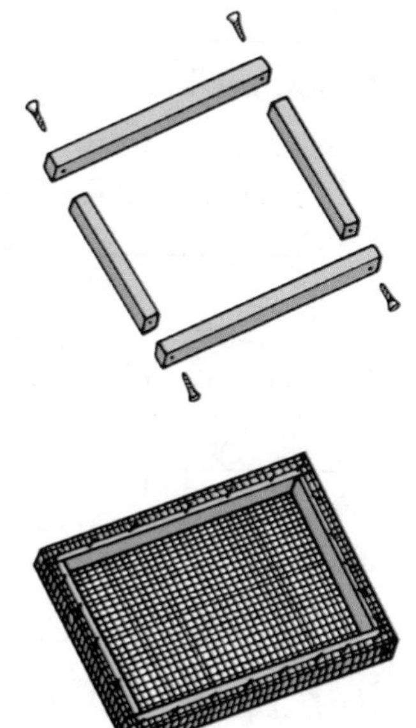

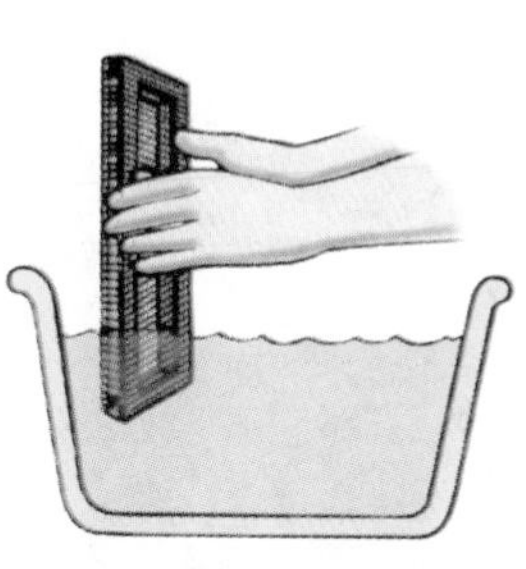

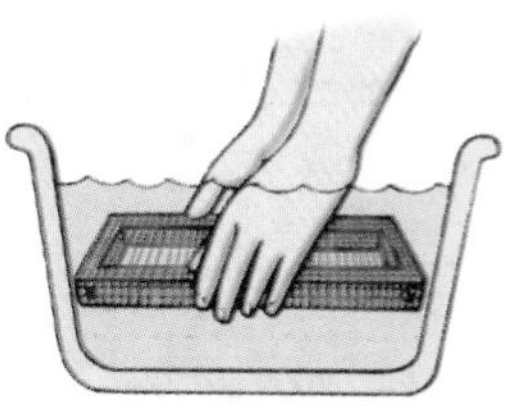

11. Carefully lift the screen frame from the recycled paper. The paper should adhere to the cloth instead of the screen. Then carefully peel the paper from the cloth.
12. There are two general ways to dry your recycled paper.
    - Sandwich your paper between two pieces of dry cloth. Put a heavy weight such as a phone book on top and let the paper dry for a day or two. Several such sandwiches can be stacked together and weighted by the same heavy weight.
    - Iron your paper with a clothes iron on an ironing board. Be sure not to use the steam setting on the iron.
13. When cleaning up, do not pour leftover pulp down the drain. Pour it through the screen frame or a sieve to remove most of the pulp from the water. This pulp can be saved for later use or discarded.

Summing Up

1. How do you think the pulp you made differs from the pulp used to make brand-new paper? How are they similar?

    ____

    ____

    ____

2. How do the characteristics of the paper you made differ from the original paper you recycled?

    ____

    ____

    ____

3. How might the large-scale production of recycled paper cause pollution?

    ____

    ____

    ____

4. What recycled paper products have you seen in use?

    ____

    ____

    ____

Going Beyond

When making the pulp, include pieces of other materials in the mix. Onion skins, short threads, and crumbled leaves make good additions.

Application

name ____________________

section __________ date __________

19a Human Skin

Directions

Fill in the missing letters in the following statements. The circled letters form a phrase that tells one of the most important functions of the skin.

1. The fluid secreted by sweat glands is called ___ ___ ___ ___ (___) ___ ___ A ___ ___ ___ ___.
2. The ___ ___ ___ D ___ (___) ___ ___ ___ is the outer layer of skin, which continuously sheds dead cells.
3. The body adjusts the amount of ___ ___ (___) O ___ in the skin to help control body temperature.
4. Intense heat or prolonged friction can cause a ___ L ___ ___ (___) ___ ___ to form.
5. The ___ (___) ___ ___ I ___ is the inner, thicker layer of the skin.
6. An area of thick, tough epidermis that protects the skin is a (___) ___ ___ ___ ___ S.
7. The yellowish pigment found in the skin is ___ ___ ___ ___ (___) E ___ ___.
8. ___ ___ L ___ ___ (___) ___ is the dark brown pigment that colors the skin.
9. The layer of loosely arranged fat cells and fibers below the skin is the ___ U ___ ___ ___ ___ ___ ___ E (___) ___ ___ layer.
10. A darkening of the skin that is caused by a buildup of melanin is a ___ A (___).
11. Blood vessels in the skin contract and the pores of the sweat glands close when the body is ___ (___) L ___.
12. Hair develops from cells in the hair (___) ___ L ___ ___ ___ ___ ___ ___.
13. Your skin is a major part of your ___ ___ ___ ___ G ___ ___ ___ ___ ___ ___ ___ (___) system.
14. The hair and skin are kept soft, flexible, and water-resistant by the (___) I ___ produced by glands in the skin.
15. Overexposure to ultraviolet rays results in a ___ (___) ___ B ___ ___ ___.

A major function of skin is the

___ ___ ___ ___ ___ ___ ___ ___ ___ ___   ___ ___   ___ ___ ___.
1 2 3 4 5 6 7 8 9 10   11 12   13 14 15

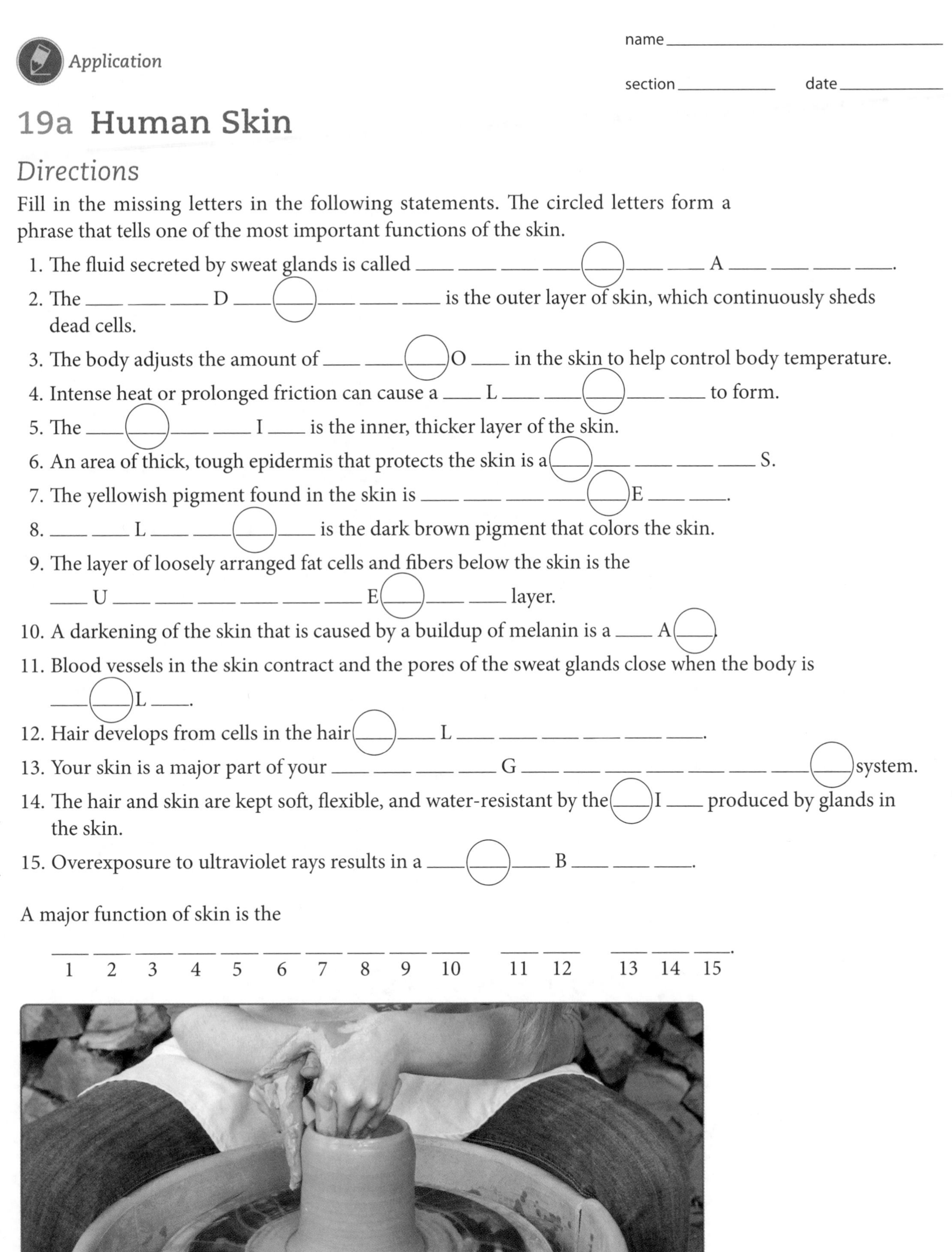

Application

name ______________________

section ____________ date ____________

19b The Skeletal System

Part 1: Bones

Directions

Label the bones numbered in the diagram below.

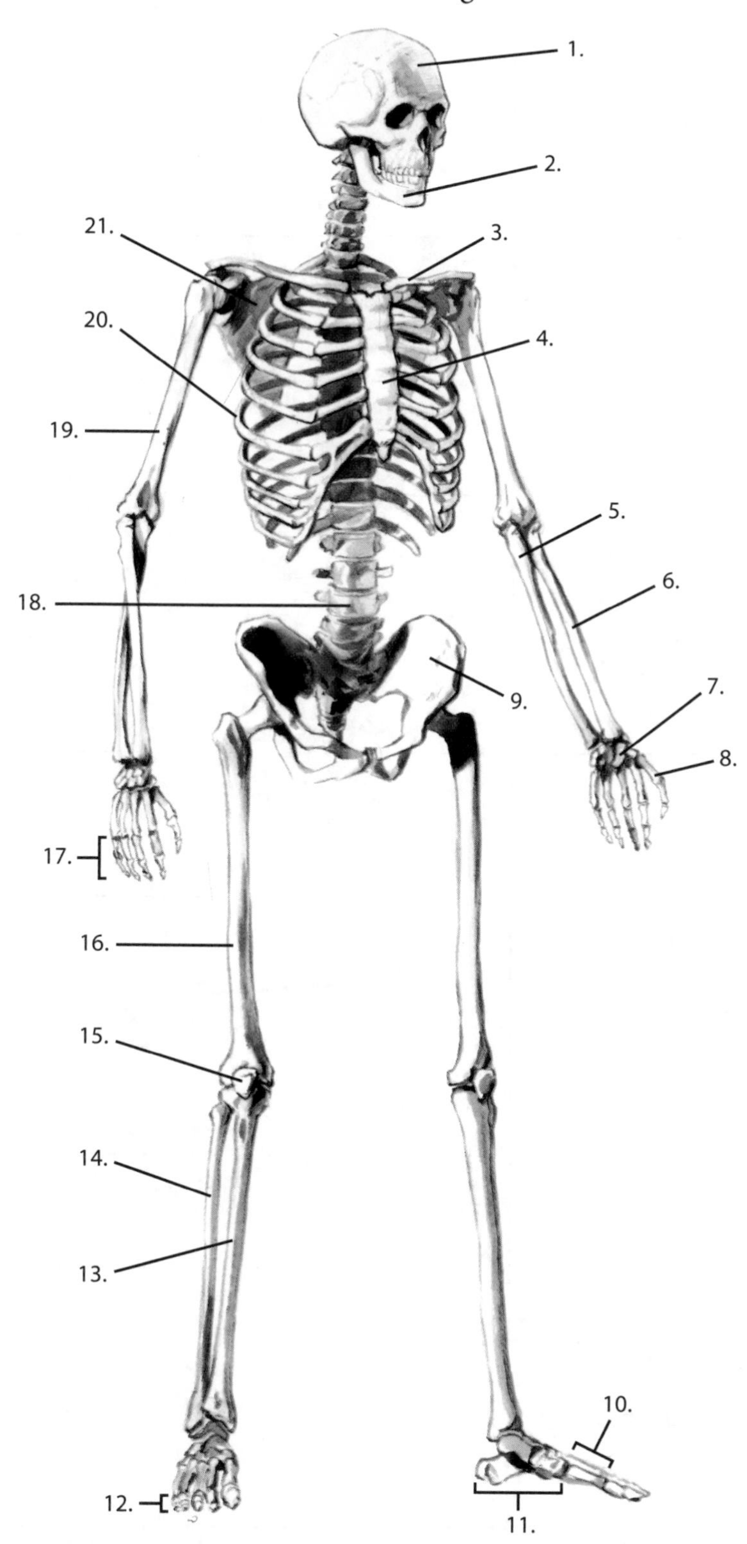

1. skull
2. mandible
3. clavicle
4. sternum
5. ulna
6. radius
7. carpal
8. metacarpal
9. pelvis
10. metatarsals
11. tarsals
12. phalanges
13. tibia
14. fibula
15. patella
16. femur
17. phalanges
18. vertabrae
19. humerus
20. rib
21. scapula

Part 2: Joints

Directions

Below is a series of diagrams of various movements. In the space provided, tell what type of joint is responsible for each action and which bones form the joint responsible for the movement.

Diagram	Type of joint	Bones forming the joint
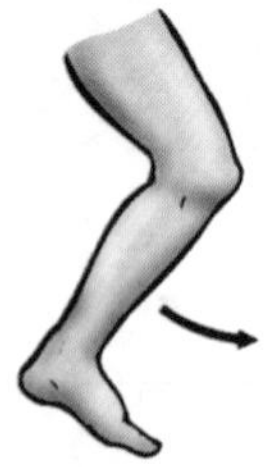	1. hinge	femur & tibia
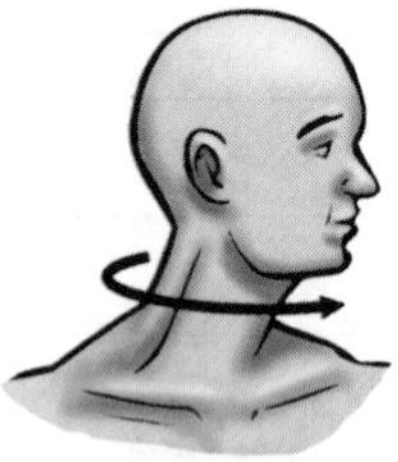	2. pivot	1st two vertebra
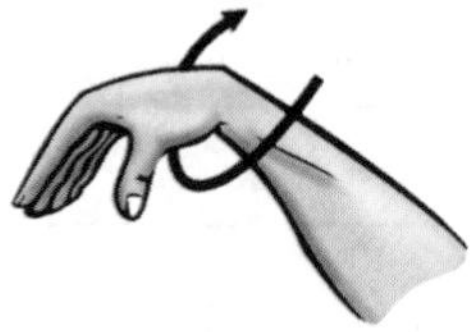	3. gliding	carpals
	4. ball and socket	pelvis & femur
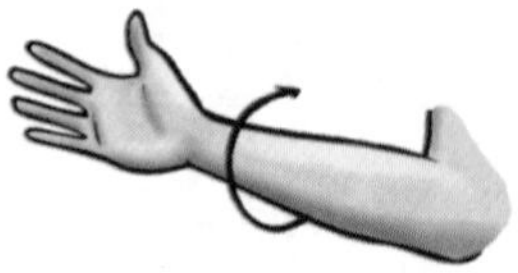	5. pivot	radius & ulna
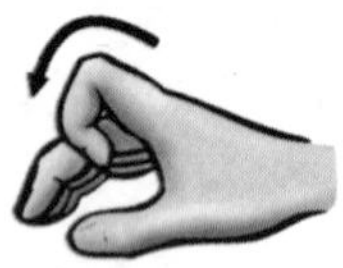	6. hinge	phalanges

Application

name ____________________

section __________ date __________

19c The Muscular System

Directions

Below is a series of diagrams of various actions and a list of muscles. Match the action with the muscle most responsible for the action by writing the muscle name in the space provided. In the diagram, color the area where the muscle is located.

biceps	gluteus	rectus femoris	trapezius
deltoid	latissimus dorsi	sartorius	triceps
external oblique	pectoralis	sternocleidomastoid	
gastrocnemius	rectus abdominis	tibialis anterior	

Application

name ____________________

section __________ date __________

19d Review

Directions

All the scrambled words listed below deal with the integumentary, skeletal, or muscular systems. Using the definitions as clues, unscramble the words and write them in the blanks.

	Scrambled word	Answer	Definition
1.	metpreiuos	periostcum	The tissue that covers bones
2.	lsitgnaem	ligaments	Tough, flexible bands that connect bones to bones
3.	tsondne	tendons	The structures that connect muscles to bones
4.	worarm	marrow	The substance found in the cavities of bones
5.	netsoso	ostcons	Tiny units that make up bone
6.	ratcigale	cartiliage	A supporting tissue that is more flexible than bone
7.	eusdf	fused	Allowing no movement
8.	sypgno	spongy	A type of bone that has many irregular spaces in it
9.	vtbererea	vertebrae	Bones of the back
10.	tcarligea aestlp	cartilage plates	Structures that permit long bones to grow in length
11.	ssniotirat	striations	The stripes seen in some muscle tissue
12.	ouepstr	posture	One of the functions of muscles
13.	revshi	shiver	A muscle movement that creates heat for the body
14.	nocratct	contract	What muscles do when nerves stimulate them
15.	aictlc daci	lactic acid	A substance produced by muscles during anaerobic cellular respiration
16.	ouayvlntr	voluntary	Muscle actions that you have control over
17.	eeoslktn	skeleton	All the bones of the body
18.	iouanvlntry	involuntary	Muscle actions that you have no control over
19.	osomht	smooth	Muscle tissue that lacks striations
20.	areht	heart	An organ that is made of involuntary striated muscle tissue

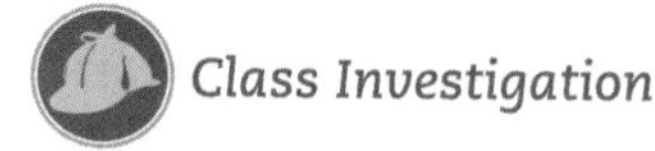

name ____________________

section __________ date __________

19e Structure of the Skin

Introduction

The skin is a major part of your integumentary system. It is very easy to take your skin for granted. But skin is actually quite complex, and it has many important functions. In this lab, you'll observe human skin under the microscope to learn about its structures.

Goal

✓ Observe and learn about the structures of the skin.

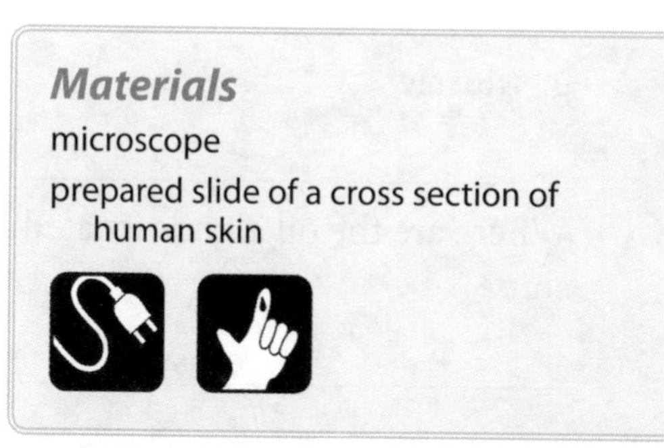

Procedure

Obtain and set up your microscope. Focus your microscope on the slide of human skin. In your field of view, the epidermis should be toward the top, and the subcutaneous layer should be toward the bottom.

1. Find and observe the epidermis.
   - Where is the epidermis?

     ____

     ____
   - Describe the epidermis.

     ____

     ____
   - What type of tissue is the epidermis made of?

     epithelial ☐ muscle ☐ connective ☐ nervous ☐
   - What substance fills epidermal cells before they die?

     melanin ☐ keratin ☐ osteon ☐
2. Find and observe the dermis.
   - Where is the dermis?

     ____
   - Look for the following structures in the dermis. If you can find them, describe their appearance. Leave the lines blank for those you cannot find.

     a. Hair

     ____

     b. Hair follicle

     ____

     c. Blood vessel

     ____

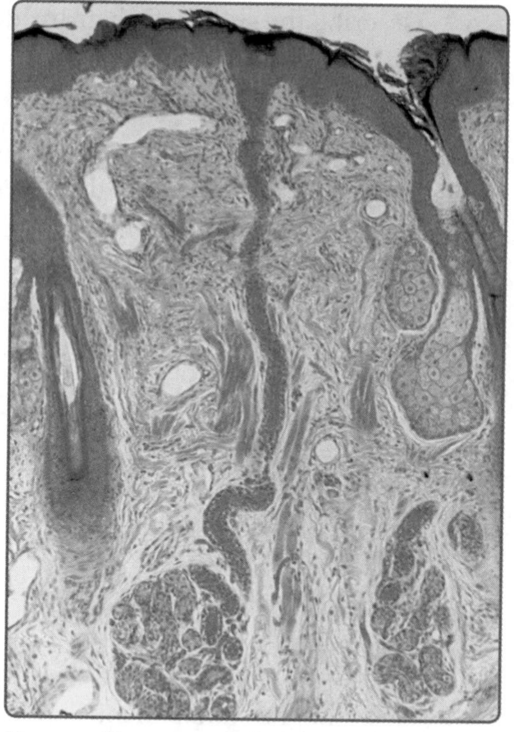

Human skin, cross section, 270×

d. Oil gland

____

e. Sweat gland

____

f. Nerve ending

____

g. Muscle

____

- Where are the oil glands located in relation to the hair follicles? What is the significance of this relationship?

____

____

- Describe the shape of a hair inside the follicle.

____

____

- Pull a hair out of your scalp. Does the end of the hair from your scalp resemble the end of the hair you observed through the microscope? yes ☐ no ☐

  If not, how does it differ?

____

____

- What type of tissue is the dermis mostly made of?

  epithelial ☐ muscle ☐ connective ☐ nervous ☐

3. Find and observe the subcutaneous layer.
   - Where is the subcutaneous layer?

   ____

   - Describe the subcutaneous layer in comparison to the dermis and epidermis.

   ____

   ____

   - What are the two main structures that make up the subcutaneous layer? (Select two.)

     keratin ☐ fibers ☐ oil ☐ fat ☐

   - What structures can you find in the subcutaneous layer?

   ____

   ____

name ______________________

section ____________ date ____________

19f Observing a Beef Bone

Introduction

The structures of a long bone are easily seen on a fresh beef bone. Refer to page 423 of your textbook as you complete this investigation.

Goal

✓ Observe and learn the structures of a bone.

Materials

fresh beef bone

Procedure

Carefully observe a beef bone and answer the questions as you make your observations. When you are asked to describe a structure, give as much of the following information as you can:

- color, shape, and texture
- firmness (Is it hard or soft?)
- anything else you can observe

1. What type of tissue makes up the bone you are observing?

   epithelial ☐ muscle ☐ connective ☐ nervous ☐

2. Locate the periosteum on your specimen.
   - Describe the periosteum.

     ____

   - What is the function of the periosteum?

     ____

   - What structures attach to the periosteum?

     ____

3. Locate the bone marrow on your specimen. You will need to look at the end of the bone where the cut was made.
   - Describe where the bone marrow is and what it looks like.

     ____

     ____

   - What are the two types of bone marrow?

     ____

   - Describe the structure and function of each type of bone marrow.

     ____

     ____

     ____

4. Locate any ligaments and tendons that are present on your specimen.
   - What is the difference between a ligament and a tendon?

     ____

     ____

   - How are ligaments and tendons similar?

     ____

     ____

5. Look for any openings and grooves along the surface of the bone. What is their function?

   ____

   ____

   ____

6. Describe any other structures that you can locate on your specimen.

   ____

   ____

   ____

   ____

   ____

   ____

name ______________________

section __________ date __________

19g Heat from Muscles

Goal

✓ Demonstrate that muscle contractions produce heat.

Materials

strip thermometers (2)
dumbbell or similar weight
stopwatch or watch with a second hand

Introduction

Your muscular system has many functions besides allowing you to move. One function is to help maintain a steady temperature for your body. In this lab, you will see that muscle contraction produces heat.

Procedure

1. Choose a student to sit where everyone can see him. He should wear a short-sleeved shirt or roll up his sleeves.
2. Put one strip thermometer on each arm, over his biceps. Allow about 15 seconds for the thermometers to indicate the correct temperature. Record these initial temperatures in the table below.
3. Choose one arm to be the exercised arm. With this arm the student should lift and lower the weight at a constant rate of about once every second. The other arm should remain motionless.
4. After 30 seconds, record the temperature of each arm. It is not necessary to stop the lifting and lowering to record the temperature.
5. Continue taking temperature readings every 30 seconds for several minutes or until the student's arm is too tired to continue.

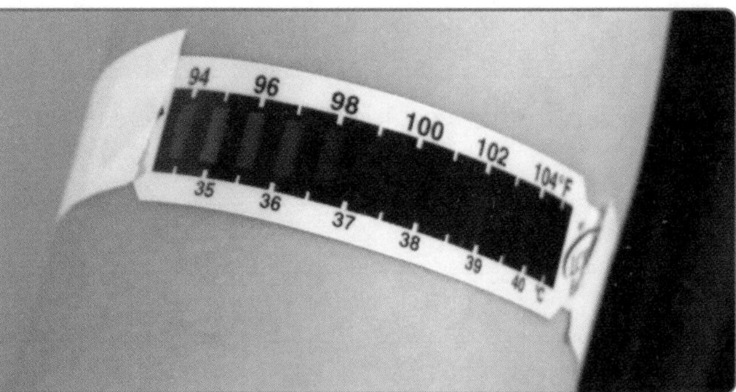

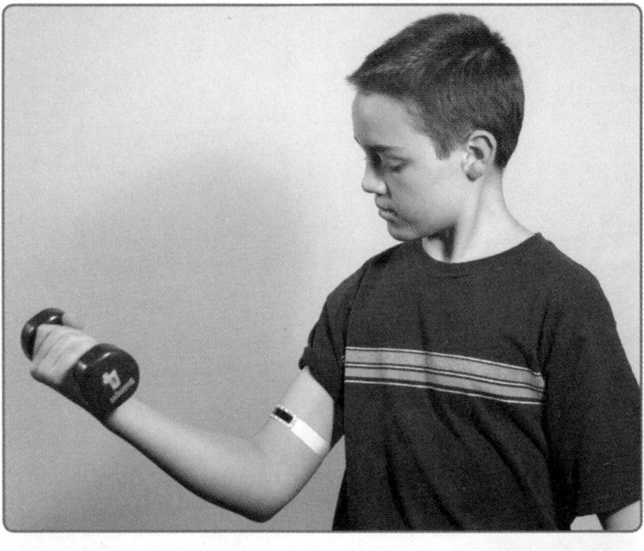

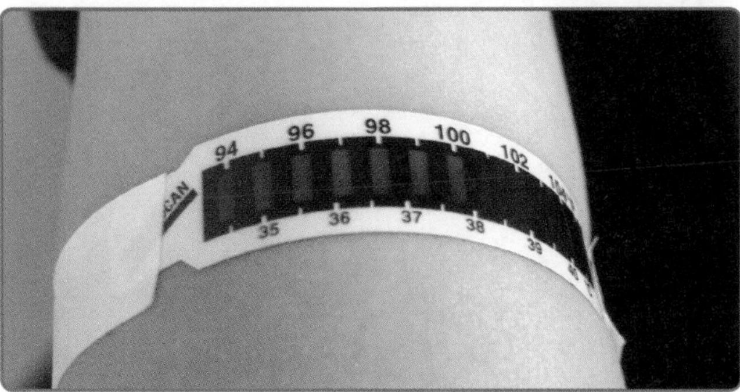

Arm Temperature Data

Time (sec)	Temperature of exercised arm	Temperature of unexercised arm
initial	94	94
30		
60		
90		
120		
150		
180		
210		
240		

Summing Up

1. Did the temperature of the exercised arm increase? Why do you think this did or did not happen?

2. Did the temperature of the unexercised arm increase? Why do you think this did or did not happen?

3. Based on what you learned in this investigation, why is shivering beneficial?

name ____________________

section __________ date __________

19h The Structure of Bones and Muscles

Goal

✓ Observe the microscopic structures of bone and muscle.

Materials

microscope

prepared slide of a cross section of dry, ground human bone

prepared slide of human skeletal muscle

Introduction

In this lab, you will practice your microscope skills as you observe the microstructure of human bone and muscle.

Procedure

Obtain and set up your microscope.

Bone

Focus your microscope on a prepared slide of human bone.

- Before the bone was made into a slide, all the cell cytoplasm and blood vessels were removed. All that you will see are the hard, "bony" structures.
- Examine the slide and compare it to the material on page 423 of your textbook. You may need to use high power in order to see some of the structures clearly.
- Name and describe the various structures that you observe.

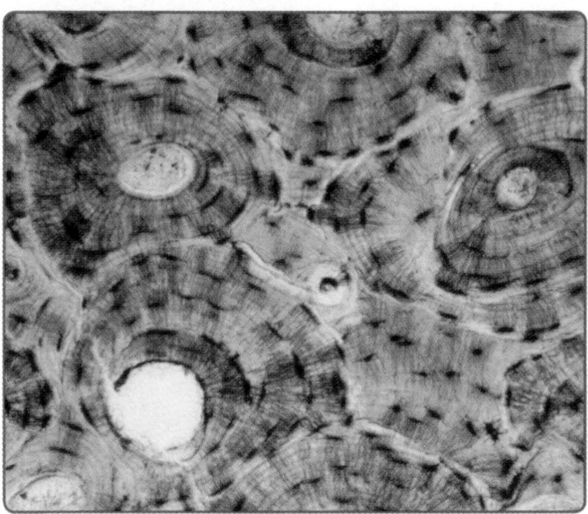

Human bone, 400×

- What is the name for one unit of bone?
- Where within a unit of bone is the blood vessel located?
- What minerals make bones strong?
- What portion of a bone is living? What is nonliving?

Muscle

Focus your microscope on a prepared slide of human muscle.

- Examine the slide and compare it to the material on page 428 of your textbook. You may need to use high power in order to see some of the structures clearly.
- What type of muscle are you observing? Check the proper box in each pair.

  voluntary ☐ involuntary ☐

  striated ☐ smooth ☐
- Name and describe the various structures that you see.

  ____

  ____

  ____
- Where in the human body would the muscle tissue you are observing most likely be found?

  in the heart ☐ in the stomach ☐ in the biceps ☐
- There are two other types of muscles besides the one you just observed. Give the following information for these two muscle types.

Name	Location	Function	Striated or nonstriated?	Voluntary or involuntary?

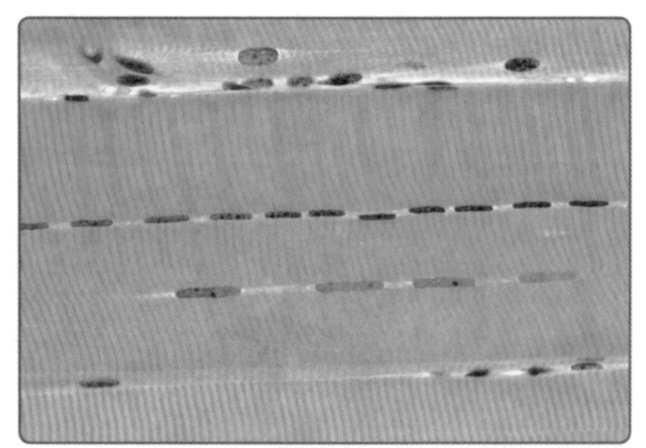
Human skeletal muscle, 1600×

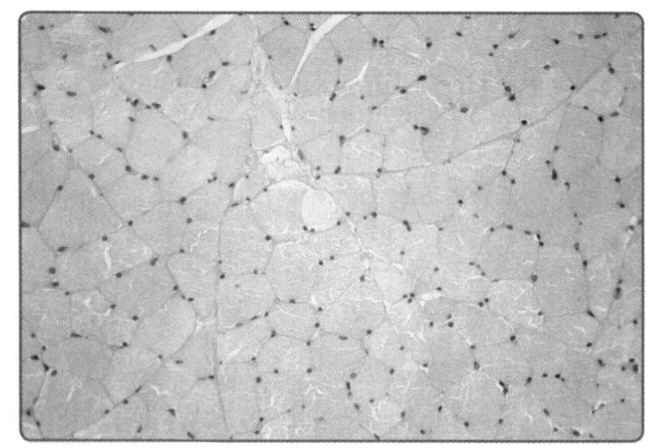
Human skeletal muscle, 64×

Application

name ______________________

section ____________ date ____________

20a The Heart

Part 1: Structure of the Heart

Directions

Supply the missing terms for each definition. Then in the blanks in the diagram, write the number of each term that indicates the proper structure in the diagram.

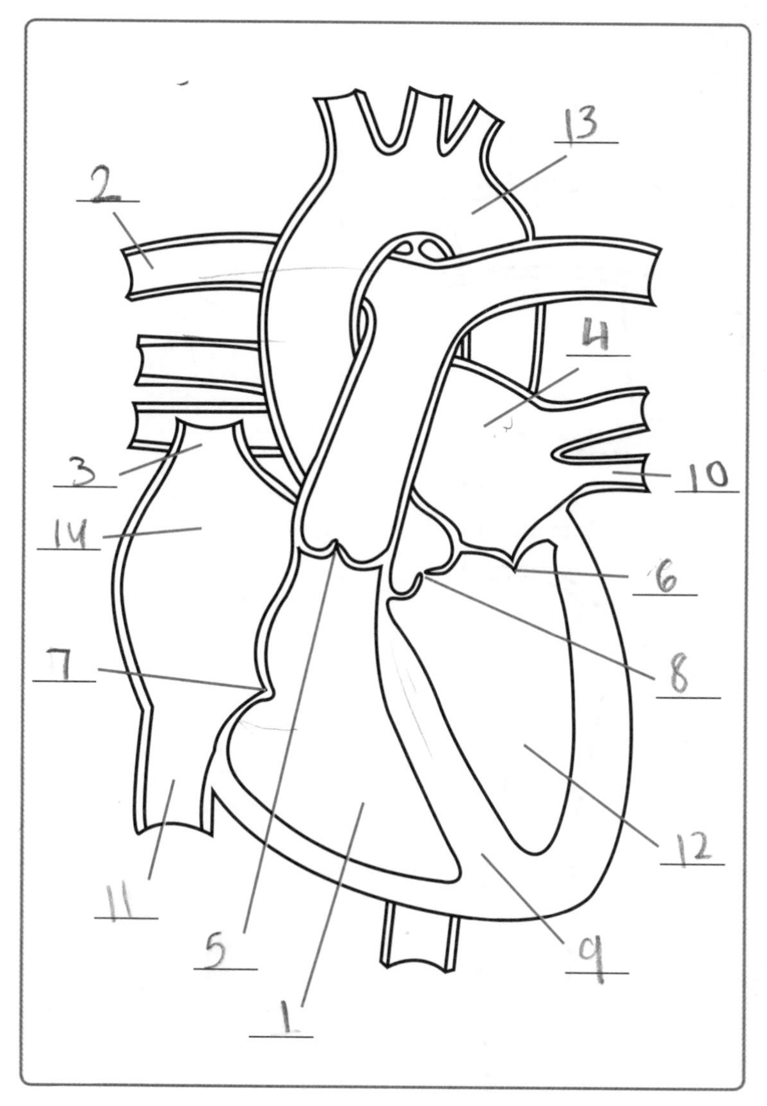

1. right ventricle
(pumps blood to the lungs)
2. pulmonary artery
(carries deoxygenated blood to the lungs)
3. superior vena cava
(brings blood from the upper parts of the body to the heart)
4. left atrium
(receives oxygenated blood from the lungs)
5. right semilunar valve
(allows blood to leave the right ventricle)
6. Left AV valve
(prevents blood from passing back into the left atrium)
7. right AV valve
(prevents blood from passing back into the right atrium)
8. left semilunar valve
(allows blood to leave the left ventricle)
9. septum
(separates the right and left sides of the heart)
10. pulmonary vein
(returns oxygenated blood to the heart)
11. inferior vena cava
(brings blood from the lower parts of the body to the heart)
12. left ventricle
(pumps blood into the aorta)
13. aorta
(carries oxygenated blood away from the heart to all parts of the body)
14. right atrium
(collects blood from the body)

Part 2: Path of Blood

Directions

On the diagram of the heart below, draw arrows indicating the flow of blood through the heart. There should be an arrow at each point where the blood enters or exits the heart or passes through a valve. Use one color for oxygenated blood and another color for deoxygenated blood. On the key, indicate which color you used for each type of blood.

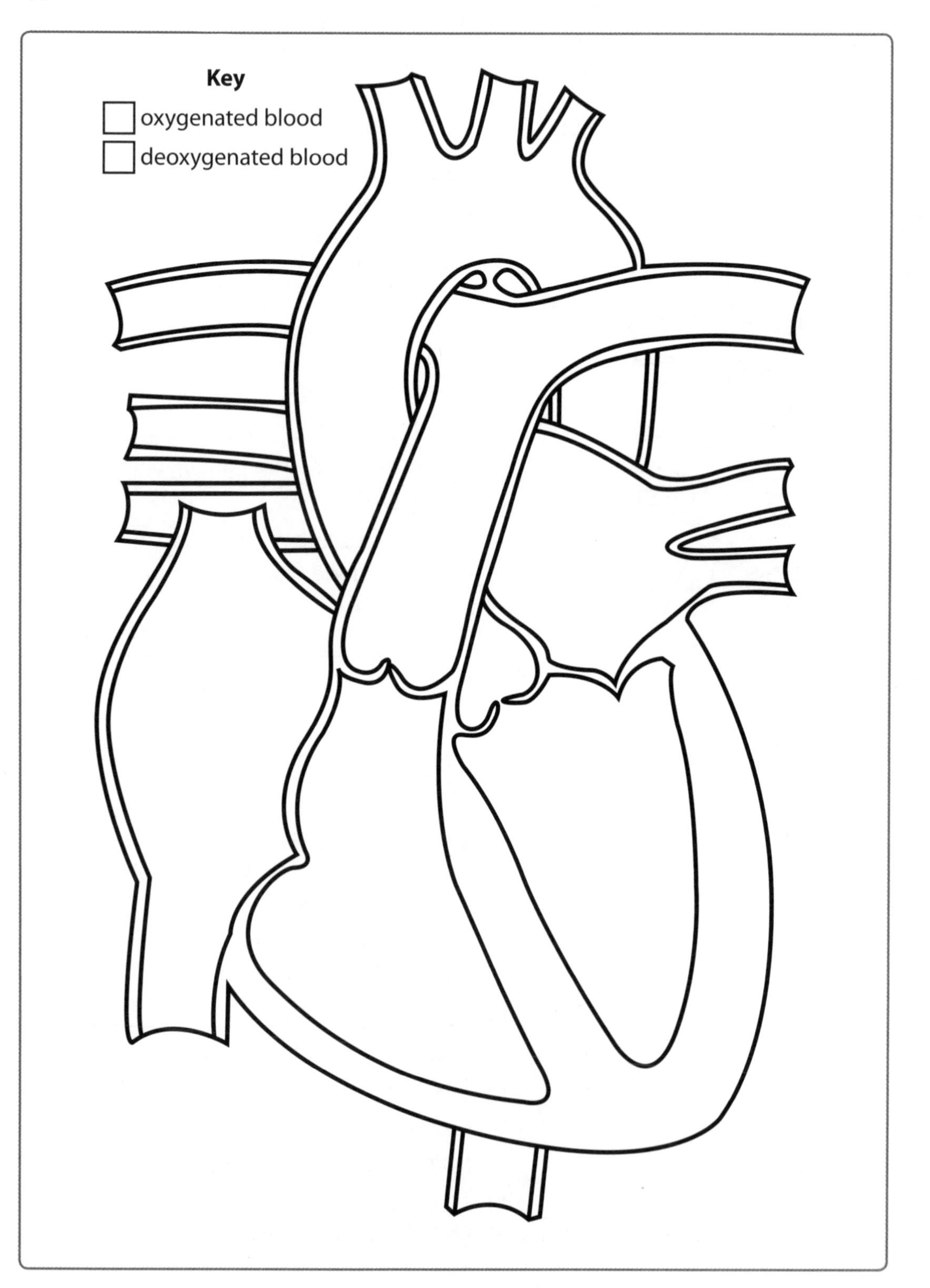

name ____________________

section __________ date __________

Application

20b The Circulatory System

Directions

Read the following statements. In the space provided, write *True* if the statement is true. If the statement is false, draw a line through the word or words that make the statement false. Then in the blank, write the word or words necessary to make the statement true.

__________ 1. Erythrocytes are shaped like disks that have been pressed in on both sides.

__________ 2. Leukocytes are smaller than erythrocytes.

__________ 3. The blockage that results when a coronary artery is clogged by clots that are floating in the bloodstream is called a coronary thrombosis.

__________ 4. Blood plasma is a straw-colored fluid that contains dissolved foods, hormones, minerals, and other materials.

__________ 5. Another name for leukocytes is red blood cells.

__________ 6. If a person's blood cannot carry enough oxygen, the person has anemia.

__________ 7. Carbon dioxide easily combines with hemoglobin at the same place that oxygen combines with hemoglobin.

__________ 8. Infections in the body cause the number of erythrocytes to increase.

__________ 9. Hemoglobin carries oxygen.

__________ 10. Atherosclerosis is the development of fatty materials inside the walls of arteries.

__________ 11. If a person's diet lacks lead, he may develop anemia.

__________ 12. Erythrocytes lack nuclei, but leukocytes have nuclei.

__________ 13. Some types of leukocytes engulf and digest foreign matter.

__________ 14. There are many more leukocytes in blood than there are erythrocytes.

__________ 15. An arrhythmia in which the heart quivers but does not pump blood is called ventricular fibrillation.

__________ 16. Platelets are irregular cell fragments that are needed to form blood clots.

__________ 17. Blood pressure is the push that blood has against artery walls.

_______________ 18. The septum separates the right side of the heart from the left.

_______________ 19. If a person's heart is beating irregularly, that person has an arrhythmia.

_______________ 20. The heart has two lower chambers called atria.

_______________ 21. A person's blood pressure normally increases as he exercises vigorously.

_______________ 22. Using a finger to push an artery against a bone will permit a person to take his blood pressure.

_______________ 23. A major cause of high blood pressure is tension.

_______________ 24. Blood moving away from the heart travels in the veins.

_______________ 25. A human body normally contains about 8–10 L of blood.

_______________ 26. Blood becomes oxygenated in the lungs and deoxygenated in other body tissues.

_______________ 27. Hemoglobin is an iron-containing pigment that makes blood appear red.

_______________ 28. Platelets are produced in bone marrow.

_______________ 29. Blood plasma is about 50% water.

_______________ 30. The right side of the heart contains deoxygenated blood.

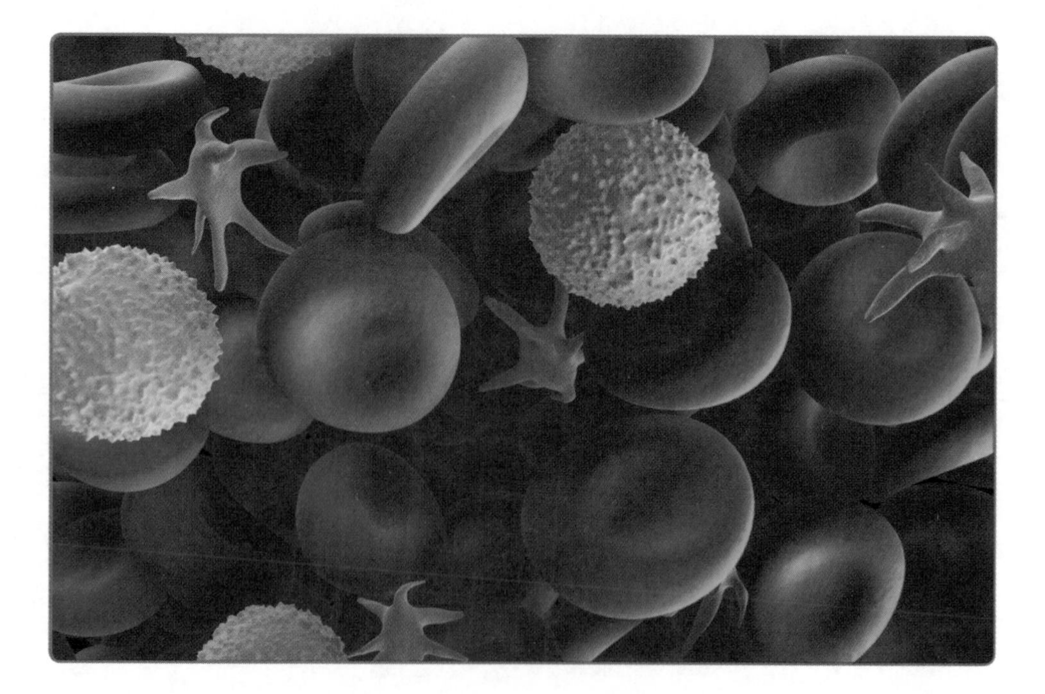

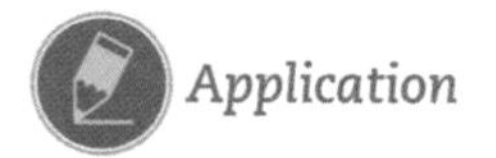

name ______________________

section ____________ date ____________

20c The Body's Defense System

Directions

Read the following statements. In the space provided, write *True* if the statement is true. If the statement is false, draw a line through the word or words that make the statement false. Then in the blank, write the word or words necessary to make the statement true.

______________ 1. A biblical worldview teaches that before the Fall, there was no death and only a few diseases.

______________ 2. The body's first line of defense is the blood plasma.

______________ 3. Inflammation is a local response to foreign invaders.

______________ 4. A fever is a decrease in the body's normal temperature.

______________ 5. The two major types of lymphocytes used in the immune system are T cells and B cells.

______________ 6. The body forms antigens, which attack disease-causing agents.

______________ 7. B cells attack and destroy foreign invaders.

______________ 8. The immune system has a memory that can respond to specific antigens.

______________ 9. An allergic response can be considered an abnormal response of the immune system.

______________ 10. If someone has an autoimmune disease, his immune system is unable to tell the difference between foreign invaders and normal body cells.

 *Application*

name ____________

section ________ date ________

20d The Excretory System

Directions

Use the clues below to choose the right words to fit in the blanks. The letters in the shaded rectangle will spell out the answer that you should put in the blanks at the bottom of the page.

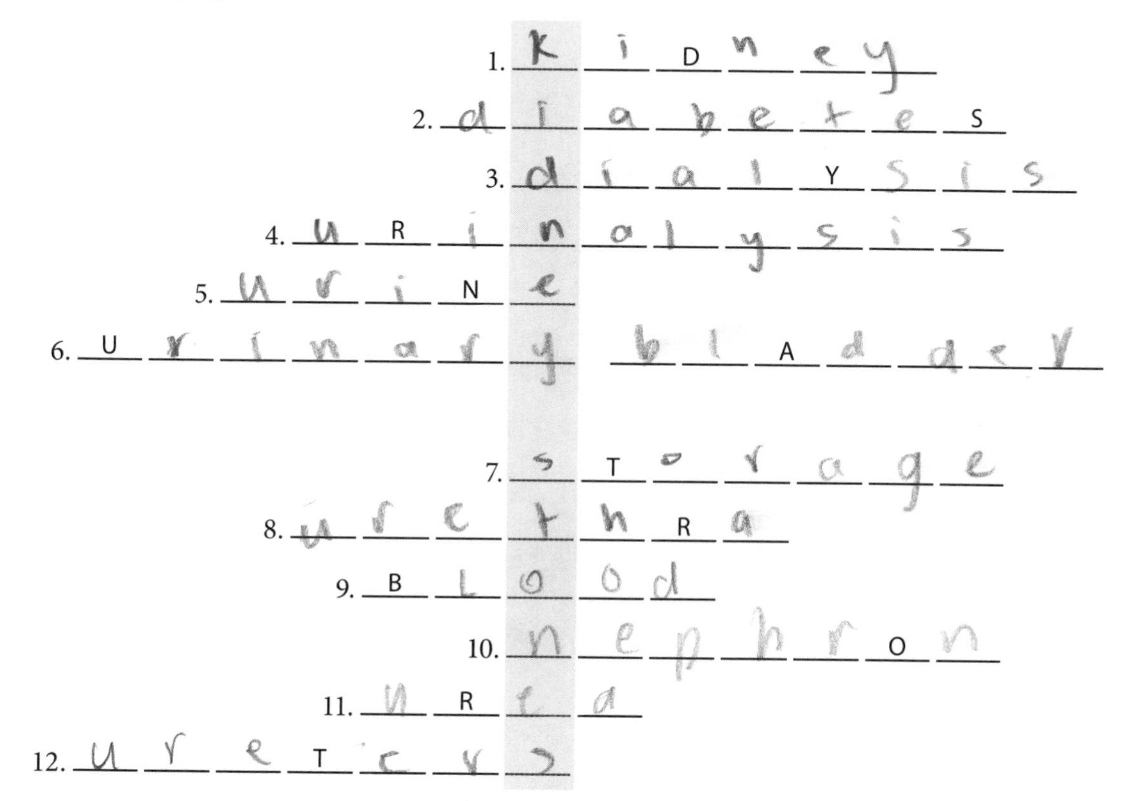

1. One of the filtering organs of the excretory system
2. A condition indicated by too much sugar in the blood and urine
3. The proper name for an artificial kidney: ______ machine
4. The test that a physician uses to determine certain properties of urine
5. The substance that is excreted by the nephron after all the useful products have been reabsorbed into the blood
6. A muscular sac that stores urine (two words)
7. The primary function of the urinary bladder
8. The tube that leads from the urinary bladder to the outside of the body
9. The substance that is filtered as it passes through the kidneys
10. A microscopic structure that filters the blood inside a kidney
11. A waste product of protein digestion that is normally found in urine
12. Tubes that carry urine from the kidneys to the urinary bladder

A common kidney disease that is painful but not usually serious is kidney stones.

name ____________________

section __________ date __________

20e Blood

Introduction

In this lab, you will study human blood under the microscope. You will also learn about some of the effects that certain diseases can have on the blood.

Goals

✓ Observe blood cells.

✓ See some of the effects that certain diseases have on the blood.

Procedure

Obtain and set up your microscope. Focus your microscope on a prepared slide of normal human blood. You will need to use high power in order to observe the blood cells clearly.

Materials

microscope

prepared slide of normal human blood

prepared slides of diseased human blood

1. Locate and observe the erythrocytes.
   - Describe their appearance.

   - Are there different types of erythrocytes? yes ☐ no ☐

     If so, describe the differences between the types you see.

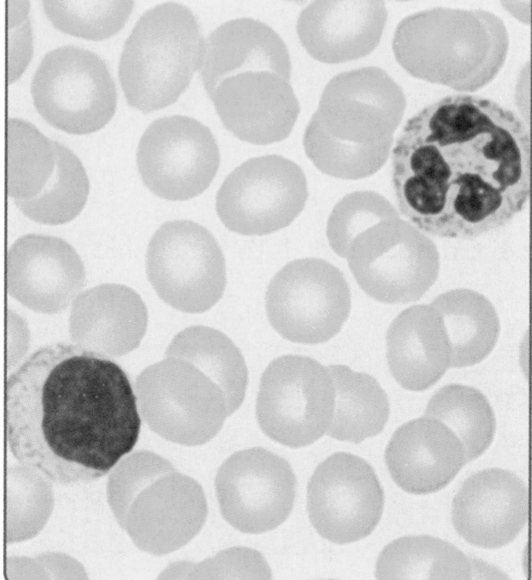

Human blood smear, 400×

   - What is the primary function of erythrocytes?

2. Locate and observe several leukocytes.
   - Describe their appearance and compare them with the erythrocytes.

- Compare the number of leukocytes to the number of erythrocytes.

  ____

- Are there different kinds of leukocytes? yes ☐ no ☐

  If so, describe the differences between the kinds you see.

  ____

  ____

  ____

- What is the primary function of leukocytes?

  ____

  ____

  ____

3. In the box provided, draw the blood cells that you are looking at under the microscope. Draw at least five erythrocytes and two leukocytes. Label your drawing.

4. Complete the following table comparing erythrocytes and leukocytes.

	Erythrocytes	Leukocytes
Color		
Size		
Shape		
Number		

5. Observe several slides of blood from people who had blood disorders. In the table below, record the name of the blood diseases you observed and describe the differences between normal blood and each diseased blood.

Blood disease	Description

Class Investigation

name ______

section ______ date ______

20f Observing a Cow Heart

Introduction

A cow heart is larger than, but similar to, a human heart. On a cow heart, you can clearly see the heart structures and easily trace the pathway of blood through the heart. Refer to pages 448–50 of your textbook as you complete this investigation.

Goals

- ✓ Observe and identify the structures of the heart.
- ✓ Trace the pathway of blood through the heart.

Materials

dissected cow heart
glass or wooden rods
large forceps
blue and red yarn

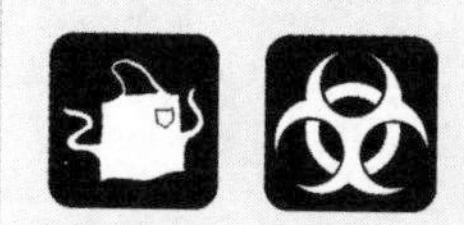

Procedure

1. Examine the outside of the cow heart.
   - What type of muscle tissue makes up the heart muscle?

     skeletal ☐ smooth ☐ cardiac ☐
   - Which terms describe the heart muscle? Select one answer from each pair.

     voluntary ☐ involuntary ☐

     striated ☐ smooth ☐
2. Locate the chambers in the cow heart. You will need to remove the top section of the heart to do this. Use the heart illustration on page 449 of your textbook as a guide.
   - Check each chamber as you locate it.

     right atrium ☐ right ventricle ☐

     left atrium ☐ left ventricle ☐

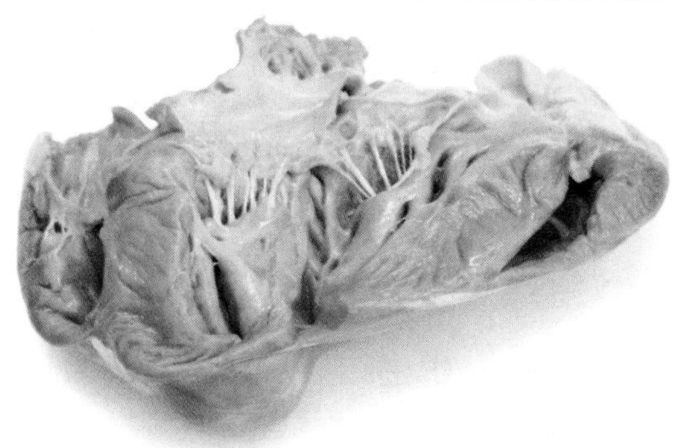

   - Which chamber(s) hold oxygenated blood? Which chamber(s) hold deoxygenated blood?

     ______

     ______
   - Notice that the wall of the left ventricle is thicker than the wall of the right ventricle. Why do you think this is so?

     ______

     ______
   - What structure separates the right side of the heart from the left side? ______
3. Locate the blood vessels and valves on the cow heart.
   - Use a blunt rod to probe into the blood vessels and see where they go. Check each vessel as you locate it.

     superior vena cava ☐ inferior vena cava ☐ pulmonary arteries ☐ pulmonary veins ☐ aorta ☐
   - Which vessels carry oxygenated blood? Which carry deoxygenated blood?

     ______

     ______

- Locate the valves in the heart. Check each valve as you locate it.

  right AV valve ☐ pulmonary semilunar valve ☐ left AV valve ☐ aortic semilunar valve ☐

- What is the function of these valves?

  ____

  ____

4. Trace the path in which the blood flows through the heart.
   - Using a blue piece of yarn, trace the path of deoxygenated blood through the heart.
   - Using a red piece of yarn, trace the path of oxygenated blood through the heart.
   - Have your teacher inspect your work.

name ____________________

section __________ date __________

20g Using a Stethoscope

Introduction

In this lab, you will use a stethoscope to listen to the sounds of your heart. Using alcohol and a tissue, clean the earplugs of the stethoscope. The earplugs should always be cleaned with alcohol and a tissue before they are put into the ears of another person. Whenever you put the earplugs of the stethoscope into your ears, be sure the diaphragm of the stethoscope does not tap against any hard object. The sound made by tapping a button or a tabletop can be very loud and can damage your ears.

Goals

- ✓ Learn how to correctly use a stethoscope.
- ✓ Listen to the sounds of your heart.
- ✓ Compare your pulse rate with your heart rate.

Materials

alcohol
tissues
stethoscope
stopwatch or clock with a second hand

Procedure

Place the earplugs of the stethoscope into your ears. Place the diaphragm of the stethoscope on another student's cheek and ask him to chew. Describe what you hear.

Spit loud noises

Listen to the sounds of your heart.

1. Place the diaphragm of the stethoscope on the center of your chest. Listen carefully.
2. Move the diaphragm of the stethoscope to the left of your sternum.
3. Move the diaphragm of the stethoscope slightly up and down to be sure it is directly over a rib.
4. Once you have found a place where you can hear your heart, listen carefully. What does it sound like?

thumbing

Determine how fast your heart beats while you are sitting quietly.

1. Sit quietly for about five minutes before doing this exercise.
2. Use the stethoscope to count the number of times your heart beats in 15 seconds. Recall that your heart makes two sounds for each beat. In other words, each "lubb-dubb" is a single beat.
3. Multiply by four the number of times your heart beats in 15 seconds. This number will tell you how many times your heart beats per minute. Record this amount in the table.
4. Repeat Steps 2 and 3 three times and, for each count, record the number of beats per minute in the table. Average your results.

Heartbeat Rate per Minute	
Count 1	60
Count 2	52
Count 3	45
Count 4	60
Average	54

54
4)217
20
17
217

Determine how fast your pulse throbs while you are sitting quietly.

1. You can feel your pulse by putting light pressure against a blood vessel that is beside a bone. Find the pulse in your neck or in your wrist by placing your fingers as illustrated in the photographs.
2. Count your pulse for 15 seconds and then multiply the number by four. This number tells you your pulse rate for one minute. Record this number in the table.
3. Repeat Step 2 three times and, for each count, record the number of beats per minute in the table. Average your results.

Pulse Rate per Minute	
Count 1	40
Count 2	44
Count 3	36
Count 4	40
Average	47

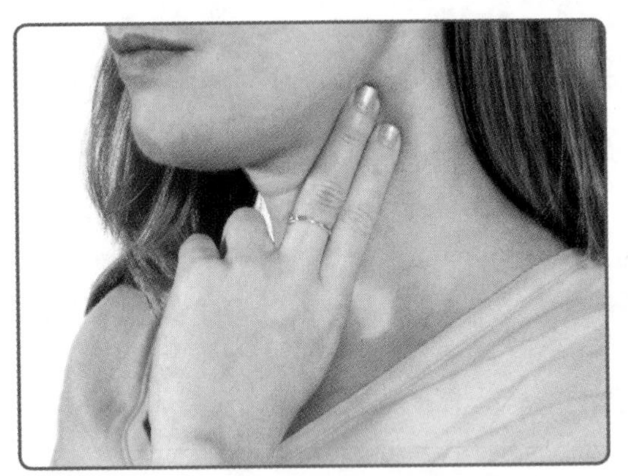
Finding the carotid pulse

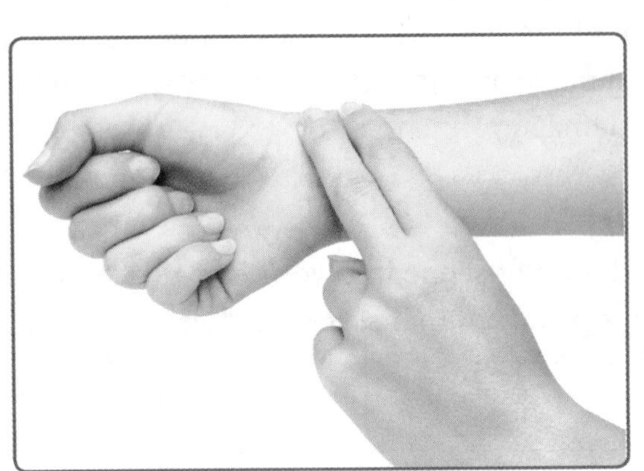
Finding the radial pulse

Summing Up

1. What is the difference between your average heartbeat rate per minute and your average pulse rate per minute?

   Pulse is slower than heartbeat

2. Should there be a noticeable difference between your heartbeat rate and your pulse rate? yes ☑ no ☐

   Why or why not?

Class Investigation

name ______________________

section ____________ date ____________

20h Increasing Heart Rate

Goals

- ✓ Determine whether heart rate is proportional to amount of exercise.
- ✓ Identify how much time the heart requires to return to its normal rate after exercise.

Materials

stopwatch or clock with a second hand

Introduction

In this lab, you will need to be able to find your pulse quickly and to measure it accurately. (See Class Investigation 20h for instructions on measuring a pulse.)

Map out a route where you and your classmates can walk and run. It should be about 134 m (440 ft) and should start and end near your classroom.

Divide your class into teams of two people each. In each team, one person should do the activities and the other should measure the pulse rate and record the results. Both people should do the Summing Up section at the end.

Each time you measure a pulse rate for this exercise, do so for 15 seconds and then multiply your answer by four to obtain the pulse rate for one minute.

Procedure

1. Lie quietly for three minutes. Record your pulse rate. _______ bpm (beats per minute)
2. Sit quietly for three minutes. Record your pulse rate. _______ bpm
3. While seated, move your arms back and forth above your head for three minutes. Record your pulse rate. _______ bpm
   - Sit quietly, checking the pulse rate periodically, until the pulse rate returns to normal. How long did you have to rest until the pulse rate became the same as the "sitting quietly" rate? _______ min _______ sec
4. Walk slowly around the mapped area. Record your pulse rate. _______ bpm
   - Rest until the pulse is the same as the "sitting quietly" rate. How long did you have to rest? _______ min _______ sec
5. Walk briskly around the mapped area. Record your pulse rate. _______ bpm
   - Rest until the pulse is the same as the "sitting quietly" rate. How long did you have to rest? _______ min _______ sec
6. Jog around the mapped area. Record your pulse rate. _______ bpm
   - Rest until the pulse is the same as the "sitting quietly" rate. How long did you have to rest? _______ min _______ sec
7. Run rapidly around the mapped area. Record your pulse rate. _______ bpm
   - Rest until the pulse is the same as the "sitting quietly" rate. How long did you have to rest? _______ min _______ sec

Summing Up

Fill out the charts by shading in the bars of the charts with the data you have obtained.

Chart A—Pulse Rate per Minute

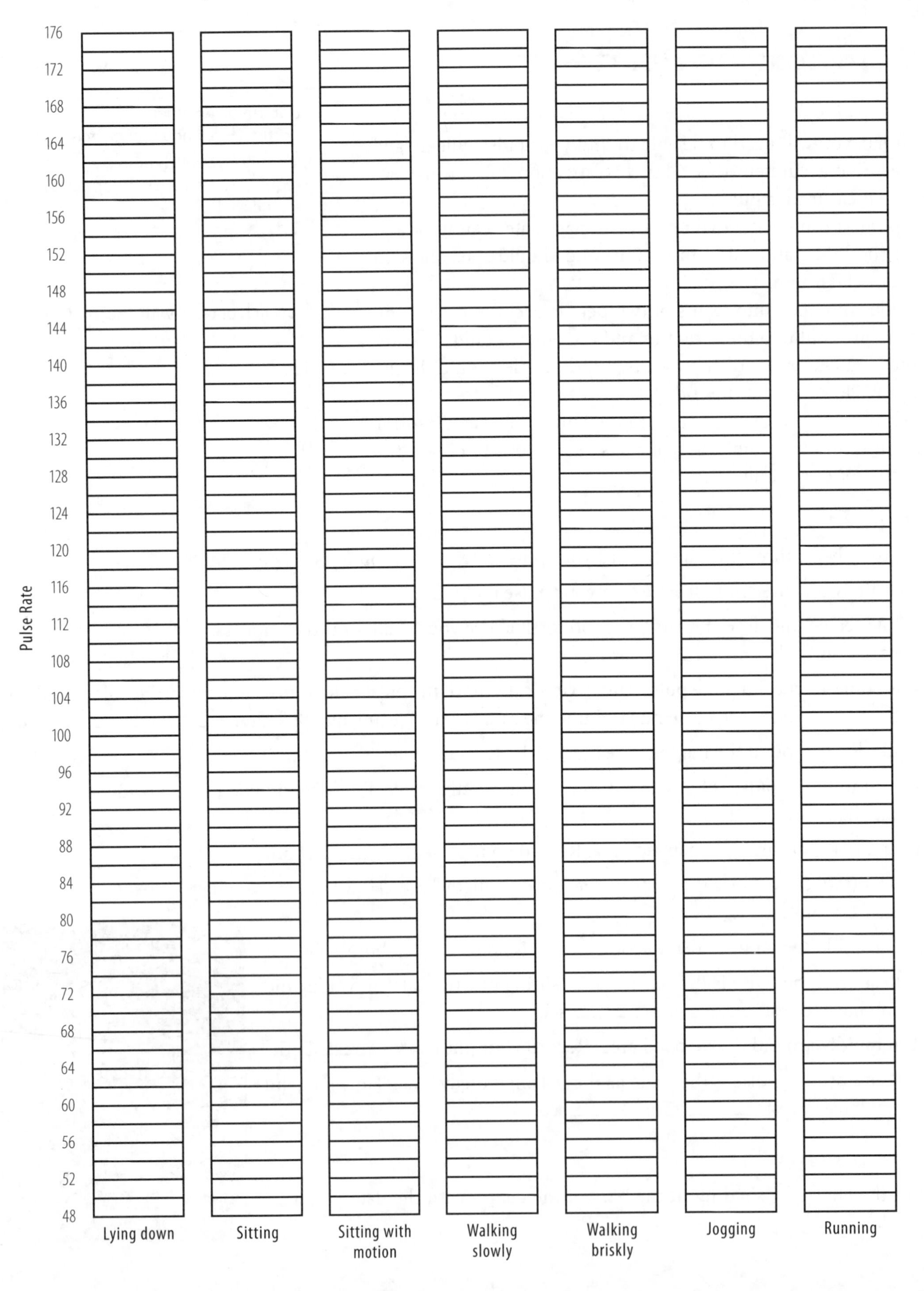

name ____________________

Chart B—Time Required for Pulse Rate to Return to Normal

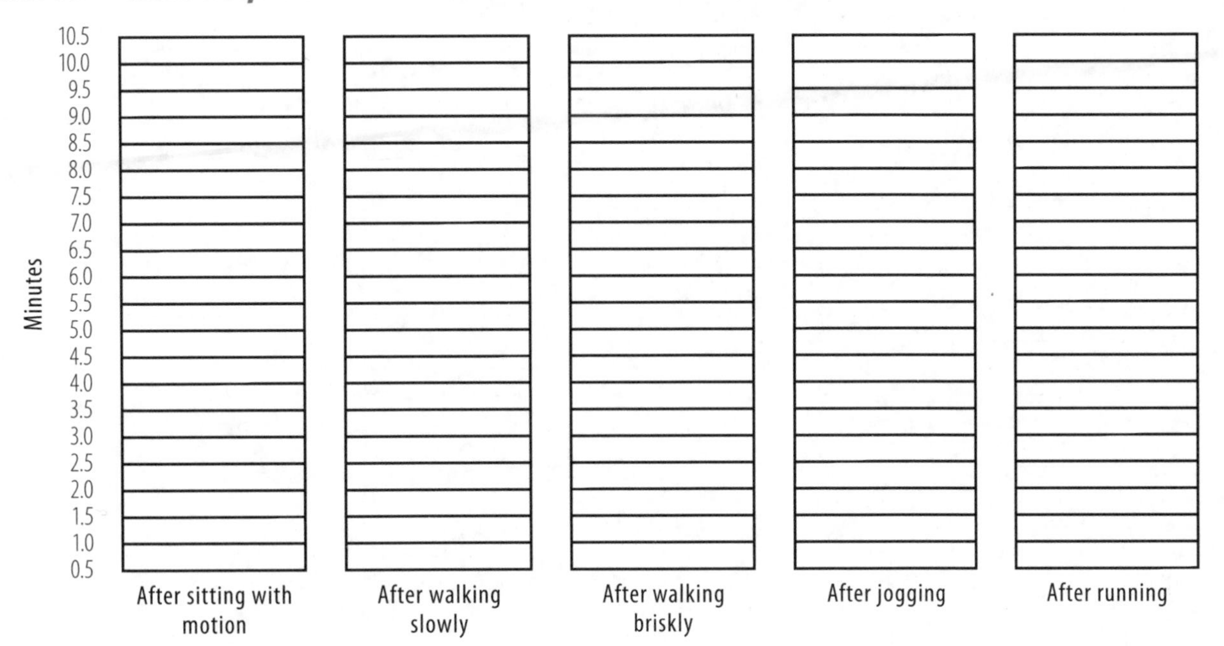

1. By comparing the charts, what are you able to determine about the relationship between pulse rate and the length of time needed for the pulse rate to return to normal?

____

____

____

____

____

2. Compare your chart to other students' charts.
   - Are they about the same? yes ☐ no ☐
   - Does any person in your class have an unusual chart? yes ☐ no ☐

     If so, what could explain the difference?

____

____

____

____

____

Application

name ____________________

section __________ date __________

21a The Respiratory System

Directions

In the space provided, describe the difference between the terms given.

1. bronchi / bronchioles

2. pharynx / larynx

3. glottis / epiglottis

4. bronchi / alveoli

5. thorax / diaphragm

6. trachea / esophagus

name ______________________

section ____________ date ____________

21b The Digestive System

Part 1: Structures of the Digestive System

Directions

Below are drawings of the human digestive system. Supply the missing terms for each definition. Then in the blanks in the diagram, write the number of each term that indicates the proper structure in the diagram. The first number has been placed on the diagram as an example.

1. ______________________ (the four pointed teeth)
2. ______________________ (the glands that produce saliva to lubricate food and begin chemical digestion)
3. ______________________ (the structure that moves food around in the mouth)
4. ______________________ (the pouch in which food is mixed with digestive juices)
5. ______________________ (the eight front teeth used for biting)
6. ______________________ (the twelve rear teeth used for grinding)
7. ______________________ (the structure that extends from the back of the mouth to the esophagus and the larynx)
8. ______________________ (the eight teeth with broad tops for crushing food)
9. ______________________ (the structure that receives food and begins mechanical and chemical digestion)
10. ______________________ (the accessory organ that produces insulin and enzymes for digestion)
11. ______________________ (the organ that stores bile until needed for digestion)
12. ______________________ (the small, tubular organ attached to the large intestine)
13. ______________________ (the tube that absorbs water and minerals)
14. ______________________ (the organ that produces bile)
15. ______________________ (the organ in which most chemical digestion and absorption occurs)
16. ______________________ (the muscular tube that leads to the stomach)

Part 2: Process of Digestion

Directions

Below is a list of scrambled words. Unscramble the words and write them in the blanks. Then match them to the definitions given below.

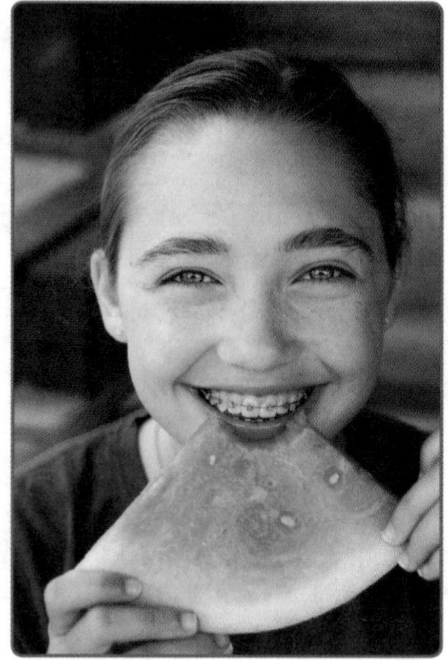

A. stucd ducts

B. iavlas saliva

C. anbosiotrp absorption

D. laptro nvie portal vein

E. sinmvtai vitamins

F. lalgrbeladd gall bladder

G. laintarmey nalac alimentary canal

H. cerlu ulcer

I. loacloh alcohol

J. pndxpaei appendix

C 1. A process that takes place primarily in the small intestine

D 2. The structure that carries blood from the digestive organs to the liver

A 3. Tiny tubes that carry the secretions of glands to the areas where they are used

F 4. The organ that stores bile

G 5. The digestive system tube that carries food completely through the body

E 6. Essential substances required for normal body functioning

I 7. A substance that the liver would try to filter out of the blood

H 8. An open sore that discharges a fluid and does not heal normally

J 9. A small, tubular organ that evolutionists once thought was vestigial

B 10. The enzyme-containing fluid secreted in the mouth

Application

name ______________________

section ____________ date ____________

21c Review

Directions

Write your responses in the spaces provided.

1. Within the body systems that you have studied so far, several changes occur as a result of vigorous exercise. Describe at least four of those changes and the purpose of each.

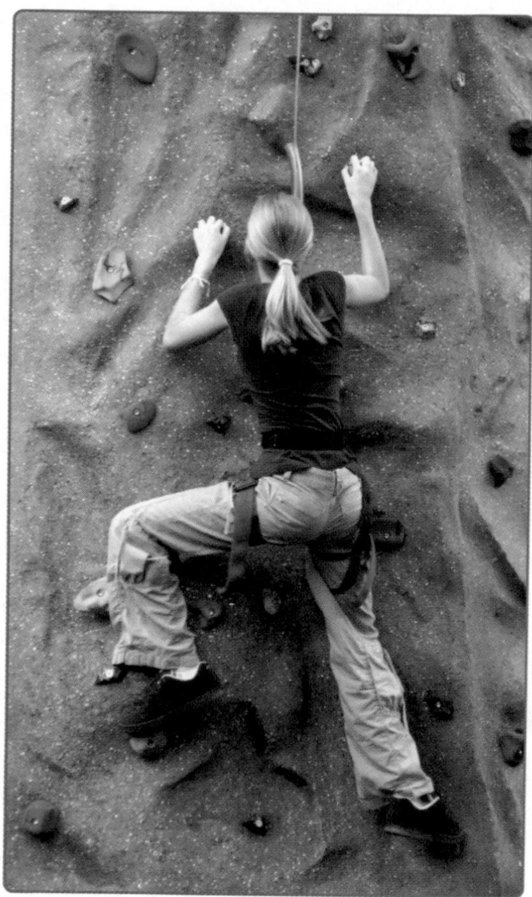

2. Why is mucus important in both the respiratory system and the digestive system?

3. List as many functions of the liver as you can.

4. Why is it important for blood from the digestive system to pass through the liver before entering the rest of the body?

5. Describe the immune system of the body. In your description be sure to use the following words: *immune*, *antibodies*, and *vaccines*.

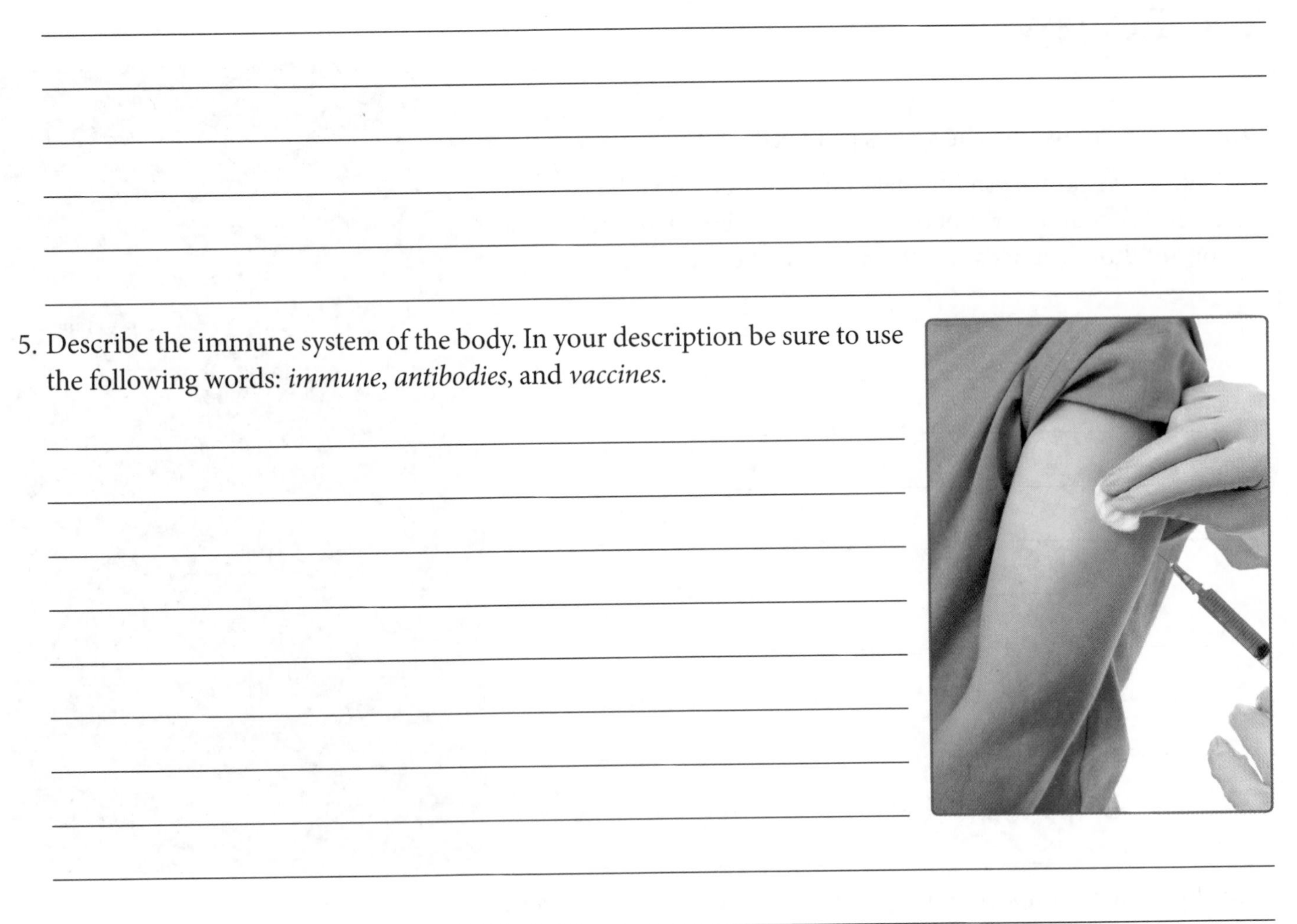

name ____________________

section ____________ date ____________

21d Respiration

Introduction

In this lab, you will perform several activities to observe the effects that various factors have on respiration. You may want to refer to page 473 of your textbook as you complete the lab.

Goals

✓ Measure your vital capacity.

✓ Observe the effects of various factors on respiration.

Materials

spirometer
a 4-gallon plastic bag
stopwatch or clock with a second hand

Procedure

Determining Vital Capacity

Your *vital capacity* is equal to the greatest amount of air that you can breathe out at one time. To determine that quantity, you will use a spirometer.

1. Take the biggest breath you can possibly take.
2. Put your mouth on the spirometer hose and breathe out all the air you possibly can.
3. Read the air volume on the spirometer, and record the volume in the table below.
4. Repeat this procedure a second time and record your results in the table.
5. Also record the results of each member of your group. (Be sure to reset the spirometer and either clean the spirometer hose or put a new mouthpiece on it before the next person uses it.)

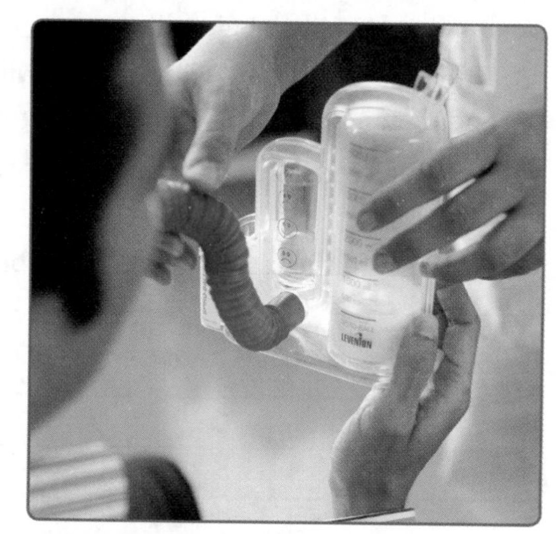

Student name	Vital capacity 1st measurement	Vital capacity 2nd measurement

Holding Your Breath

Have another member of your group time you to see how long you can hold your breath.

1. Take as big a breath as you can, and hold it for as long as you can. Keep your mouth closed and your nose pinched closed. Record your time in the table at the top of page 328.
2. Rest quietly for several minutes, and then repeat this procedure a second time and record your results in the table.
3. Also record the results of each member of your group.
4. Now blow out as much air as you can and have a group member time you as you hold your breath as long as you can. Record your time in the table.

5. Rest quietly for several minutes, and then repeat this procedure a second time and record your results in the table. Also record the results of each member of your group.

Student name	Inhalation time #1	Inhalation time #2	Exhalation time #1	Exhalation time #2

The Effect of the Air You Breathe on Your Ability to Hold Your Breath

1. Fill a plastic bag with air. Do this by holding the bag open and moving it through the air, then squeezing it at the opening to hold the air inside.
2. Breathe into the bag for 30 seconds while keeping it tightly sealed around your mouth and nose.
3. After 30 seconds and with the bag still tightly sealed around your mouth, breathe in as deeply as you can and then hold your breath while a group member times you. Record your time in the table below.
4. Rest quietly for several minutes, and then repeat this procedure a second time and record your results in the table.
5. Also record the results of each member of your group.

Student name	Time #1	Time #2

The Effect of Exercise on Your Ability to Hold Your Breath

1. Jog in place rapidly for one minute.
2. Take as big a breath as you can, and hold it for as long as you can. Keep your mouth closed and your nose pinched closed. Record your time in the table below.
3. Rest quietly for several minutes, and then repeat this procedure a second time and record your results in the table.
4. Also record the results of each member of your group.

Student name	Time #1	Time #2

name ____________________

Summing Up

1. When you reached the point where you had no breath left to blow out, was there still any air in your lungs? yes ☐ no ☐
   - If so, why couldn't you blow it out?

   ____

   ____

   ____

2. Average vital capacity is approximately 4500 mL. Would the vital capacities of your group members be considered average? yes ☐ no ☐
   - If not, what factors could account for the difference?

   ____

   ____

   ____

3. After you breathed out all the air that you could, why could you still hold your breath?

   ____

   ____

4. How is the air in the bag different after breathing into the bag for 30 seconds?

   ____

   ____

5. Compare your breathing into the bag with your breathing in normal air. What effect did breathing into the bag have on how long you could hold your breath? Why?

   ____

   ____

6. Compare your group members' vital capacities with the length of time that they can hold their breath. Is there any relationship between the two amounts?

   ____

   ____

7. How does your ability to hold your breath after jogging compare to your ability earlier when you were not jogging? Why is there a difference?

   ____

   ____

8. When you are holding your breath, what is it that makes you want to breathe?

   ____

   ____

name ______________________

section ____________ date ____________

21e Digestive Enzymes

Goal

✓ Observe starch being broken down into sugar by digestive enzymes.

Procedure

Use a marking pencil to label five test tubes *A* through *E*.

Test A

1. In test tube A place a crushed piece of cracker. Add enough water to moisten the cracker.
2. Add 5 mL (1 tsp) of Benedict's solution to the test tube and heat the contents to a boil. Place it in the test tube rack to cool.

Test B

1. Rinse out your mouth with water. Then collect in test tube B about 5 mL of your saliva.
2. Add 5 mL of Benedict's solution and heat the contents to a boil. Place it in the test tube rack to cool.

Test C

1. Place a cracker on your tongue. Do not chew it. Hold it there for five seconds.
2. Break the cracker into small pieces and place it into test tube C.
3. Add 5 mL of Benedict's solution and heat the contents to a boil. Place it in the test tube rack to cool.

Test D

1. Chew a cracker only five chews. Place the chewed cracker into test tube D.
2. Add 5 mL of Benedict's solution and heat the contents to a boil. Place it in the test tube rack to cool.

Test E

1. Chew a cracker thoroughly. It should be a soft mass. Place the chewed cracker into test tube E.
2. Add 5 mL of Benedict's solution and heat the contents to a boil. Place it in the test tube rack to cool.

Materials

test tubes (5)
marking pencil
plain saltine crackers
water
graduated cylinder
Benedict's solution
Bunsen burner or butane lab burner
test tube rack
test tube tongs

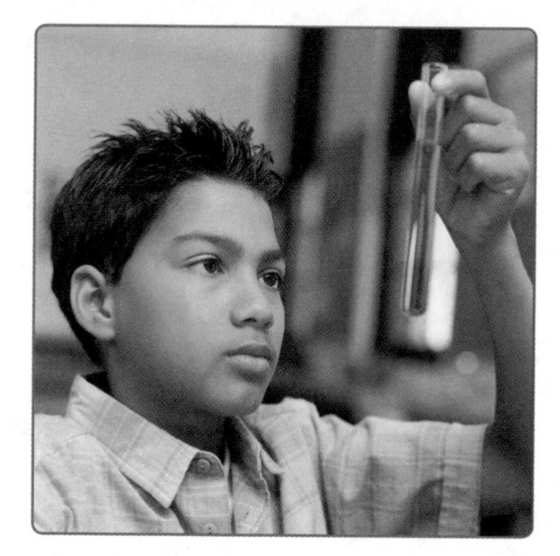

Data

When heated, Benedict's solution will change color if sugar is present.

- If no sugar is present, it will remain blue.
- If a small amount of sugar is present, it will turn yellow.
- If a medium amount of sugar is present, it will turn orange.
- If a large amount of sugar is present, it will turn brick red.

Compare the color of the five test tubes. Record your responses below.

Test tube	Color	Amount of sugar present
A	blue	none
B	blue	none
C	yellow/green	small amount
D	yellow	some sugar
E	yellow/orange	moderate

Summing Up

1. Which test tube or tubes have the most sugar? E
2. Which test tube or tubes have the least sugar? A, B
3. Crackers are predominantly starches (carbohydrates). When starches are digested, what are they broken down into? sugar
4. From your data, does the amount of sugar increase as the cracker is chewed more? yes ☒ no ☐
   If so, explain why.
   The amount of saliva increases when the cracker is chewed which increase the amount of sugar present.

Application

name ______________________

section ____________ date ____________

22a The Nervous System

Directions

Match each term with its definition.

axons	dendrites	interneuron	reflex
brain	endocrine	motor neuron	sense organs
cell body	eye	nervous	sensory neuron
central	hormones	neurons	spinal cord
coordination	impulse	peripheral	synapse

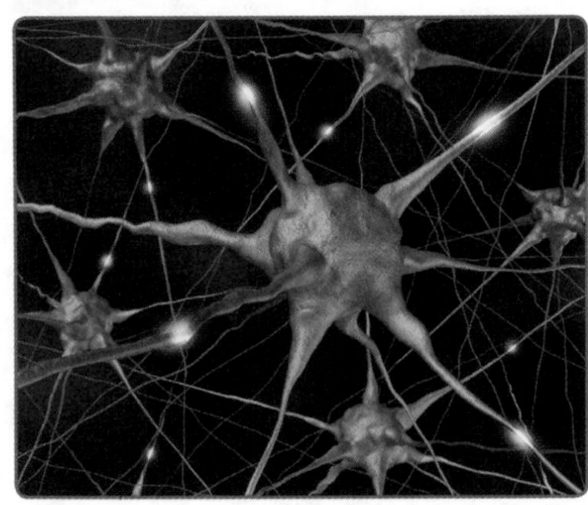

coordination 1. The organization of the systems and processes of the body

endocrine 2. The system that produces hormones to control and coordinate the body

cell body 3. The part of the neuron that contains the nucleus

neurons 4. Cells of the nervous system that are capable of transmitting impulses

brain 5. The part of the central nervous system that is found in the skull

nervous 6. The system of the body that includes the brain, eyes, ears, and nerves

axons 7. Extensions of a neuron that carry impulses away from the cell body

eye 8. The organ responsible for sensing light

hormones 9. Chemicals produced by the glands of the endocrine system

impulse 10. The membrane change that travels along a neuron

sense organs 11. Structures, such as the eyes, that receive various kinds of stimuli

Central 12. The division of the nervous system made of the brain and spinal cord

interneuron 13. A neuron that is in a reflex arc and serves as a go-between for the other cells in the reflex arc

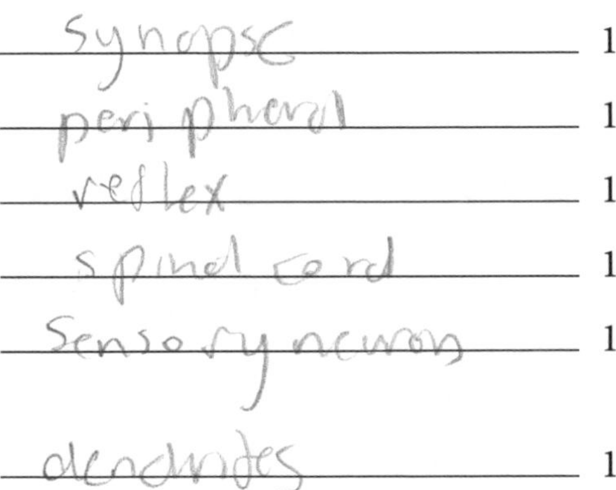

synapse 14. The space that impulses jump across by means of neurotransmitters

peripheral 15. The division of the nervous system made of nerves and sense organs

reflex 16. An immediate, inborn response to a stimulus

spinal cord 17. The part of the central nervous system not found in the skull

Sensory neuron 18. In a reflex arc, the neuron that receives the stimulus and initiates an impulse

dendrites 19. Extensions of a neuron that carry impulses toward the cell body

motor neuron 20. In a reflex arc, the neuron that carries an impulse to a muscle

name ______________________

section __________ date __________

22b Bob Uses His Brain

Directions

Below is a list of the divisions of the brain, followed by a list of statements describing Bob's actions. For each statement, choose the brain division that is most involved with Bob's action.

A. brain stem
B. cerebellum
C. cerebrum, frontal lobe
D. cerebrum, occipital lobe
E. cerebrum, parietal lobe
F. cerebrum, temporal lobe

__C__ 1. Bob decides to go outside.

__B__ 2. Bob walks out the door.

__F__ 3. Bob takes a deep breath.

__E__ 4. Bob feels heat from the sun.

_____ 5. Bob realizes he could get sunburned.

_____ 6. Bob smells something.

__F__ 7. Bob hears a loud noise.

__F__ 8. Bob sees a lawn mower across the street.

__C__ 9. Bob understands why he smelled mowed grass.

_____ 10. Bob steps into the street.

_____ 11. Bob hears something nearby.

_____ 12. Bob decides to look to his left.

_____ 13. Bob decides he should move out of the way.

__B__ 14. Bob jumps back onto the sidewalk.

__A__ 15. Bob's heart begins to beat faster, and his blood pressure goes up.

_____ 16. Bob feels rushing air as a truck passes.

name ______________________

section __________ date __________

22c The Eye and Ear

Part 1: The Eye

Directions

Below is a drawing of the human eye. Write the definition for each term. Then in the blanks in the diagram, write the number of each term that indicates the proper structure in the diagram. The first number has been placed on the diagram as an example.

1. sclera ______________________
2. aqueous humor ______________________
3. cornea ______________________
4. retina ______________________
5. vitreous humor ______________________
6. iris ______________________
7. choroid ______________________
8. lens ______________________
9. pupil ______________________
10. optic nerve ______________________

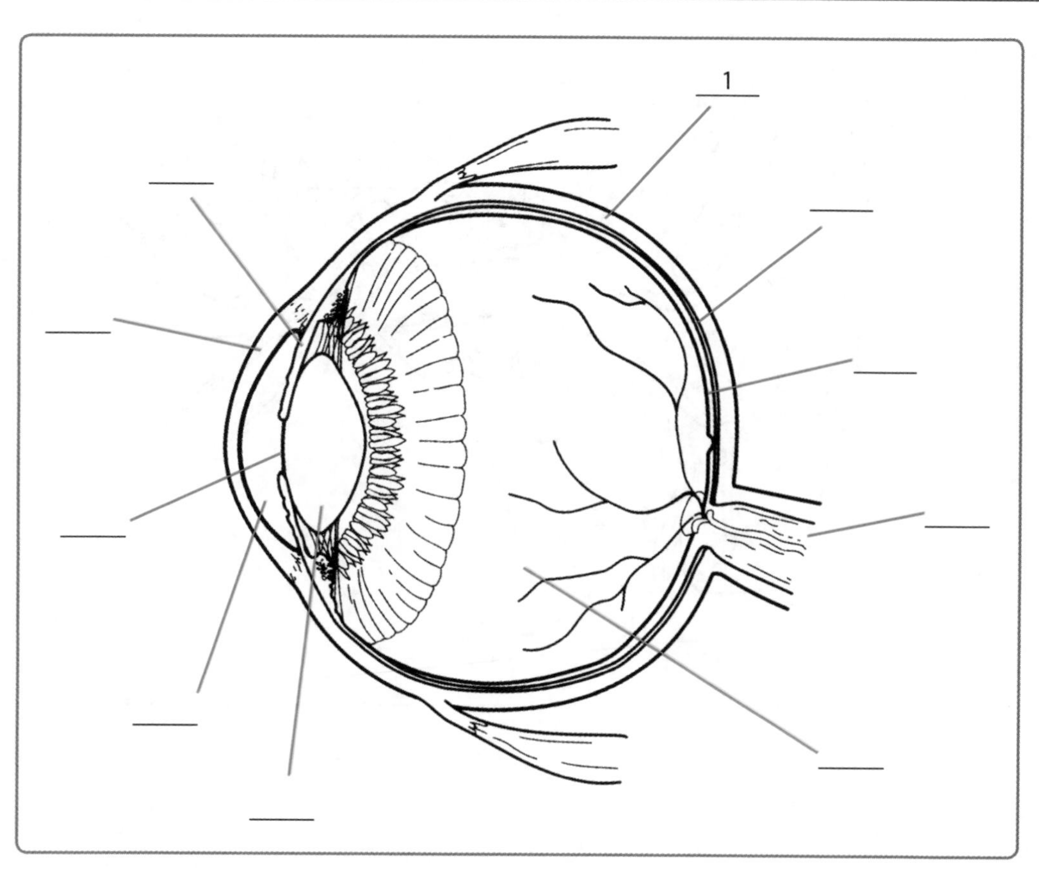

Part 2: The Ear

Directions

Below is a drawing of the human ear. Write the term for each definition. Then in the blanks in the diagram, write the number of each term that indicates the proper structure in the diagram. The first number has been placed on the diagram as an example.

1. ______________________ the structure that collects sound waves
2. ______________________ the ear bone that connects the anvil and the cochlea
3. ______________________ the ear bone that connects the tympanic membrane and the anvil
4. ______________________ the structures that sense body balance and position
5. ______________________ the thin membrane that makes up the innermost part of the outer ear
6. ______________________ the air-filled chamber that contains the ear bones
7. ______________________ the tube that connects the pharynx and the middle ear
8. ______________________ the section of the ear that contains the cochlea and the semicircular canals
9. ______________________ the tube that permits sound waves to reach the tympanic membrane
10. ______________________ the ear bone that connects the stirrup and the hammer
11. ______________________ the coiled, tubular structure in the inner ear that contains fluid

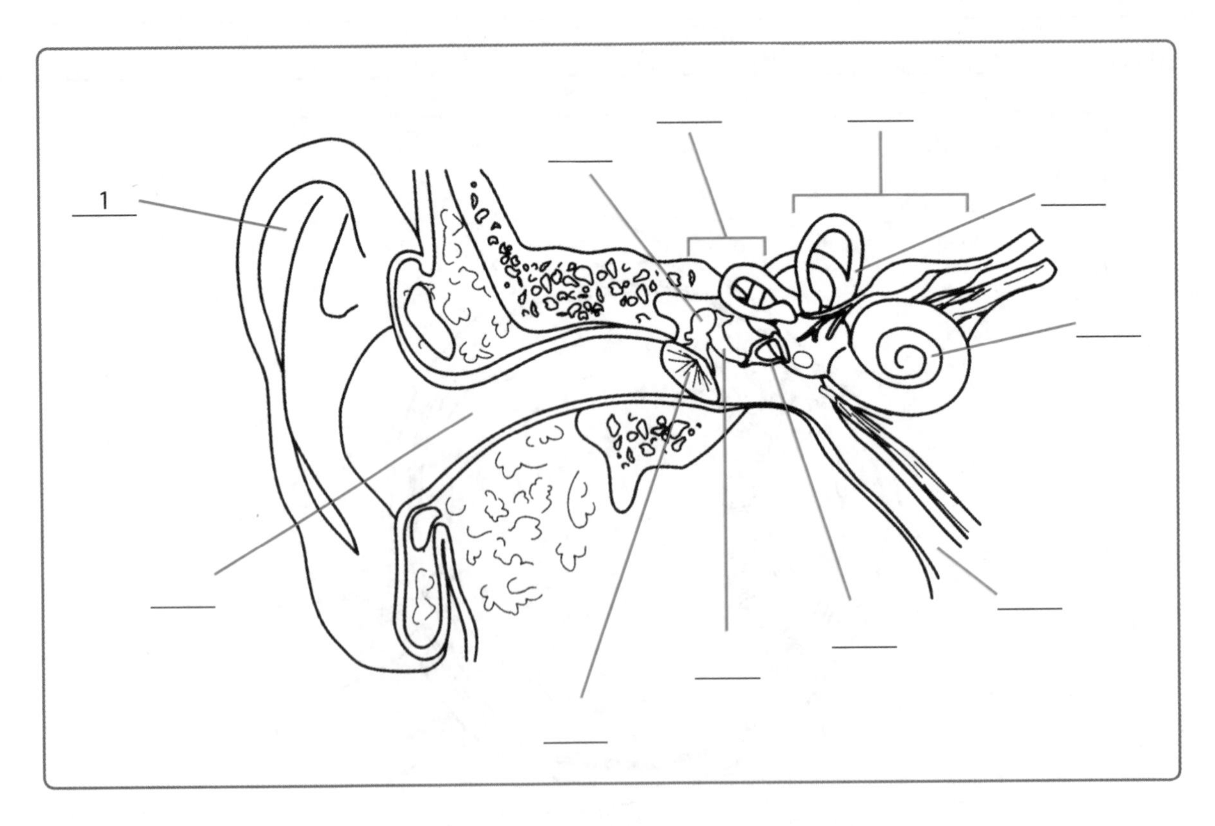

name ______________________

section ____________ date ____________

22d The Endocrine System

Directions

Fill in the chart by selecting the correct descriptions from the lists. All the boxes on the chart will have at least one entry; some will have two.

Locations *(Use only five.)*

behind the stomach
below the brain
in the chest
in the lower abdomen
in the neck
on top of the kidneys
under the sternum

Hormones *(Use all.)*

epinephrine
growth hormone
insulin
reproductive hormones
thyroxine

Notes *(Use all.)*

are called the glands of emergency
controls the body's metabolic rate
is called the master gland of the body
produce gametes (ova or sperm)
produce hormones that cause puberty
produces digestive enzymes
produces more hormones than any other gland in the body
supply the blood with more oxygen and food when necessary
undersecretion that can cause a goiter
undersecretion that can cause diabetes mellitus

Gland	Location	Hormones produced	Notes
adrenal glands			
ovaries or testes			
pancreas			
pituitary gland			
thyroid gland			

name ______________________

section ____________ date ____________

22e Review

Directions

Below are several groups of terms. In each group, three of the four terms are related to one another. Draw a line through the least related term and then write a sentence using the remaining terms. Your sentence should show how the terms are related. (You may slightly change the form of the terms in your sentence.)

1. internal coordination / synapse / nervous system / endocrine system

2. dendrite / axon / cell body / cerebellum

3. peripheral nervous system / nerve impulse / neurotransmitters / synapse

4. interneuron / motor neuron / synapse / sensory neuron

5. hemispheres / lobes / cerebrum / brain stem

6. spinal cord / cerebrum / brain stem / cerebellum

7. sclera / synapse / choroid / retina

8. choroid / retina / iris / pupil

9. aqueous humor / vitreous humor / lens / iris

10. lens / rods / cones / retina

11. outer ear / ear bones / eardrum / ear canal

12. eustachian tube / cochlea / pharynx / middle ear

13. smell / pain / cold / touch

14. stirrup / cochlea / inner ear / semicircular canals

15. tympanic membrane / ear bones / cochlea / semicircular canals

16. pancreas / insulin / pituitary gland / thyroid

17. endocrine / sugar / hormones / ductless

18. diabetes / thyroid / goiter / thyroxine

19. dwarfism / insulin / pancreas / sugar

20. growth hormone / pituitary gland / dwarfism / ductless

name ____________________

section __________ date __________

22f The Skin's Sensation of Temperature

> **Goals**
> ✓ Demonstrate the skin's ability to detect differences in temperature.
> ✓ Observe the fallibility of the senses.

> **Materials**
> large glasses or cups (7)
> cold water
> hot water
> thermometers (1–7)
> paper
> dish

Introduction

Your skin responds to many different sensations—temperature, touch, pressure, pain, and more. In this lab you will study the sensation of temperature by testing your skin's ability to detect differences in temperature.

Procedure

Set up your experiment.

1. Put some tap water into a glass. Place two fingers into the water. Add hot or cold water to make the water feel lukewarm (around 80 °F, neither cool nor warm).
2. When the water is lukewarm, use a thermometer to measure its temperature.
3. You will prepare seven glasses, each containing water of a different temperature. One glass should contain water at the lukewarm temperature, as determined in Step 1.
4. Three glasses should have hotter water: 5 °F hotter than the lukewarm water, 10 °F hotter, and 15 °F hotter. Similarly, prepare three glasses of colder water: 5 °F colder than the lukewarm water, 10 °F colder, and 15 °F colder.
5. Label the glasses appropriately: *hot*, *very warm*, *warm*, *lukewarm*, *cool*, *very cool*, and *cold*.
6. Prepare 21 small pieces of paper. On three of them write *hot*, on three write *very warm*, on three write *warm*, and so on. Fold these pieces of paper and place them in a dish.

Run your experiment.

You should frequently test the temperatures of the various glasses of water and, if necessary, add hot or cold water so that they maintain their original temperatures throughout the experiment.

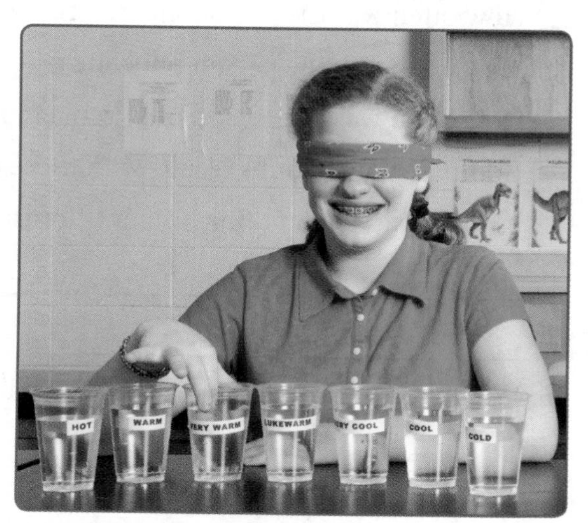

1. Choose a person to test the water. Make sure the person looks away (or is blindfolded) so he cannot see the glasses. He will use the same index finger in each glass, briefly drying his finger before testing the next glass.
2. Determine which glass you dip his finger into by drawing a piece of paper out of the dish. For each test, move the glass to the person testing the water. If you move his hand to the glass, he may be able to tell which glass it is by its location.

3. Dip his finger into the glass for 5 seconds and then remove it. Have him tell you which glass he thinks it was.
4. Fill in the chart by putting a check for the correct water temperature and an *X* for the temperature that the person said it was. (If the person got it right, there will be a check and an *X* in the same box.) Repeat Steps 2–4 until the chart is filled in.

Data

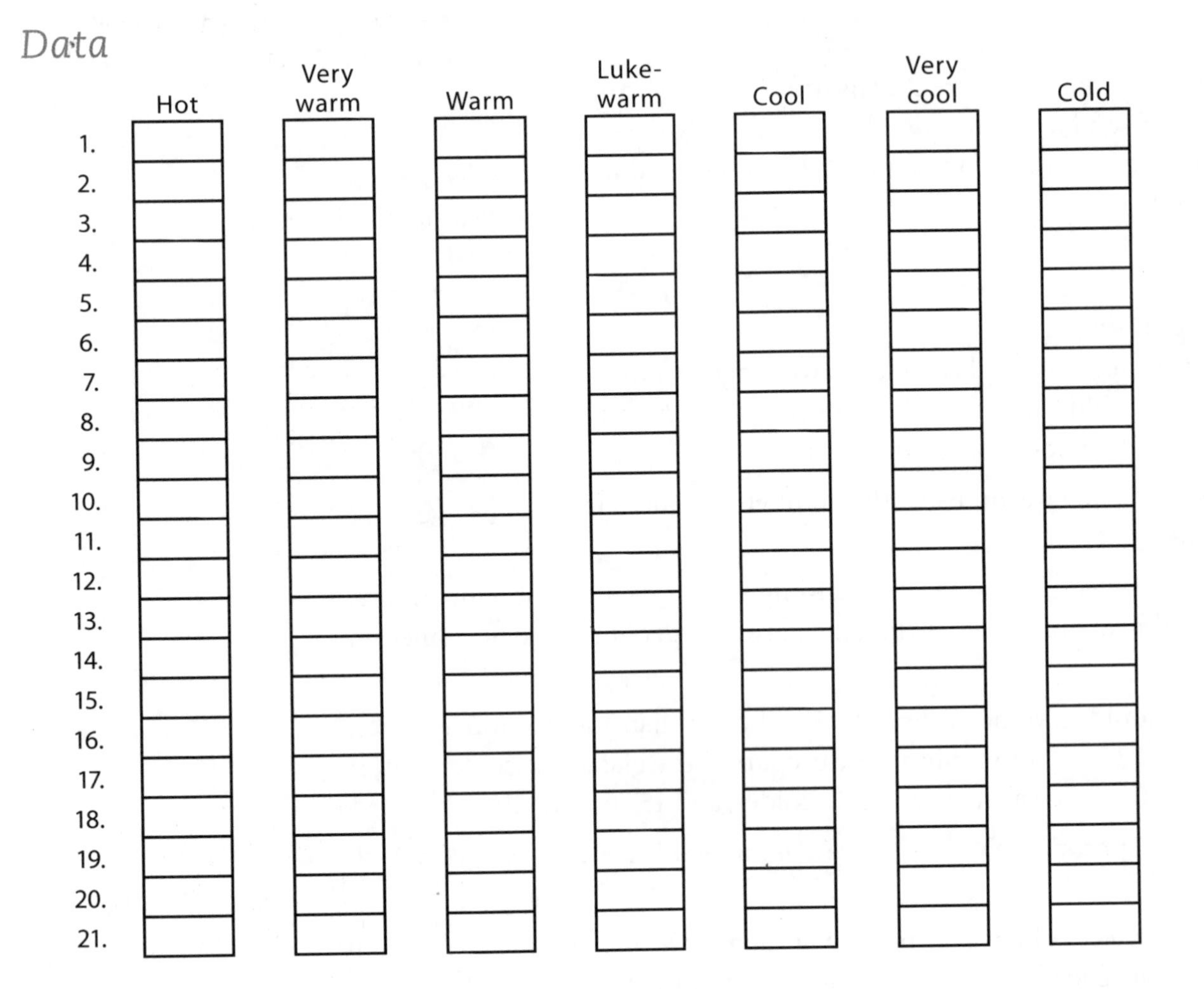

	Hot	Very warm	Warm	Luke-warm	Cool	Very cool	Cold
1.							
2.							
3.							
4.							
5.							
6.							
7.							
8.							
9.							
10.							
11.							
12.							
13.							
14.							
15.							
16.							
17.							
18.							
19.							
20.							
21.							

Summing Up

1. How often was the person incorrect? ______________ How often was he correct? ______________
2. How often was the person only one temperature off? ______________
3. How often was the person only two temperatures off? ______________
4. Compare your group's results with those of other groups. Are they about the same? yes ☐ no ☐

   If not, what do you think accounts for the difference?

   ____

   ____

5. What are your conclusions about the skin's ability to determine temperatures?

   ____

   ____

Class Investigation

name ______________________

section __________ date __________

22g The Pupil Reflex

Introduction

The iris (colored portion) of the eye controls the size of the pupil (black portion). The pupil is actually an opening into the eye. When the pupil is large, a great amount of light enters the eye. When the pupil is small, very little light enters the eye. The size of the pupil is controlled by a reflex. This reflex is stimulated by the amount and intensity of light available to the eye.

Goals

✓ Demonstrate a reflex.
✓ Understand the purposes of reflexes.

Materials

darkened room
penlight (small flashlight)

Procedure

You will need to perform the following procedures with a partner.

1. Sit in a darkened area for several minutes. This should cause your pupils to become large. If they do not, go to a darker area.
2. Shine a penlight into the right eye of your partner, being careful not to shine it into his left eye.
   - What happens to the pupil of the right eye?
     It became smaller
   - What happens to the pupil of the left eye?
     it stayed large
   - How fast does the reflex take place?
     immediandly

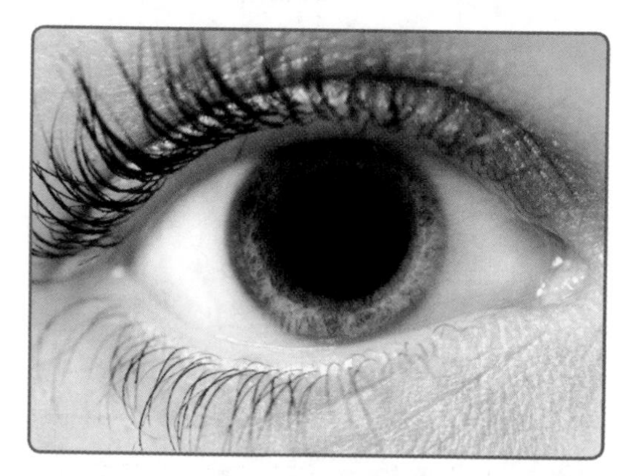

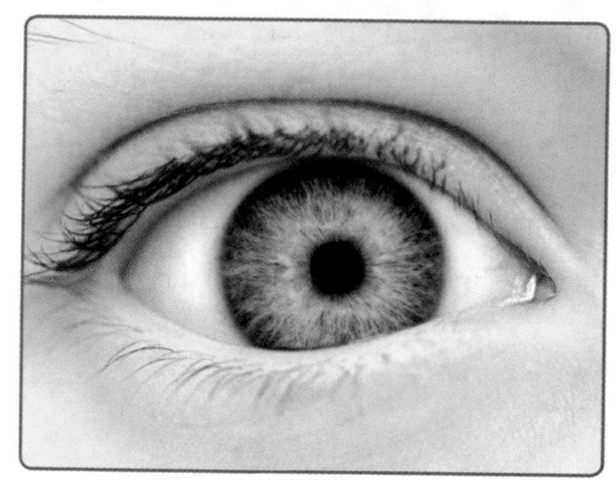

3. Turn off the penlight and allow the eyes to readjust to the dim light.
4. Repeat the above experiment but shine the penlight into the left eye. Does the same thing happen? yes ☒ no ☐
   If not, what does happen? ______________________

Summing Up

1. Why is the pupil reflex necessary?
   To keep unnessosary light out of the eye, and to bring in light when it is dark
2. Why must the reflex happen quickly?
   If it does not extra light might enter the eye and damage it

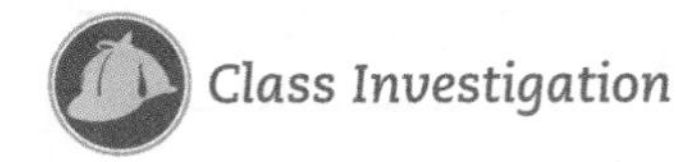

name ____________________

section __________ date __________

22h Afterimages

Introduction

An afterimage is the image you see after you stop looking at an object. Afterimages are most common when you stop looking at something that is in sharp contrast to its background. In this lab, you will observe afterimages as an illustration of how the cones in your eyes work.

Goals

- ✓ Demonstrate afterimages.
- ✓ Evaluate the functioning of the cones of the eye.

Materials

colored construction paper (both dark and bright colors)
scissors
glue or tape
white paper
brightly lit area
stopwatch or clock with a second hand
color wheel (optional)

Procedure

Set up your experiment.

1. Cut circles, triangles, squares, and other simple shapes from colored construction paper. You should have at least four different colors of each shape. Each figure should be about 5 cm (2 in.) square.
2. Glue or tape each of these shapes in the center of a sheet of white paper (one shape per sheet of paper). If you use tape, use tiny rolls of tape behind the shape so that none of the tape is visible.
3. Using a pencil, place a tiny dot in the center of each shape.

Perform your experiment.

1. Place a sheet of white paper with a colored shape on it in a brightly lit area about 50 cm (20 in.) away from your face.
2. Stare at the dot in the center of the shape for 20 seconds. Keep your eyes on the dot for the entire time.
3. Look at a light-colored area in the distance (the ceiling is good) and then close your eyes. What you see immediately after you close your eyes is called an afterimage. Describe the afterimage you saw. (Be sure to describe its color and its shape in relation to the color and shape you stared at.)

   ____

   ____

   ____

   ____

4. After you have performed this experiment and have seen an afterimage, you should wait until you no longer can see that afterimage before you do the experiment again.
5. Try obtaining other afterimages using different colors and shapes. Record your findings on the chart on the next page. In the "Notes" column, record anything unusual you observe about the afterimages.
6. If time permits, you may want to form some afterimages by using colored shapes on pieces of colored paper. What are the results?

Shape	Shape color	Afterimage color	Notes

Summing Up

The cones in your eyes have different chemicals that break down when exposed to different colors. Thus when you look at something blue, a certain chemical breaks down. When you look at something red, a different chemical breaks down. Different shades of color are seen when different amounts and combinations of these chemicals break down.

Afterimages result when you break down a large amount of a particular color's chemical and then look away. The temporary lack of that particular chemical causes the afterimages.

1. About how long did the afterimages last?

2. What observations can you make about different colors of afterimages?

3. List normal, everyday situations in which afterimages occur.

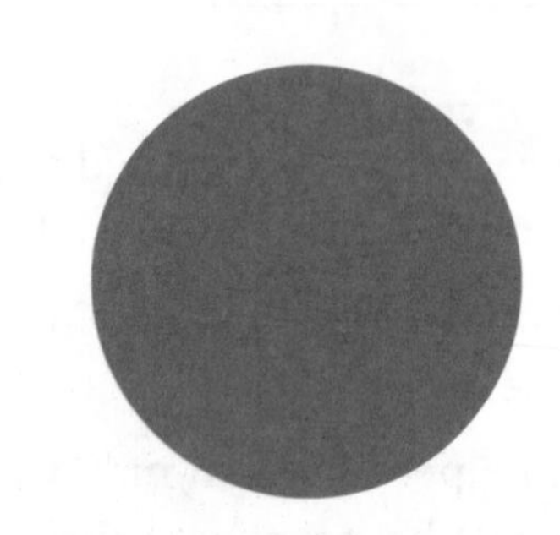

Stare at the center of each of these images for 30 seconds, and then immediately look at a white sheet of paper. What do you see?

name ______________________

section __________ date __________

23a Metabolism

Directions

Below is a series of examples. Choose which term is being described in each example. Some choices will be used more than once.

A. basal metabolic rate

B. digestive system

C. metabolic rate

D. metabolism

E. respiratory system

_______ 1. All the processes your body carries on to keep you alive

_______ 2. How quickly your body uses energy

_______ 3. The structures responsible for supplying oxygen to the body

_______ 4. The rate at which your body uses energy when you are resting quietly

_______ 5. The structures responsible for supplying food for the body to use

_______ 6. Decreases as a person ages

_______ 7. The structures that exchange carbon dioxide and oxygen

_______ 8. Increases as you engage in strenuous physical activity

_______ 9. The measurement of body activity at rest

_______ 10. The structures that supply the glucose for aerobic cellular respiration

name ______________________

section ____________ date ____________

23b Metabolic Rate

Part 1

Directions

Below is a list of factors that result in either an increased metabolic rate or a decreased metabolic rate. Write each factor in the correct space in the table below.

active	inactive	overweight
calm	jogging	sleeping
fever	lean	stress
hypothermia (low body temperature)	old	young

How Various Factors Affect Metabolic Rate

	Increased metabolic rate	Decreased metabolic rate
Activity amount		
Activity example		
Age		
Body temperature		
Body type		
Emotional responses		

Part 2

Directions

Write your responses in the spaces provided.

1. Suppose that a person's BMR (basal metabolic rate) causes him to use 1500 Calories per day. He exercises every day, causing him to use an additional 1800 Calories per day. If the person consumes 4000 Calories per day, what will probably happen? Why?

   ____

   ____

   If the same person consumes only 3000 Calories per day, what will probably happen? Why?

   ____

   ____

2. If an overweight person consumes fewer Calories than his metabolism uses, and he reaches a healthy weight, what might happen if he continues to consume fewer Calories?

3. Why might your BMR be an even more important factor in your overall health after your teenage years?

4. What are some of the things you eat that do not supply energy for metabolism but are still necessary for good health?

5. Since metabolism cannot be measured directly, how can it be measured?

name ____________________

section __________ date __________

23c Nutrition and Food Labels

Introduction

In this activity you will evaluate several foods based on the labels found on their packaging. Be sure you understand the information about food labels given in your textbook (p. 526). You will also need to keep the following in mind:

- Calories: 40 Cal per serving is low; 100 Cal per serving is moderate; 400 Cal per serving is high.
- Percent Daily Values: 5% or less is low; 20% or more is high.
- Protein content: A good protein source has 5 or more grams of protein per serving (or 10 or more grams of protein per 100 grams of food).

A

Nutrition Facts	
Serving Size 1/2 cup (78g)	
Amount Per Serving	
Calories 25	Calories from Fat 0
	%Daily Value*
Total Fat 0g	**0%**
Saturated Fat 0g	**0%**
Trans Fat 0g	
Cholesterol 0mg	**0%**
Sodium 60mg	**3%**
Potassium 190mg	**5%**
Total Carbohydrate 6g	**2%**
Dietary Fiber 2g	**9%**
Sugars 4g	
Protein < 1g	
Vitamin A 220% •	Vitamin C 4%
Calcium 2% •	Iron 4%
Vitamin K 10% •	Niacin 2%
Vitamin B6 4% •	Folate 6%
Pantothenic acid 4% •	Phosphorus 2%
Magnesium 2% •	Copper 4%
Manganese 6%	

* Percent Daily Values are based on a 2,000 calorie diet. Your Daily Values may be higher or lower depending on your calorie needs.

B

Nutrition Facts	
Serving Size 6 oz (170g)	
Amount Per Serving	
Calories 360	Calories from Fat 140
	%Daily Value*
Total Fat 16g	**25%**
Saturated Fat 6g	**30%**
Trans Fat 0g	
Cholesterol 150mg	**50%**
Sodium 105mg	**4%**
Potassium 630mg	**18%**
Total Carbohydrate 0g	**0%**
Dietary Fiber 0g	**0%**
Sugars 0g	
Protein 50g	
Vitamin A 0% •	Vitamin C 0%
Calcium 4% •	Iron 20%
Vitamin D 4% •	Vitamin E 4%
Vitamin K 4% •	Thiamin 8%
Riboflavin 15% •	Niacin 70%
Vitamin B6 50% •	Folate 4%
Vitamin B12 50% •	Pantothenic acid 10%
Phosphorus 40% •	Zinc 60%
Selenium 80% •	Copper 8%

* Percent Daily Values are based on a 2,000 calorie diet. Your Daily Values may be higher or lower depending on your calorie needs.

C

Nutrition Facts	
Serving Size 1 cup (225g)	
Amount Per Serving	
Calories 200	Calories from Fat 0
	%Daily Value*
Total Fat 0.5g	**1%**
Saturated Fat 0g	**0%**
Trans Fat 0g	
Cholesterol 0mg	**0%**
Sodium 0mg	**0%**
Potassium 810mg	**23%**
Total Carbohydrate 51g	**17%**
Dietary Fiber 6g	**24%**
Sugars 28g	
Protein 2g	
Vitamin A 2% •	Vitamin C 35%
Calcium 0% •	Iron 4%
Niacin 8% •	Vitamin B6 40%
Folate 10% •	Phosphorus 6%
Magnesium 15%	

* Percent Daily Values are based on a 2,000 calorie diet. Your Daily Values may be higher or lower depending on your calorie needs.

D

Nutrition Facts	
Serving Size 4 oz (113g)	
Amount Per Serving	
Calories 180	Calories from Fat 0
	%Daily Value*
Total Fat 0.5g	**1%**
Saturated Fat 0g	**0%**
Trans Fat 0g	
Cholesterol 0mg	**0%**
Sodium 95mg	**4%**
Potassium 730mg	**21%**
Total Carbohydrate 35g	**12%**
Dietary Fiber 10g	**40%**
Sugars 0g	
Protein 11g	
Vitamin A 0% •	Vitamin C 0%
Calcium 6% •	Iron 15%
Thiamin 20% •	Riboflavin 8%
Niacin 4% •	Vitamin B6 10%
Folate 10% •	Phosphorus 10%
Magnesium 15% •	Zinc 6%
Selenium 2% •	Copper 4%
Manganese 30%	

* Percent Daily Values are based on a 2,000 calorie diet. Your Daily Values may be higher or lower depending on your calorie needs.

E

Nutrition Facts	
Serving Size 1 cup (244g)	
Amount Per Serving	
Calories 150	Calories from Fat 70
	%Daily Value*
Total Fat 8g	**12%**
Saturated Fat 4.5g	**23%**
Trans Fat 0g	
Cholesterol 25mg	**8%**
Sodium 105mg	**4%**
Potassium 320mg	**9%**
Total Carbohydrate 12g	**4%**
Dietary Fiber 0g	**0%**
Sugars 12g	
Protein 8g	
Vitamin A 8% •	Vitamin C 0%
Calcium 30% •	Iron 0%
Vitamin D 30% •	Thiamin 8%
Riboflavin 25% •	Vitamin B6 4%
Folate 4% •	Vitamin B12 20%
Phosphorus 20% •	Magnesium 6%
Zinc 6% •	Selenium 15%

* Percent Daily Values are based on a 2,000 calorie diet. Your Daily Values may be higher or lower depending on your calorie needs.

Directions

Choose the best answer for each of the following questions.

_______ 1. Based on the food labels, which food would be best to eat often, due to its high levels of more than one vitamin that needs to be replenished regularly? (Be sure to consider the nutrients that should be limited.)

A. food A
B. food B
C. food C
D. food D
E. food E

_______ 2. Which food would be best for bone health?

A. food A
B. food B
C. food C
D. food D
E. food E

_______ 3. Which food contains the greatest percentage of calories from fat?

A. food A
B. food B
C. food C
D. food D
E. food E

_______ 4. Which food does *not* contain a large amount of a mineral that is good for your muscles and nerves?

A. food A
B. food B
C. food C
D. food D
E. food E

_______ 5. Which food contains the most nutrients that are needed for the formation of blood cells?

A. food A
B. food B
C. food C
D. food D
E. food E

_______ 6. Which of the groups of the USDA food plate is *not* represented in these labels?

A. grains
B. vegetables
C. proteins
D. dairy products

Match the food label with the most likely food that it represents.

A. bananas
B. beans
C. broccoli
D. carrots
E. oranges
F. potatoes
G. steak
H. whole milk
I. whole wheat bread

_______ 7. food A

_______ 8. food B

_______ 9. food C

_______ 10. food D

_______ 11. food E

Application

name ____________________

section __________ date __________

23d Drugs

Directions

Use the clues below to fill in the blanks. The letters in the shaded rectangle will spell out the answer to the question at the bottom of the page.

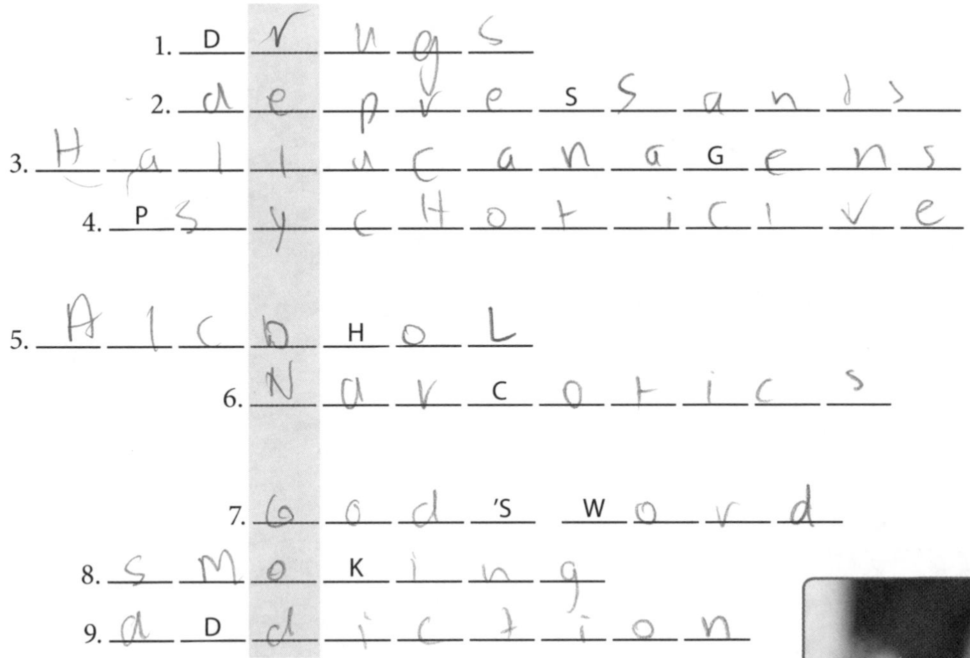

1. Substances that are used either to treat or prevent diseases or disorders or to cope with problems
2. Drugs that slow down the central nervous system
3. Drugs that cause people to see things that are not real
4. Drugs that primarily affect a person's mental or emotional condition
5. One of the most widely used and abused substances
6. Drugs that dull the senses and cause a feeling of happiness
7. Where the cause of our problems is described (two words)
8. A habit that has many harmful effects on the body
9. Enslavement to a substance that is physically or psychologically habit-forming

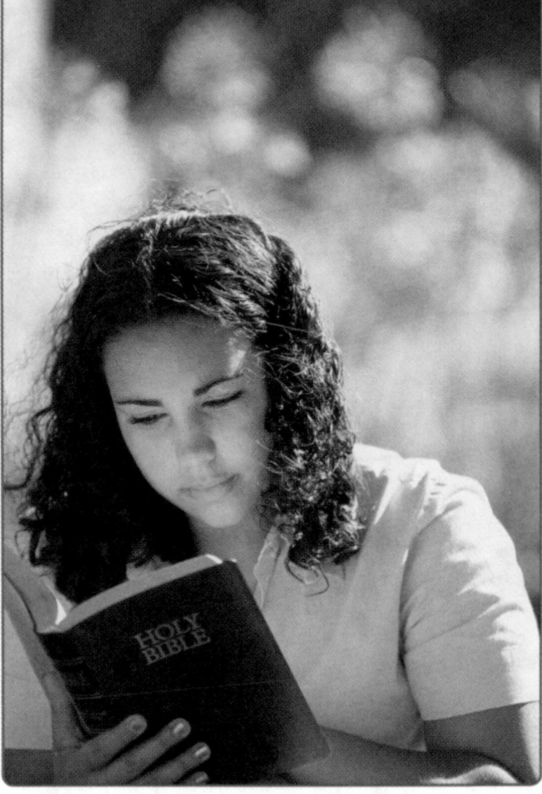

What should a person do rather than turn to drugs to cope with difficulties?

Rely on God

name____________________

section__________ date__________

23e Disease

Directions

Below is a list of terms related to disease. Choose which term is best for each description or example. Some choices will be used more than once.

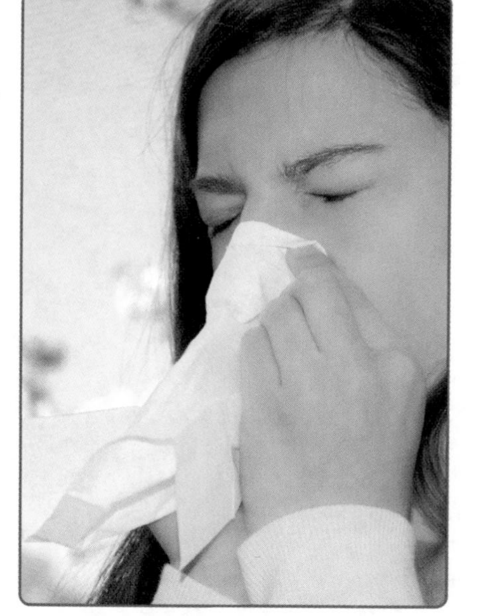

A. airborne infection

B. contact infection

C. contamination infection

D. immune system

E. inflammation, white blood cells, and fever

F. medical treatment

G. skin and mucous membranes

H. vector-carried infection

I. wound infection

C 1. Washing your hands, wearing gloves, and cooking food properly help prevent this type of infection.

G 2. Providing a barrier is the primary function of this line of defense.

A 3. Inhaling pathogens can result in this type of infection.

B 4. Washing your hands often, washing dishes, getting vaccinations, and not drinking after others help prevent this type of infection.

E 5. Swelling, redness, warmth, and pain are evidence of this line of defense being used.

G 6. Trapping particles and inhibiting microorganisms are part of this line of defense.

I 7. *Streptococcus* and *Staphylococcus* bacteria can cause this type of infection if a patient's skin is not cleaned properly before his surgery.

B 8. Mononucleosis, meningitis, and cold sores are spread this way.

H 9. West Nile virus, Lyme disease, and malaria are spread this way.

I 10. Carefully cleaning a skinned knee helps prevent this type of infection.

G 11. Lysozyme is a powerful enzyme involved with this line of defense.

D 12. The production of antibodies is a major portion of this line of defense.

F 13. This can involve the use of antibiotics to kill pathogens.

name ______________________

section ____________ date ____________

Field Investigation

23f Collecting Bacteria

Introduction

Bacteria are ubiquitous (yoo BIK wih tuss). That means they are all around you. They are even found floating in the atmosphere at more than three miles up! In this lab, you will test various places around your home for the presence of bacteria.

Goals

- ✓ Demonstrate the prevalence of bacteria.
- ✓ Observe bacterial colonies on culture plates.
- ✓ Evaluate the conditions needed for bacterial growth.
- ✓ Consider methods to prevent the growth of harmful bacteria.

Materials

prepared culture plates (or petri dishes and nutrient agar)
sterile cotton swabs
permanent marker
tape
zippable bags

Procedure

Collect samples of bacteria.

1. Choose six of the following surfaces to test for the presence of bacteria.
   - bathroom counter
   - bathroom doorknob
   - bottom of purse or backpack
   - computer keyboard
   - kitchen counter
   - kitchen sink
   - outdoor doorknob
   - palm of hand
   - telephone
   - toilet seat
   - other: ______________________
   - other: ______________________

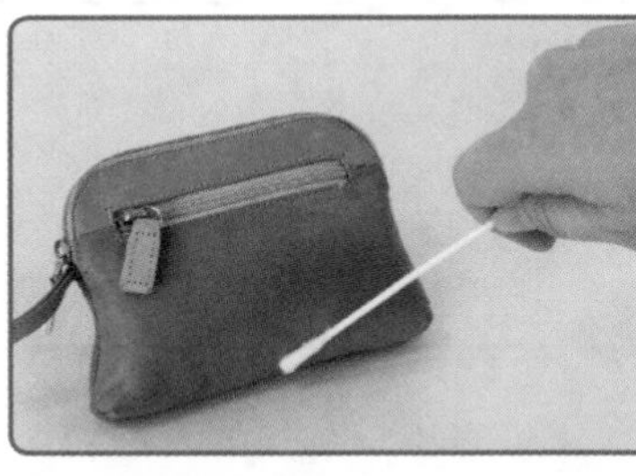

2. Label your culture plates with the six locations that you have chosen. This can be done by writing directly on the lid with a permanent marker or by writing on a piece of tape placed on the lid. Be sure the culture plates remain sterile until the bacterial samples are placed in them.
3. To collect your samples, swipe a sterile cotton swab back and forth five times across a three-inch-wide area of each surface. After you collect a sample on your cotton swab, lift the lid of a culture plate and swipe the cotton swab back and forth three times in a zigzag pattern on the surface of the agar. Then turn the dish 90 degrees and repeat. Replace the lid quickly.
4. Place all the culture plates in a large zippable bag, and put the bag in a warm, dark location (such as a cabinet). Check the plates each day for bacterial growth. It may take 2–4 days for good-size colonies to appear on the plates.

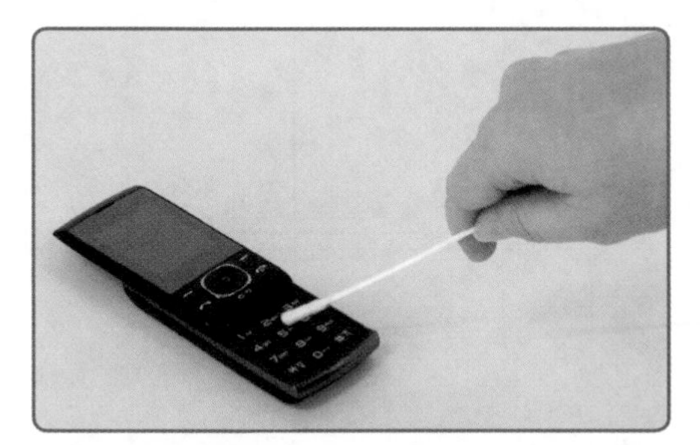

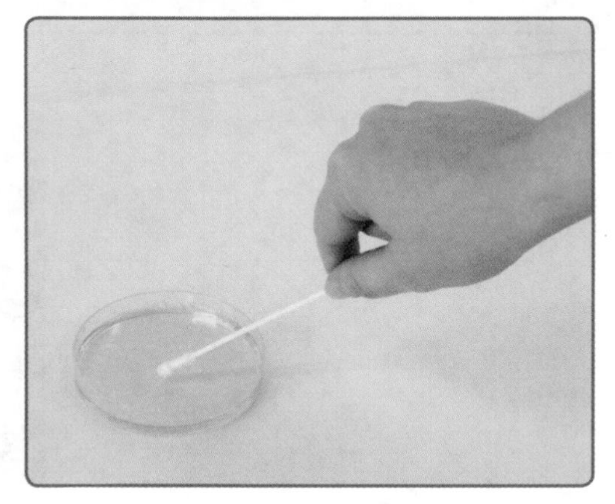

Record your observations.

Describe the size, shape, color, and texture of any bacterial colonies growing in the culture plates.

Location	Description
Kitchen sink	fifteen 1cm white colonies
keyboard	three colonies
bathroom	six small
phone	four 1 cm white
palm	one 2 cm
kitchen	two 2cm

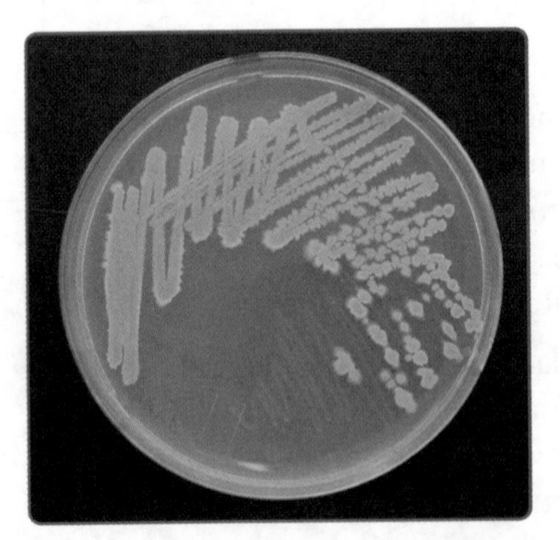

name ____________________

Summing Up

1. Why was it important to use sterile cotton swabs when you collected your bacterial samples?

2. Why was it important to replace the lid quickly when you were transferring your sample from the cotton swab to the culture plate?

3. Explain why some surfaces had few bacteria. Explain why some surfaces had many bacteria.

4. Could there have been other kinds of bacteria (besides those that grew on your plates) in the places you tested? Why or why not?

5. Did the different kinds of bacteria all grow at the same rate? Why would different bacteria grow at different rates?

6. The bacteria in this experiment were all grown on nutrient agar. Could it be possible for the bacteria that grew the slowest in your experiment to grow faster on some other type of medium? Why or why not?

7. What could you do to reduce the amount of bacteria on the surfaces where the most was found?

8. What else could you do to prevent being infected by harmful bacteria?

9. By looking at the bacterial colonies on the culture plates, could you tell whether they were cocci, bacilli, or spirilla? yes ☐ no ☐

   If yes, tell what shapes you saw. If no, explain why you could not tell and suggest a way to find out what shape the bacteria were.

name ____________________

section ____________ date ____________

Personal Investigation

23g Counting Calories

Goals

- ✓ Understand the relationship between diet, exercise, and weight.
- ✓ Recognize the importance of a healthy lifestyle.

Materials

calculator

Introduction

You probably already realize that diet and exercise are closely linked to weight. But it can be hard to figure out precisely how they are related. In this activity, you will perform the following tasks:

- Calculate your basal metabolic rate (BMR).
- Carefully monitor the energy content (Calories) of the food you eat.
- Calculate and record the energy expended in the activities you engage in.
- Determine the effect your BMR, food intake, and activities have on your weight over a five-day period.

Many factors can affect the results of this experiment—differences in metabolic rates due to a person's genes, gender, and weight; differences in the amount of effort each person uses to perform a particular activity; differences in the way food is processed or prepared; and many more that cannot possibly be accounted for in this exercise.

Still, by carefully considering the basic energy input (foods eaten) and output (activities engaged in) over a period of time, you should gain a better understanding of how these factors can affect your weight. Although your weight is only one aspect of your overall health, it is an important one that will become even more important as you get older. Understanding this at an early age will help you become a better steward of the body that God has given you.

Procedure

Calculate your basal metabolic rate in Chart A.

1. Use the formula given below to calculate your BMR.
   - For males: BMR = 66 + (6.2 × weight in pounds) + (12.7 × height in inches) – (6.8 × age in years)
   - For females: BMR = 655 + (4.35 × weight in pounds) + (4.7 × height in inches) – (4.7 × age in years)
2. Record your BMR in Chart A. Multiply by five to determine the total Calories burned due to BMR for the five days of this activity, and record this in the chart.

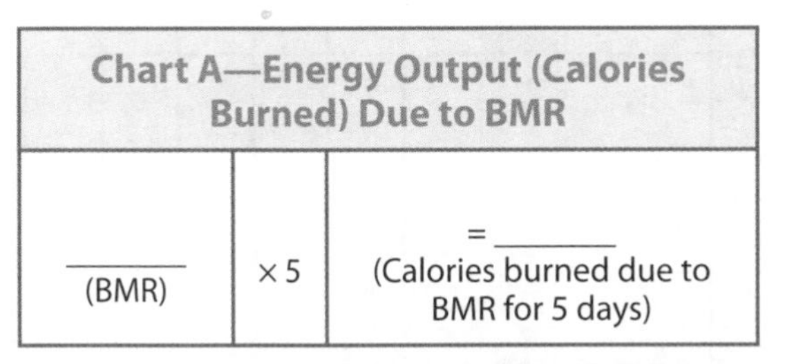

Chart A—Energy Output (Calories Burned) Due to BMR		
______ (BMR)	× 5	= ______ (Calories burned due to BMR for 5 days)

Keep track of your weight and Calories in Chart B.

1. Each morning of the five days, soon after you get up, weigh yourself as precisely as possible. Also do this on the morning of the sixth day. Each day, record your weight in the top row of Chart B on page 364.
2. Keep track of the amounts and types of food that you eat throughout the day. Be sure to include food items that you eat between meals. Record this information in Chart B.

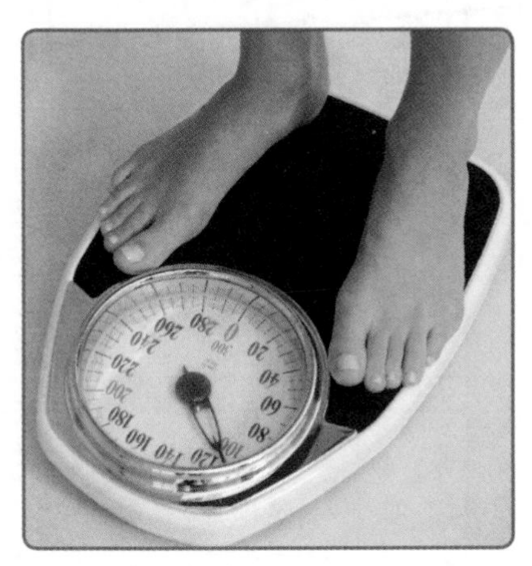

Chart B—Energy Input (Calories Taken In from Food)

	Example	Cal	Day 1	Cal	Day 2	Cal	Day 3	Cal	Day 4	Cal	Day 5	Cal	Day 6
Weight	125												
Breakfast	2 eggs	160											
	2 sausage patties	326											
	8 oz orange juice	122											
	1 slice of toast	70											
Lunch	2 slices of white bread	140											
	2 slices of ham	92											
	1 slice of cheddar cheese	110											
	1 tbsp mayonnaise	110											
	1 snack bag of potato chips	230											
	1 apple	70											
	8 oz lemonade	70											
	1 candy bar	280											

name ______________________

Chart B—Energy Input (Calories Taken In from Food) (continued)

	Example	Cal	Day 1	Cal	Day 2	Cal	Day 3	Cal	Day 4	Cal	Day 5	Cal	Day 6
Dinner	7 oz meat loaf	380											
	½ cup cooked broccoli	25											
	1 cup mashed potatoes	237											
	1 roll	90											
	2 tbsp gravy	27											
	8 oz sweet tea	92											
Daily Calorie Total		2631											Total Calorie Input for 5 Days = ______

3. Calculate the number of Calories in each of the foods you ate, and record this in Chart B.
   - If the food has nutrition information on its packaging, find the number of Calories per serving and multiply that number by the number of servings you ate. For example, if you eat two servings of a food that has 60 Calories per serving, you would have eaten 120 Calories.
   - If there is no food label, use the food table "Selected Foods and Calorie Values" on page 368 to estimate the number of Calories the food contains.
   - If the particular food you eat is not listed, you can try to find it online, or you can estimate based on a similar type of food that is listed in the table.
4. At the end of each day, calculate the total number of Calories you consumed that day.
5. At the end of the five days, calculate the total number of Calories you consumed over the five-day period.

Keep track of your Calories burned during activities in Chart C.

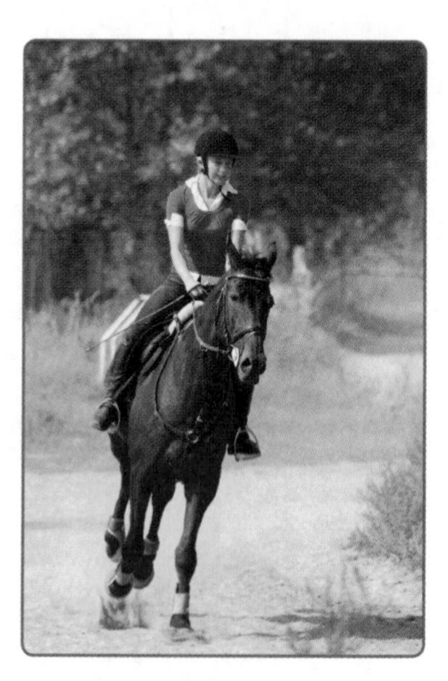

1. Keep track of how long (in minutes) you participate in any physical activities other than the usual walking that you do every day, and record this in Chart C on page 367. For example, record that you played a soccer game for 45 minutes, ran a mile in 9 minutes, did 30 pushups in 1 minute, walked for 30 minutes, and so on.
2. Use the table "Calories Used for Selected Activities" on page 368 to estimate the number of Calories you used during each activity, and record this number next to each activity on Chart C.
   - Note that the values in the table are for one hour of the activity. If you did not perform the activity for one hour, multiply the value by the percentage of the hour that you performed the activity. For example, suppose you ran a mile in 8.5 minutes. Since the Calorie values in the table are based on an activity lasting an hour, divide your activity time by an hour (60 min) to get the percentage of the hour that you performed the activity: (8.5 min ÷ 60 min) × 100% = 14.2% of an hour. Find on the table the number of Calories used per hour based on running a mile every 8.5 minutes (626 Calories). Then multiply that number by 14.2% to get the number of Calories you used: 626 Calories × 0.142 = 88.9 Calories.
   - Now suppose you ran a mile in 8 minutes. You would find the percentage of an hour: (8 min ÷ 60 min) × 100% = 13.3%. But the table gives Calorie values for running 7.5 minutes and 8.5 minutes, not 8 minutes. You can average the Calorie values given for these two times and then multiply the average by 13.3%: (626 + 654) ÷ 2 = 640 Calories; 640 × 0.133 = 85.1 Calories.
3. In the bottom row for each day, list the total time you spent in activity for the day and the total number of Calories you burned due to activity.
4. At the end of the five days, record in Chart C your total activity time and your total Calories burned due to activity.

Calculate your energy change in Chart D.

Finally, use Chart D on page 369 to subtract your total output (Calories burned) from your total input (Calories taken in from food). Your result may be negative (if you used more Calories than you ate) or positive (if you ate more Calories than you used).

name________________________

Chart C—Energy Output (Calories Burned) Due to Activities

	Example	Cal	Day 1	Cal	Day 2	Cal	Day 3	Cal	Day 4	Cal	Day 5	Cal	
Activity	ran mile—8 min	85											
Activity	played soccer—1 hr	568											
Activity	played piano—30 min	37.5											
Activity	brushed teeth—4 min	6.7											
Activity	eating—1 hr total	25											
Activity													
Activity													
Activity													
Daily Activity and Calorie Totals	Total Activity Time (min)	Total Calories	Total Activity Time (min)	Total Calories	Total Activity Time (min)	Total Calories	Total Activity Time (min)	Total Calories	Total Activity Time (min)	Total Calories	Total Activity Time (min)	Total Calories	Total Calories Burned in 5 Days
	162 min	722.2											
													Total Activity Time for 5 Days

Selected Foods and Calorie Values			
Food	**Calories**	**Food**	**Calories**
Fruits		**Meats, continued**	
apple (1 large)	70	beef stew (1 cup)	250
banana (1 large)	85	chicken, fried (half breast, 3⅓ oz)	154
cantaloupe (½)	40	egg (1)	80
orange (1 large)	70	ham (slice)	46
orange juice (1 cup)	122	hamburger, on bun (1/4 lb)	416
raisins (1 cup)	460	hot dog (1)	155
strawberries (1 cup)	55	meat loaf (3½ oz)	190
watermelon (2 lb slice)	120	perch, fried (3 oz)	195
Vegetables		sausage patty	163
broccoli (1 cup)	50	turkey (1 cup)	238
carrots, cooked (1 cup)	50	**Seeds and Nuts**	
celery stalk (8 in.)	5	almonds, shelled (1 cup)	850
corn (5 in. ear)	65	peanut butter (1 tbsp)	90
cucumber (1 in. slice)	5	peanuts, shelled (1 cup)	840
green beans (1 cup)	46	**Breads and Cakes**	
green peas (1 cup)	110	angel food cake (2 in. slice)	110
green pepper (1 raw)	15	Boston cream pie (3⅓ oz)	329
onion (1 in. slice)	80	cheesecake (4 oz)	215
pickle, dill (1 large)	15	doughnut, powdered sugar (1⅘ oz)	233
potato, baked (5 oz)	90	pancake (4 in. diameter)	60
potatoes, French-fried (2 oz)	200	pumpkin pie (4 in. section)	265
potatoes, mashed (1 cup)	237	roll	90
pinto beans (½ cup)	157	wheat bread (1 slice)	70
pork 'n' beans (1 cup)	231	white bread (1 slice)	70
Dairy Products		**Miscellaneous**	
butter or margarine (1 tbsp)	100	chicken soup (1 cup)	75
cheddar cheese (1 slice)	110	cola (6 oz)	73
cottage cheese (1 oz)	30	French salad dressing (1 tbsp)	90
ice cream (1 cup)	295	fudge (1 oz)	115
whole milk (1 cup)	165	honey (1 tbsp)	60
yogurt (1 cup)	120	ketchup (1 tbsp)	15
Meats		mayonnaise (1 tbsp)	110
beef, roast (3 oz)	265	potato chips (1½ oz bag)	230
beef sirloin (6 oz)	360	sugar (1 tbsp)	50

Calories Used for Selected Activities (average values for a 105 lb 13-year-old; averaged for gender as well)			
Activity	**Calories/hour**	**Activity**	**Calories/hour**
basketball	369	running (7 mi/hr) (1 mi/8.5 min)	626
bicycling (5.5 mi/hr)	199	running (8 mi/hr) (1 mi/7.5 min)	654
bowling	216	running (10 mi/hr) (1 mi/6 min)	738
brushing teeth or hair	100	shoveling	300
dusting furniture	132	sit-ups	214
eating	25	skiing (cross country)	542
golfing	273	soccer	568
hiking	301	swimming (laps vigorously)	557
jumping jacks	384	swimming (leisurely)	341
jumping rope	479	table tennis	228
mopping floors	200	tennis	415
mowing lawn	270	typing	25
playing piano	75	volleyball (competitive)	341
pull-ups	354	volleyball (noncompetitive)	171
pushups	239	walking (2.5 mi/hr) (1 mi/24 min)	171
roller-skating (recreational)	427	walking (4 mi/hr) (1 mi/15 min)	285
running (6 mi/hr) (1 mi/10 min)	556		

name ______________________

Chart D—Energy Change						
____________ (Energy input—Cal taken in from food for 5 days—last row of Chart B)	–	____________ (Energy output—Cal burned due to BMR for 5 days—last column of Chart A)	–	____________ (Energy output—Cal burned during activities for 5 days—last row of Chart C)	=	____________ **(Energy change)**

Summing Up

1. Is your net energy change for the five-day period positive or negative? positive ☐ negative ☐
2. Was there a change in your weight over the five-day period? yes ☐ no ☐
3. Does your change in weight correspond with your net energy change? If so, how? If not, why not?

   ____

   ____

   ____

4. What food that you regularly eat contains the most Calories?

   ____

5. What activity that you regularly participate in burns the most Calories?

   ____

6. How is your metabolism likely to change over the next 12–13 years?

   ____

7. How will your answer to Question 6 affect the relationship between your food intake and your ability to stay healthy?

   ____

   ____

8. How will your answer to Question 6 affect the relationship between your need for exercise and your ability to stay healthy?

   ____

   ____

9. Some young people may take dieting to an extreme. Besides depriving themselves of necessary energy, what other important materials might they be lacking?

   ____

   ____